D1445336

Welcome to TCN

This study guide is intended to prepare you to challenge the **Excelsior College** examination related to this specific subject matter. The guide is designed to provide you with comprehensive yet condensed information that will help you focus your efforts in studying for the particular examination. As you progress through the guide, you will accumulate knowledge that will assist you to confidently take the exam.

Using the Study Guide

Keep in mind that the examination you will be taking is a standardized test. These tests are structured to measure the skills you would receive in a conventional classroom setting: **your comprehension of facts, your understanding of concepts**, and **your ability to think critically** (combining several facts to describe or apply to a new situation). When you take the practice exam at the end of this guide, you will see questions that measure each of these three skills. For this reason, you may not find an explicit answer to specific practice exam questions in the guide. However, you will find the "pieces" from which you can derive the correct answer. If you are unsure about the process used to arrive at the correct answer, call our toll-free number at 1-800-634-1443, and a member of our academic staff will be happy to assist you.

Registering for Tests

To register for an **Excelsior College** exam (offered through Prometric Testing Centers), refer to the exam test sites bulletin included in your **original welcome letter**. Once you have determined the site nearest you, call the phone number listed to get information on testing dates and registration procedures. Then, determine when you will be ready to test, and register according to the individual test site instructions.

A Note about Guides

The course content for proficiency examinations administered by Excelsior College is periodically revised to stay abreast of current educational requirements. In response to curriculum changes, it is necessary to update The College Network, Inc., study guides. Therefore, there is a chance that course materials and contents may change as you progress through the study guide program. **To assure your success in pursuing your degree and to activate our Success Guarantee, please call us or visit our Web site to verify that you have the current version of this guide prior to studying.** If we determine that your study guide is outdated, we will be happy to replace it with an updated guide at no additional cost.

Please call us if you have any questions—we're here to help you succeed. **Please call the Academic Support Department at 1-800-634-1443, or visit us on the Internet at www.college-net.com/support/index.asp.**

The College Network
1-800-634-1443
www.college-net.com/support/index.asp

Nursing Concepts 4

3815 River Crossing Parkway, Suite 260 • Indianapolis, IN 46240 • www.college-net.com

NC4 113001 v1.0
2006 Edition

Let's Go!

Do you have the current version?

At The College Network (TCN), we want you to go forward with your education! We are committed to providing quality study material that provides you with the latest and most up-to-date information available. Our authors are constantly improving the content of our study guides, as course content for proficiency examinations is periodically revised to stay abreast of current educational requirements.

In order to activate our Success Guarantee*, before you start studying this guide, we require you to either call our Academic Support Department or visit our Web site to verify that you have the current version of the guide. If the version is not current, we will be happy to replace the guide at no additional cost.

Call us at 1-800-634-1443
or visit us online at
www.college-net.com/support/index.asp

*TCN's Success Guarantee is applicable only to study guides required for your program and the related costs.

About the Author

 Judy Halstead, BSN, MSN, DNS, has achieved recognition for her excellence as a scholar, educator, author, researcher, and clinician. She currently holds an academic appointment as an Associate Professor at the University of Southern Indiana, School of Nursing and Health Professions, Evansville, Indiana. She is also the Director of Instructional Services and Resources and a Director for the Center for Community Health Care Practice and Research.

Judy's research interests include the effectiveness of sexually transmitted disease education with incarcerated women; the effect of learning style preferences on Web-based student learning; learning style preferences and disposition toward critical thinking in baccalaureate nursing students; nursing students' perceptions of the advantages and disadvantages of using case studies and lectures in the classroom; the effects of interactive teaching strategies on critical thinking and knowledge acquisition and retention in BSN students; the extent of collegiality in student-faculty interactions as perceived by baccalaureate nursing students and faculty; and the importance of preoperative teaching.

Dr. Halstead's work can be found in these prestigious publications: *Journal of Nursing Profession, Enhancements: How Using Technology Changes What Faculty Do; Journal of Nursing Education; Review of Research in Nursing Education;* and *Computers in Nursing*. In addition to teaching numerous graduate courses and directing independent studies, Judy has taught undergraduate courses in Foundations of Nursing Practice, Health Patterns of the Adult, Health Patterns of Clients with Chronic Illness, Foundations for Nursing of Children and Adults, and Nursing and Health Care Issues.

Judy Halstead received her BSN from the University of Evansville, her MSN from University of Evansville with a specialty in Medical/Surgical Nursing, and her DNS from Indiana University.

Acquisitions Editor: Laura Williams

Editors: Carolyn Lamontagne and Miriam Klein

Content Editors: Kathleen Kaufman, RN, MS, Tara Watson, RN, MSN, CFNP, and Nancy J. Crigger, Ph.D., M.A., A.R.N.P.

TABLE OF CONTENTS

PREFACE

The content of the *Nursing Concepts 4* study guide provides an overview of nursing care related to cardiovascular problems, respiratory problems, abnormal cellular growth, and congenital and genetic disorders. Topics covered for each disorder include risk factors, clinical manifestations, diagnostic and laboratory tests, and therapeutic interventions. Also included are discussions of nursing assessments, diagnoses, goals, treatments, and expected patient outcomes.

Units I, II, and III cover cardiovascular and respiratory problems. Disorders discussed include upper and lower respiratory tract disorders, cardiac dysrhythmias, coronary vascular disorders, hypertension, peripheral vascular disease, hematologic disorders, and shock. Unit IV covers disorders related to abnormal cell growth, including tissue hypertrophy, benign abnormal cellular growth, and various forms of cancer. And Unit V discusses congenital and genetic disorders. At the end of each chapter you will find study questions designed to aid your understanding of the material. At the end of this study guide, a comprehensive practice examination attempts to simulate the Excelsior College examination for *Nursing Concepts 4*.

UNIT I: THEORETICAL BASES FOR RESPIRATORY AND CARDIOVASCULAR DISORDERS

Chapter 1: Cardiovascular and Respiratory Disorders

Key Terms

Alveolar-capillary membrane
Dead space
Diffusion
Expiration
Hypercapnia
Hyperventilation
Hypoventilation
Hypoxemia
Hypoxia
Inspiration
Respiratory acidosis
Respiratory alkalosis
Shunting
Silent unit
Ventilation
Ventilation-perfusion (V/Q) ratio

Introduction

The lungs are responsible for oxygenating blood and eliminating carbon dioxide from the body. The heart is responsible for transporting oxygenated blood throughout the body to meet the metabolic demands of tissue cells. This chapter describes the pathophysiological changes that can lead to the development of cardiovascular or pulmonary health problems. These pathophysiological changes can be categorized as problems of oxygen (1) intake and supply, (2) absorption, and (3) transportation.

Problems of Oxygen Intake and Supply

Ventilation

Air is moved into and out of the lungs through the process of **ventilation**. Ventilation is the process by which gases are exchanged in the respiratory system. Oxygen is brought into the lungs and carbon dioxide is eliminated from the lungs through this process.

Inspiration is the movement of air into the lungs. Inspiration is an active process caused by the contraction of the diaphragm and the intercostal and accessory respiratory muscles. As the diaphragm contracts and moves downward, the chest cavity expands.

The expansion of the chest cavity causes the intrathoracic pressure to decrease and become less than atmospheric air, thus allowing air to flow into the lungs. The intercostal and accessory muscles assist in enlarging the chest cavity by elevating the rib cage.

Expiration is the movement of air out of the lungs. Expiration is a passive process that occurs as a result of the elastic recoil properties of lung tissue and the chest wall. As the lungs and chest wall structures passively recoil, the intrathoracic pressure within the lungs becomes greater than the atmospheric air, thus forcing the air out of the lungs.

Hyperventilation

Hyperventilation is increased ventilation that exceeds the body's need for carbon dioxide elimination. Hyperventilation is characterized by a rapid respiratory rate. Prolonged hyperventilation can lead to **respiratory alkalosis**, which is a state of carbon dioxide deficit (PCO_2 less than 35 mm Hg) in the blood. Common causes of hyperventilation are anxiety, hypoxia, fever, and salicylate toxicity. If respiratory alkalosis is not corrected, the patient may develop convulsions and cardiac arrhythmias.

Hypoventilation

If ventilation is decreased (hypoventilation), then the intake and supply of oxygen will be decreased. A variety of respiratory and neurological problems can lead to **hypoventilation**, which is a decreased ability to ventilate the lungs and provide an adequate exchange of oxygen and carbon dioxide. Hypoventilation is characterized by a decreased respiratory rate or a decreased respiratory effort that impairs chest wall movement, thus affecting the depth of ventilation. Hypoventilation is caused by alterations in either the mechanics of breathing or the neurological mechanisms that control breathing.

Causes of Hypoventilation

Respiratory Center Depression

Various patient problems can lead to hypoventilation. For example, one common cause of hypoventilation is depression of the respiratory center. **Respiratory center depression** can develop as a result of an overdose of any drug that has a respiratory depressant action, such as opiates, barbiturates, and antidepressants, or it can develop as a result of neurological damage. In respiratory depression, the patient's respiratory rate becomes shallow and slow. The patient may become restless, anxious, and/or confused. In the later stages of respiratory depression, the patient becomes lethargic and may be cyanotic.

Chronic Obstructive Pulmonary Disease

Another cause of hypoventilation is **chronic obstructive pulmonary disease (COPD)**, which is characterized by air trapping in the alveoli, thus decreasing the exchange of gases.

Increased Airway Resistance

Another cause of hypoventilation that results in a decreased intake and supply of oxygen is **increased airway resistance** that prevents air from reaching the lung tissues. Examples of respiratory problems that can lead to increased airway resistance include laryngeal edema (swelling), croup, asthma, lodging of a foreign body, and thick, tenacious secretions that obstruct the airway. All of these respiratory problems decrease the radius (diameter) of the airway, thus increasing resistance to airflow and decreasing ventilation.

- **Laryngeal edema** is caused by an allergic reaction or inflammation of the larynx, resulting in swelling (edema) that occludes the patient's airway. *Laryngeal edema is a medical emergency.* If an airway is not quickly established, either through the administration of medication that reduces the swelling or through intubation, the patient will die.
- **Croup** is a childhood condition caused by an upper respiratory infection that leads to laryngeal or tracheal swelling, potentially occluding the child's airway.
- In **asthma**, a narrowing of the patient's airways within the lungs leads to difficulty moving air into and throughout the lungs.
- Thick, tenacious **secretions**, such as those that develop in response to a lower respiratory infection or chronic obstructive lung disorder (COPD), can also block the patient's airways and restrict the intake of oxygen into the lungs.

In all of the above examples, there is a narrowing or obstruction of the patient's airway that impedes the intake of oxygen. The patient will typically display acute respiratory distress, as evidenced by difficulty breathing. (These respiratory problems are discussed in greater depth in chapters 6 and 7.)

Effects of Hypoventilation

Hypoventilation can cause the patient to develop hypoxia, hypoxemia, and hypercapnia.

- **Hypoxia** is a decreased supply of oxygen to the tissues.
- **Hypoxemia** is a decreased level of oxygen in the blood.
- **Hypercapnia** is an increased level of carbon dioxide in the blood.

Hypoxia and hypoxemia develop as a result of the decreased availability of oxygen due to the hypoventilation. Hypercapnia develops because ventilation is insufficient to remove carbon dioxide from the system.

If the hypoventilation is not corrected, the patient can develop low arterial oxygen blood levels (low **PaO$_2$**) and high arterial carbon dioxide blood levels (high **PaCO$_2$**), leading to **respiratory acidosis**. Respiratory acidosis is a state of carbonic acid excess (PaCO$_2$ over 50 mmHg) in the blood.

Assessment

It is important that the nurse closely assess the respiratory status of patients who are at risk for developing hypoventilation and ultimately, respiratory acidosis. In addition to drug sedation and overdose, other conditions that lead to respiratory acidosis are any respiratory disorders that cause a decrease in the amount of lung tissue available for gas exchange or neuromuscular disorders that lead to weakness of the respiratory muscles. Respiratory acidosis can develop quickly or gradually, depending upon the etiology and acuity of the problem, as well as the patient's general health and respiratory status. Primary nursing interventions for preventing hypoventilation and respiratory acidosis are to promote adequate lung ventilation and oxygenation through encouraging coughing and deep breathing, turning frequently, and administering oxygen as ordered.

If not corrected, respiratory acidosis can eventually lead to **respiratory failure**. In respiratory failure, the patient is not capable of sustaining the ventilation necessary to adequately oxygenate the blood and eliminate carbon dioxide. A patient with respiratory failure requires intubation and mechanical ventilation to provide enough oxygen to the body's tissues and to eliminate excess carbon dioxide. (Respiratory failure is discussed further in chapter 7.)

Decreased Lung Expansion

Oxygenation is also dependent upon the adequate expansion of the lungs. There are a variety of conditions that decrease expansion of the lungs or decrease movement of the respiratory muscles and affect the patient's ability to adequately ventilate and take in enough oxygen. For example, the patient who has fractured ribs or who is recovering from abdominal or chest surgery can experience pain that is severe enough to prevent the patient from taking deep breaths, thus decreasing chest excursion and the intake of oxygen. In these cases, it is important that the nurse implement a plan of care that will effectively manage the patient's pain and allow the patient to take deep breaths more comfortably. In addition to administering pain medication, the nurse can help the patient splint the chest or abdomen with pillows or a folded blanket while taking deep breaths and coughing.

Any disorder that decreases or paralyzes diaphragm movement can lead to hypoventilation and decreased oxygenation. Through weakness and debilitation, the aging process can also decrease a patient's ability to breathe deeply enough to adequately expand the lungs.

Decreased Supply of Atmospheric Oxygen

And finally, a decreased supply of atmospheric oxygen can lead to a decrease in the intake and supply of oxygen. For example, **smoke inhalation**, such as that which occurs in a house fire, can cause a decrease in the intake and supply of oxygen to the lungs. A decrease in oxygen occurs because carbon monoxide in the bloodstream binds with hemoglobin, displacing the oxygen. **High altitudes** can also lead to the development of hypoxemic hypoxia due to decreased oxygen intake.

Problems of Oxygen Absorption

Some problems with oxygenation are caused by an inability to absorb oxygen into the bloodstream at the cellular level. Ventilation of the lungs and intake of oxygen is adequate, but the oxygen is not absorbed into the bloodstream for use by the body's tissues.

Insufficient Diffusion

Oxygen absorption and carbon dioxide elimination are achieved through the process of diffusion. The diffusion of oxygen and carbon dioxide takes place in the lungs at the level of the **alveolar-capillary membrane**. **Diffusion** is the movement of gases, such as oxygen and carbon dioxide, from higher levels of concentration to lower levels of concentration.

The alveolar-capillary membrane is normally very thin, which allows the gases to diffuse easily between the alveoli and the capillaries. Oxygen diffuses across the alveolar-capillary membrane from the alveoli to be absorbed into the bloodstream, and carbon dioxide diffuses across the alveolar-capillary membrane from the capillaries to be removed from the bloodstream and eliminated through expiration.

Causes of Insufficient Oxygen Diffusion and Absorption

Problems with oxygen absorption develop when the process of diffusion is altered. The patient can have proper lung ventilation and breathe into the lungs an adequate amount of oxygen, but the gas exchange (diffusion) of oxygen and carbon dioxide is insufficient at the alveolar-capillary membrane level.

Blocked alveoli are one cause of insufficient oxygen diffusion and absorption. For example, in lower respiratory tract infections, inflammation, swelling, and secretions can develop within the alveoli, thus blocking the alveoli and decreasing gas exchange across the alveolar-capillary membrane.

A **decrease in the amount of oxygen-absorbing surfaces of the lungs** will also affect the absorption of oxygen. For example, one condition in which poor oxygen diffusion occurs because of a decrease in available oxygen-absorbing surfaces is **atelectasis**, which is the actual collapse of alveoli. The resulting lack of air in the collapsed alveoli leads to a lack of gas exchange within the affected alveoli. Atelectasis frequently occurs as a postoperative complication when the patient does not breathe deeply enough to move secretions out of the alveoli and air into the alveoli to keep them inflated.

Other conditions that cause a decrease in the absorption of oxygen due to a decrease in the absorbing surfaces of the lungs include pneumonia, lung surgery, pulmonary edema, pneumothorax (collapsed lung), and adult respiratory distress syndrome (ARDS).

Treatment

When caring for a patient who has a problem with oxygen absorption, the primary goal of nursing care is to promote adequate diffusion of oxygen at the cellular level. Encouraging the patient to cough and take deep breaths at frequent intervals to mobilize and remove secretions and to prevent the development of atelectasis will help achieve this goal. If the patient cannot cough effectively, the nurse may need to suction the patient to remove secretions. Supplemental oxygen is administered as ordered.

Ventilation-Perfusion Imbalances

Adequate diffusion of gases also depends upon an adequate **ventilation-perfusion ratio** in the lungs. As discussed previously, ventilation is the process by which gases are moved into and out of the lungs. **Perfusion** is the amount of blood flow through the pulmonary capillaries. When a specific amount of capillary blood flows past an alveolus and is equally matched by gas, the ventilation-perfusion ratio is considered to be normal.

Ventilation-perfusion (V/Q) imbalances can be caused by decreased ventilation and/or decreased perfusion. For example, when there is decreased ventilation, blood will perfuse the capillary and flow past the alveoli without any gas exchange occurring. This results in **shunting**, a condition in which blood flows through the lungs without any gas exchange. Carbon dioxide cannot be eliminated, and oxygen cannot be absorbed due to the inadequate ventilation. Obstruction of distal airways is a common cause of shunting.

On the other hand, when there is adequate ventilation but inadequate capillary perfusion, there is not enough blood available to support gas exchange. This condition results in **dead space**—the "space" that is lacking blood flow is essentially unavailable or "dead" to the exchange of carbon dioxide and oxygen, even though ventilation is sufficient. Conditions that lead to decreased blood flow, such as pulmonary emboli, can cause dead space to develop. If ventilation or perfusion is either inadequate or nonexistent, a **silent unit** is said to exist. **Pneumothorax** is a condition in which a silent unit commonly occurs.

Problems of Oxygen Transportation

The transportation of oxygen is dependent upon the cardiovascular system's ability to carry oxygenated blood to the tissues. The patient can have an adequate intake and supply of oxygen that is promptly absorbed into the bloodstream, but if the cardiovascular system cannot transport the oxygen to where it can be used by the tissues, the peripheral tissues will remain unoxygenated.

Blocked Arterial Blood Vessels

Several conditions can lead to problems with transportation of oxygenated blood. First of all, the patient may have an impairment of arterial blood vessels that interferes with blood flow. A common cause of blocked arterial blood vessels is atherosclerosis. In **atherosclerosis**, plaque accumulates within the arteries and creates a narrowed arterial lumen, thus impeding the flow of oxygenated blood throughout the vessels.

Hypertension, coronary artery disease, angina pectoris, myocardial infarction, abdominal aortic aneurysms, peripheral vascular disease, and gangrene are all cardiovascular conditions that can develop as a result of atherosclerosis and narrowed arterial lumens. (These cardiovascular health problems are discussed in chapters 11, 12, and 13.)

Pulmonary Embolus

Another example of a condition that impedes the transportation of oxygenated blood is pulmonary embolus. **Pulmonary embolus** is a condition in which a thrombus (clot) breaks loose and travels through the bloodstream until it lodges in a vessel in the lungs, obstructing the vessel and impeding the flow of oxygenated blood beyond the location of the clot. The clot is usually a blood clot, but it may also be a fat embolus. The acuity of the condition depends upon the size of the clot and the vessel that is obstructed. Pulmonary emboli can be fatal.

Heart Failure

Another potential oxygenation transportation problem is failure of the heart to pump effectively, leading to a decrease in cardiac output. If cardiac output is decreased, oxygenated blood is not adequately circulated to tissues to meet the oxygen demands. Examples of conditions that can lead to a decrease in cardiac output and a decrease in oxygenated tissues include dysrhythmias, myocardial infarction, and congestive heart failure. These health problems are discussed in further depth in chapters 11 and 12.

Shock

Shock is a life-threatening disorder that leads to inadequate tissue perfusion. Because of inadequate perfusion, the tissues do not receive the oxygen and nutrients necessary to maintain function.

There are a variety of problems that lead to the development of shock. For example, a decrease in blood volume can cause inadequate tissue perfusion and **hypovolemic shock**. Hemorrhage is an example of a decrease in blood volume that can lead to hypovolemic shock. Severe dehydration is another example. Hypovolemic shock develops when there is a loss of intravascular fluid volume, leading to a decrease in circulating fluid. The decreased fluid volume leads to a decrease in cardiac output and a decrease in blood flow to peripheral tissues.

Another type of shock is **cardiogenic shock**. Cardiogenic shock occurs when the heart's pumping ability is impaired, decreasing cardiac output.

Septic shock, **neurogenic shock**, and **anaphylactic shock** are all forms of **distributive shock**, in which the vascular tone of the vessels is affected, thus causing vasodilation and resulting hypovolemia. Shock is discussed further in chapter 15.

Decreased Red Blood Cells or Hemoglobin Level

Oxygen is transported to the tissues by **hemoglobin** in the red blood cells. Any condition that decreases the number of red blood cells or the hemoglobin level will cause an alteration in oxygen-carrying ability of the hemoglobin. Examples of conditions that can lead to this type of transportation problem are the anemias, e.g., sickle-cell anemia, iron-deficiency anemia, and pernicious anemia. Polycythemia vera, in which there is an increase in the number of red blood cells, can lead to hypoxia as a result of hyperviscosity and stagnation of blood flow. Conditions of anemia are covered in chapter 14.

Alterations in Blood Coagulation

An alteration in blood coagulation that leads to the development of a hemorrhagic condition can also affect tissue oxygenation. Examples of two conditions that can result in hemorrhage and tissue hypoxia are **disseminated intravascular coagulation (DIC)** and **thrombocytopenia purpura.**

- **DIC** is a bleeding disorder that causes an alteration in clotting factors, leading to hemorrhage.
- In **thrombocytopenia purpura**, platelets are destroyed, resulting in a decreased number of circulating platelets and causing the patient to be susceptible to hemorrhage.

Chapter 1 Study Questions

1.   Define the process of ventilation.

2.   Define hyperventilation and identify the condition that prolonged hyperventilation can cause.

3.   Identify three common causes of hyperventilation.

4.   Define hypoventilation.

5.   Identify two common causes of hypoventilation.

                                                   NC4 113001 v1.0

6.   Define hypoxia, hypoxemia, and hypercapnia.

7.   If hypoventilation is not corrected, what condition can develop?

8.   Describe the primary nursing interventions that can help prevent the development of hypoventilation.

9.   Identify three pathophysiological conditions that can cause problems with oxygen intake and supply.

10.   Identify two pathophysiological changes that can cause problems with oxygen absorption.

11.   Describe the process of diffusion.

12.   What is the primary goal of nursing care and appropriate nursing interventions when caring for a patient who has problems with oxygen absorption?

13.   Describe the significance of the ventilation-perfusion ratio.

14.   Describe three common ventilation-perfusion imbalances.

15.   Identify five pathophysiological changes that can cause problems with oxygen transportation.

Answers to Chapter 1 Study Questions

1. Ventilation involves the movement of air in and out of the lungs, and it is the process by which gases are exchanged in the respiratory system. Oxygen is brought into the lungs and carbon dioxide is eliminated from the lungs through the process of ventilation.

2. Hyperventilation is increased ventilation that exceeds the body's need for carbon dioxide elimination. Hyperventilation is characterized by a rapid respiratory rate. Prolonged hyperventilation can lead to respiratory alkalosis, which is a state of carbon dioxide deficit (PCO_2 less than 35 mm Hg) in the blood.

3. Common causes of hyperventilation are anxiety, hypoxia, fever, and salicylate toxicity.

4. If ventilation is decreased (hypoventilation), then the intake and supply of oxygen will be decreased. A variety of respiratory and neurological problems can lead to hypoventilation, which is a decreased ability to ventilate the lungs and provide an adequate exchange of oxygen and carbon dioxide. Hypoventilation is characterized by a decreased respiratory rate or a decreased respiratory effort that impairs chest wall movement, thus affecting the depth of ventilation. Hypoventilation is caused by alterations in either the mechanics of breathing or the neurological mechanisms that control breathing.

5. One common cause of hypoventilation is depression of the respiratory center. Respiratory center depression can develop as a result of an overdose of any drug that has a respiratory depressant action, such as opiates, barbiturates, and antidepressants, or it can develop as a result of neurological damage. Another cause of hypoventilation is chronic obstructive pulmonary disease (COPD), which is characterized by air trapping in the alveoli, thus decreasing the exchange of gases.

6. Hypoventilation can cause the patient to develop hypoxia, hypoxemia, and hypercapnia. Hypoxia is a decreased supply of oxygen to the tissues. Hypoxemia is a decreased level of oxygen in the blood. Hypercapnia is an increased level of carbon dioxide in the blood. Hypoxia and hypoxemia develop as a result of the decreased availability of oxygen due to the hypoventilation. Hypercapnia develops because ventilation is insufficient to remove carbon dioxide from the system.

7. If the hypoventilation is not corrected, the patient can develop low arterial oxygen blood levels (low PaO_2) and high arterial carbon dioxide blood levels (high $PaCO_2$) leading to respiratory acidosis. Respiratory acidosis is a state of carbonic acid excess ($PaCO_2$ over 50 mmHg) in the blood.

8. Primary nursing interventions for preventing hypoventilation and respiratory acidosis are to promote adequate lung ventilation and oxygenation through encouraging coughing and deep breathing, turning frequently, and administering oxygen as ordered.

9. Hypoventilation can cause problems with oxygen intake and supply. Depression of the respiratory center is one cause of hypoventilation. A blocked airway can also lead to a decreased intake and supply of oxygen. Any condition that alters expansion of the lungs or decreases movement of the respiratory muscles will affect the lung's ability to adequately take in enough oxygen.

10. Blocked alveoli are one cause of an alteration in oxygen absorption. A decrease in the absorbing surfaces of the lungs will also affect the absorption of oxygen. Problems with oxygen absorption develop when the process of diffusion is altered.

11. Oxygen absorption and carbon dioxide elimination is achieved through the process of diffusion. The diffusion of oxygen and carbon dioxide takes place in the lungs at the level of the alveolar-capillary membrane. Diffusion is the movement of gases, such as oxygen and carbon dioxide, from higher levels of concentration to lower levels of concentration.

12. When caring for a patient who has a problem with oxygen absorption, the primary goal of nursing care is to promote adequate diffusion of oxygen at the cellular level. Encouraging the patient to cough and breathe deeply at frequent intervals to mobilize and remove secretions and to prevent the development of atelectasis will help achieve this goal. If the patient cannot cough effectively, the nurse may need to suction the patient to remove secretions. Supplemental oxygen is administered as ordered.

13. Adequate diffusion of gases depends upon an adequate ventilation-perfusion ratio in the lungs. As discussed previously, ventilation is the process by which gases are moved into and out of the lungs. Perfusion is the amount of blood flow through the pulmonary capillaries. When a specific amount of capillary blood flows past an alveolus and is equally matched by gas, the ventilation-perfusion ratio is considered to be normal.

14. Ventilation-perfusion (V/Q) imbalances can be caused by decreased ventilation and/or decreased perfusion. For example, when there is decreased ventilation, blood will perfuse the capillary and flow past the alveoli without any gas exchange occurring. This results in shunting, a condition in which blood flows through the lungs without any gas exchange. Carbon dioxide cannot be eliminated, and oxygen cannot be absorbed due to the inadequate ventilation. Obstruction of distal airways is a common cause of shunting. On the other hand, when there is adequate ventilation but inadequate capillary perfusion, there is not enough blood available to support gas exchange. This condition results in dead

space, which occurs when the "space" that is lacking blood flow is essentially unavailable or "dead" to the exchange of carbon dioxide and oxygen, even though ventilation is sufficient. Conditions that lead to decreased blood flow, such as pulmonary emboli, can cause dead space to develop. If ventilation or perfusion is either inadequate or nonexistent, a silent unit is said to exist. Pneumothorax is a condition in which a silent unit commonly occurs.

15. The patient may have an impairment of blood vessels that interferes with blood flow. Another potential oxygenation transportation problem is failure of the heart to pump effectively, leading to a decrease in cardiac output. A decrease in blood volume can also cause a problem with the heart's ability to deliver enough oxygenated blood to the tissues. Any condition that decreases the number of red blood cells or the hemoglobin level will cause an alteration in oxygen-carrying ability of the hemoglobin. An alteration in blood coagulation that leads to the development of a hemorrhagic condition can also affect tissue oxygenation.

Chapter 2: Factors That Influence Patient Susceptibility and Response to Cardiovascular and Respiratory Disorders

Key Terms

Aging factors
Cultural factors
Economic factors
Gender factors
Familial history
Psychological factors
Socioeconomic factors

Introduction

This chapter reviews the factors that influence the patient's susceptibility and response to cardiovascular or respiratory problems. These factors may be intrinsic to the patient, such as aging, familial history, and the presence of other preexisting conditions, or they may be extrinsic to the patient, such as exercise and activity patterns, nutritional habits, stress, and other controllable lifestyle choices.

Age, Gender, and Physiological Factors

Age and gender affect a person's susceptibility to the development of cardiovascular and respiratory problems. Certain **physiological changes** occur as we age that predispose us to these problems. If individuals have engaged in lifestyle behaviors that encourage pathophysiological changes to occur in the heart and lungs, the normal aging process will only exacerbate these pathophysiological changes.

Cardiovascular Physiological Differences

There are several physiological differences in cardiac anatomy based upon gender. A woman's heart is smaller in size, weighs less, and has smaller coronary arteries. Because of the smaller coronary arteries, atherosclerotic plaques can more easily occlude a woman's vessels. Also, the smaller diameter can make cardiac catheterization and other invasive procedures more technically difficult to perform.

Another gender difference is the presence of hormones in females that are thought to provide some protection against the development of coronary artery disease. After menopause when estrogen levels decline, women's risk of developing coronary artery disease is equal to that of men. Many women take hormone replacement therapy (HRT) to continue this beneficial side effect of estrogen.

Historically, heart disease in women has not been diagnosed as early as it was in men. Symptoms of heart disease may be subtler in women, and are frequently dismissed or overlooked as stress-related discomfort. Because of the subtleness of the symptoms, women may not seek prompt medical attention.

Aging also has an impact on cardiovascular status. In the United States, more elderly are hospitalized and die as a result of cardiovascular disease than any other disease. Most of the incidences of cardiovascular disease are related to atherosclerosis. While the development of atherosclerosis is pathophysiologic in nature, some of the changes that occur within the blood vessels to promote atherosclerosis are part of the normal process of aging.

As individuals age, it is normal for the elastin in the heart to decrease, while the amount of collagen increases. These physiological changes gradually contribute to a decrease in the contractility and distensibility of the heart muscle. The myocardium gradually loses its ability to respond to increased workload demands.

Arterial vessels throughout the body gradually thicken and lose their elasticity. These changes can contribute to the development of an increased systolic blood pressure.

Additional changes that occur within the heart include a thickening of the heart valves due to lipid accumulation and calcification and a decrease in the number of sinoatrial node (SA node) pacemaker cells. The changes in the heart valves can result in a murmur, while the decreased number of pacemaker cells can lead to bradycardia.

Respiratory Physiological Differences

The aging process also affects the respiratory system. Normal physiological changes in lung tissue include the loss of elasticity in lung recoil and chest excursion. The anteroposterior diameter of the thorax enlarges as a result of these changes. The strength of an elderly individual's cough is weakened and cilia function is decreased, thus adversely affecting the ability to mobilize secretions. These changes can predispose an individual to respiratory infections. Functioning alveoli gradually decrease in number, causing a lower arterial blood oxygen level (PaO_2) in the elderly. The respiratory rate does not compensate as rapidly for changes in oxygen and carbon dioxide levels.

While all of the above physiological respiratory changes are normal in the aging process, the individual's lifestyle can have an impact on the degree of change. For example, individuals with a history of smoking greatly increase their chances of exacerbating these normal changes and developing a chronic, pathophysiological lung problem, such as chronic obstructive pulmonary disease or cancer.

Socioeconomic, Cultural, and Psychological Factors

Other factors that influence a patient's susceptibility and response to cardiovascular or respiratory problems are socioeconomic, cultural, and psychological factors. The nurse should carefully assess these areas not only to determine their impact on the patient's susceptibility to cardiovascular or respiratory problems but also to determine how likely a person is to make lifestyle changes and follow a prescribed treatment plan.

Familial Tendency

Many cardiovascular and respiratory problems demonstrate a **familial tendency**. Patients should be carefully questioned about their family history. Respiratory problems such as emphysema, cystic fibrosis, and asthma have a familial or genetic component. Disorders such as atherosclerosis, coronary artery disease, diabetes mellitus, and hypertension also demonstrate familial tendencies. Knowledge of a patient's family history can help the nurse structure health promotion teaching plans that will guide the individual to consider and select appropriate lifestyle choices in light of their family history.

Lifestyle Risk Factors

The following risk factors need to be assessed:

- Cigarette smoking
- A diet high in fat and cholesterol
- Obesity
- Sedentary lifestyle

These are common risk factors that promote the development of cardiovascular or respiratory problems.

Occupation

A patient's occupation can predispose or affect the response to cardiovascular or respiratory problems. A sedentary job may not provide the patient with enough opportunity for aerobic exercise. A job environment that exposes the individual to fumes, toxins, chemicals, or potential allergens can predispose the person to the development of respiratory problems (such as asthma) or exacerbate preexisting ones.

Socioeconomic Status

The **economic status** of the patient can impact how the patient will respond to prescribed treatment. Many cardiovascular and respiratory problems are chronic in nature. Patients may find that their health problems have affected their ability to work productively and to maintain a regular job. Health-care benefits may be affected. The nurse needs to carefully assess if the patient can afford the monthly costs of prescribed medications and help the patient locate community resources for assistance. There are an increasing number of individuals who live in poverty or who are homeless in our society. These individuals are at an increased risk for cardiovascular and respiratory problems because of they lack access to health care and poor nutrition and often live in unsanitary, crowded living conditions.

Psychological Condition

Psychological factors can also affect a patient's susceptibility and response to cardiovascular and pulmonary health problems. Stress, anger, and hostility have been shown to have some correlation to the development of cardiac disease. Patients with respiratory problems may become anxious when they experience difficulty breathing. Stress may also precipitate an episode of dyspnea.

It is not uncommon for patients who develop a chronic health problem to experience changes in relationships and interactions with others. Respiratory and cardiovascular problems can place limitations on activity levels, thus causing the patient to curtail normal activities that may lead to a sense of isolation from others. Difficulty breathing and fatigue can impact sexuality. Some medications used to treat cardiovascular problems can cause impotence; because of this, patients may refuse to adhere to medication regimens.

Patients who can no longer work at their previous level of productivity and experience a change in their role relationships may develop a lower level of self-esteem. Depression can develop, further depleting the patient's energy levels. The nurse needs to carefully assess these areas to develop an appropriate plan of care for the patient.

Cultural Factors

Cultural factors may also influence a patient's susceptibility and response to pulmonary and cardiovascular problems. An individual's culture can affect lifestyle choices, values and beliefs, and health practices. For example, food habits are frequently influenced by an individual's ethnic background. An individual's culture will influence the selection and preparation of foods. Geographic location will also dictate the availability of foods, thus influencing the ethnic diet. Individuals whose ethnic background promotes a diet high in fat, cholesterol, sodium, and starch will be at risk for obesity and cardiovascular disease.

An individual's decision to seek medical help for a health problem can be influenced not only by previous health practices but also personally held and culturally influenced values and beliefs. For example, a man who fears that diagnosis of a chronic, potentially debilitating cardiovascular or pulmonary disease will threaten his role as breadwinner for his family may be reluctant to seek medical care. An individual who believes that a health problem is "God's punishment" and is fatalistic and accepting about the outcome of the illness is less likely to seek medical intervention or follow recommended treatment, especially for chronic health disorders.

Cultural factors need to be carefully assessed by the nurse so that an individualized plan of care can be developed with the patient that considers and respects the patient's cultural beliefs. It is important that the nurse specifically ask if the patient holds any cultural or religious beliefs that will influence treatment of pulmonary or cardiovascular conditions.

Nutritional Factors

The patient's respiratory and cardiovascular status can be affected by his or her nutritional status. For example, a diet high in fat and cholesterol can predispose the individual to the development of cardiovascular disease. A high sodium intake in a patient with congestive heart failure can cause fluid retention that eventually impacts cardiac functioning and leads to pulmonary congestion with dyspnea.

In turn, the patient's nutritional status can be affected by the development of a cardiovascular or respiratory problem. Patients who are fatigued or experiencing difficulty breathing frequently have difficulty eating and ingesting enough calories to meet their body's energy requirements. Fluid intake and sodium intake may need to be restricted if the patient experiences fluid volume excess as a result of a cardiovascular problem.

The nurse should carefully assess the patient's dietary habits, paying particular attention to the intake of fat, cholesterol, and sodium. The type and amount of fluid intake should also be noted to determine the potential for developing a fluid volume excess or deficit.

Any history of weight gain or loss should be determined. A rapid weight gain may indicate fluid retention; a rapid weight loss may indicate fluid depletion. Total caloric intake should be compatible with the individual's daily exercise patterns. Obviously, a sedentary individual cannot expect to consume the same amount of calories as someone who is reasonably active without gaining weight. Obesity may predispose an individual to the development of cardiovascular disease, as well as diabetes mellitus. Individuals who have diabetes mellitus are at a higher risk for developing cardiovascular disease, and they must carefully follow their prescribed diet to potentially avoid cardiovascular complications commonly associated with diabetes, such as coronary artery disease and peripheral vascular disease.

The development of a chronic respiratory or cardiac condition can interfere with the patient's normal nutritional patterns. The onset of pulmonary problems may lead to anorexia and weight loss. Dyspnea and fatigue can make it difficult for a patient to eat regular meals. Sputum production is sometimes increased by the ingestion of certain foods. Excessive sputum production can also affect appetite and sense of taste. Many medications used to treat cardiovascular and respiratory disorders can lead to the development of anorexia or other gastrointestinal symptoms.

Environmental Factors

Environmental factors can also influence an individual's cardiovascular and respiratory status. For example, we have already discussed the importance of diet on the development of cardiovascular disease. If the home and work environment of the individual does not support healthy dietary changes, it will be difficult for the individual to adhere to a heart-healthy diet. As another example, living in an environment that is contaminated by secondhand smoke can be harmful to patients with cardiovascular or respiratory health problems. Living in crowded, unsanitary conditions can predispose an individual to respiratory infections and the development of tuberculosis. Air pollution can also exacerbate chronic respiratory conditions.

Other Factors

Other factors that can influence a patient's response to cardiovascular or pulmonary problems include the existence of other health problems, the location of the problem, and whether the problem is acute or chronic.

Preexisting Conditions

Respiratory and cardiovascular disorders frequently develop as a result of **preexisting conditions**. For example, individuals who have chronic health problems that affect their mobility, neuromuscular strength, or immunocompetence are frequently predisposed to the development of potentially life-threatening respiratory infections, such as pneumonia. Patients with diabetes mellitus or hypertension have a greater chance of developing coronary artery disease (CAD) or peripheral vascular disease. A patient with CAD and hypertension may be predisposed to congestive heart failure (CHF).

Location of the Problem

The **location of the problem** is another factor to consider. A patient who develops an atrial dysrhythmia is likely to experience less serious adverse effects than the patient who develops a ventricular dysrhythmia. A spontaneous pneumothorax (lung collapse) in a young, otherwise healthy adult may not lead to serious hypoxia, depending upon size and location of the pneumothorax and promptness of treatment. However, in a patient with a preexisting respiratory problem, a pneumothorax of the same size may cause the patient to develop major respiratory problems. Emphysema, a condition that can affect the total lung field, can produce profound changes in oxygenation. An embolus that lodges in a small artery, as opposed to one in a large, primary vessel, is less likely to cause life-threatening symptoms. The nurse needs to remember, however, that respiratory and cardiovascular problems generally have the potential to impact the body systemically and affect the functioning of other body organs and tissues.

Nature of the Problem

The **acute** versus **chronic** nature of the problem is another factor that must be considered. A problem of acute onset, such as a myocardial infarction or pulmonary embolus, may lead to death of the patient almost immediately. Other acute problems such as pneumonia can be treated effectively, albeit such problems require time for the patient to recover and return to normal activity.

A patient who has a preexisting chronic health problem and develops an acute onset of a cardiovascular or respiratory complication may become seriously ill or die as a result of the complication. The nurse must be particularly vigilant in assessing for cardiovascular and respiratory complications in the chronically ill. Initial signs and symptoms may be very subtle in nature, such as feelings of anxiety, restlessness, or subtle mental changes.

Patients who develop a chronic cardiovascular or respiratory problem may only notice a gradual diminishing of their functional abilities. It is important that the nurse work closely with patients and their families to develop a plan of care that will promote adherence to a therapeutic regimen and help identify and develop the coping skills necessary to live with a chronic illness.

Chapter 2 Study Questions

1.   Describe the normal physiological changes that occur in the cardiovascular
        system due to aging.

2.   Describe the normal physiological changes that occur in the respiratory system
        due to aging.

3.   Identify common risk factors associated with cardiovascular or pulmonary
        problems.

4.   How can an individual's occupation predispose the person to a cardiovascular or
        respiratory condition?

5.   Identify three psychological factors that have been correlated with the development of cardiac disease.

6.   Describe how cultural factors can influence a patient's susceptibility and response to cardiovascular/pulmonary problems.

7.   What specific dietary habits should the nurse assess in the patient who has a cardiovascular problem?

Answers to Chapter 2 Study Questions

1.   As individuals age, it is normal for the elastin in the heart to decrease, while the amount of collagen increases. These physiological changes gradually contribute to a decrease in the contractility and distensibility of the heart muscle. The myocardium gradually loses its ability to respond to increased workload demands. Arterial vessels throughout the body gradually thicken and lose their elasticity. These changes can contribute to the development of an increased systolic blood pressure. Additional changes that occur within the heart include a thickening of the heart valves due to lipid accumulation and calcification and a decrease in the number of SA pacemaker cells. The changes in the heart valves can result in a murmur, while the decreased number of pacemaker cells can lead to bradycardia.

2.   Normal physiological changes in lung tissue include the loss of elasticity in lung recoil and chest excursion. The anteroposterior diameter of the thorax enlarges as a result of these changes. The strength of an elderly individual's cough is weakened and cilia function is decreased, thus adversely affecting the ability to mobilize secretions. These changes can predispose an individual to respiratory infections. Functioning alveoli gradually decrease in number, causing a lower PaO_2 in the elderly. The respiratory rate does not compensate as rapidly for changes in oxygen and carbon dioxide levels.

3.   Cigarette smoking, a diet high in fat and cholesterol, obesity, and a sedentary lifestyle are common risk factors that promote the development of cardiovascular or pulmonary problems.

4.   A sedentary job may not provide the patient with enough opportunity for aerobic exercise. A job environment that exposes the individual to fumes, toxins, chemicals, or potential allergens can predispose the person to the development of respiratory problems (such as asthma) or exacerbate preexisting ones.

5.   Stress, anger, and hostility have been shown to have some correlation to the development of cardiac disease.

6.   An individual's culture can affect lifestyle choices, values and beliefs, and health practices. For example, food habits are frequently influenced by an individual's ethnic background. An individual's culture will influence the selection and preparation of foods. Geographic location will also dictate the availability of foods, thus influencing the ethnic diet. Individuals whose ethnic background promotes a diet high in fat, cholesterol, sodium, and starch will be at risk for obesity and cardiovascular disease. An individual's decision to seek medical help for a health problem can be influenced not only by previous health practices, but also personally held and culturally influenced values and beliefs. For example, a man who fears that diagnosis of a chronic, potentially debilitating cardiovascular or pulmonary disease will threaten his role as breadwinner for his family may be reluctant to seek medical care. An individual who believes that a health problem

is "God's punishment" and is fatalistic and accepting about the outcome of the illness is less likely to seek medical intervention or follow recommended treatment, especially for chronic health disorders.

7. The nurse should carefully assess the patient's dietary habits, paying particular attention to the intake of fat, cholesterol, and sodium. Type and amount of fluid intake should also be noted to help determine the potential for developing a fluid volume excess or deficit. Total caloric intake should be compatible with the individual's daily exercise patterns. For example, a sedentary individual cannot expect to consume the same amount of calories as someone who is reasonably active without gaining weight. Obesity may predispose an individual to the development of cardiovascular disease as well as diabetes mellitus.

UNIT II: DISORDERS OF THE RESPIRATORY SYSTEM

Chapter 3: Clinical Manifestations of Respiratory Disorders

Key Terms

Adventitious breath sounds
    Crackles
    Rhonchi
    Pleural friction rub
    Wheezes
Apnea
Barrel chest
Bradypnea
Cheyne-Stokes respirations
Clubbing
Cyanosis
Dyspnea
Kussmaul's respirations
Normal breath sounds
    Bronchial
    Bronchovesicular
    Vesicular
Orthopneic position
Pursed-lip breathing
Tachypnea

Introduction

This chapter discusses the clinical manifestations of respiratory disorders. The nurse needs to carefully assess the patient to detect the frequently subtle respiratory changes that can indicate the patient is developing a pulmonary problem. Prompt detection of changes in the patient's condition is important to avoid potential life-threatening complications.

Altered Respiratory Rate

An important aspect of detecting respiratory problems is the nurse's assessment of the patient's respiratory rate. The nurse should note the quality of the patient's respirations, observing rate, rhythm, and depth. A normal adult respiratory rate is twelve to eighteen breaths per minute. Children and elderly patients may have a slightly increased rate. Respirations should be quiet, with passive expiration. Inspiration normally takes approximately half as long as expiration.

The patient's other vital signs should also be assessed. An elevated pulse rate (**tachycardia**) may be noted in patients who are developing hypoxia. An elevated temperature can indicate the presence of respiratory disorders that are caused by inflammation and infection. The temperature elevation can be either low-grade or high-grade.

Altered Breathing Patterns

Altered breathing patterns develop in a number of respiratory problems. **Dyspnea**, which is defined as difficulty breathing, is the most common symptom of respiratory disorders. Dyspnea is a subjective experience for patients and may be difficult for the nurse to evaluate because of this subjectivity. Some common altered breathing patterns easily evaluated by the nurse include bradypnea, tachypnea, Kussmaul's respirations, Cheyne-Stokes respirations, and apnea.

- **Bradypnea** refers to slow, deep respirations that are usually regular in rhythm. Bradypnea is an indication of respiratory depression. Common causes of respiratory depression include drug overdose and increased intracranial pressure.
- **Tachypnea** refers to rapid, shallower respirations that may be regular or irregular in rhythm. Tachypnea frequently occurs in the presence of respiratory infections, fever, anxiety, and any condition that leads to the development of hypoxemia.
- **Kussmaul's respirations** are characterized by deep, regular, rapid respirations (hyperventilation) that are caused by metabolic acidosis. **Metabolic acidosis** is caused by either a base bicarbonate deficit or an increased accumulation of acid that exhausts the body's supply of plasma bicarbonate in an attempt to neutralize the excess acid. One common cause of Kussmaul's respirations is **ketoacidosis**, which can develop in patients with diabetes mellitus. The respiratory system attempts to compensate for the body's state of acidosis by increasing the respiratory rate to increase carbon dioxide elimination, thus decreasing the body's acidosis.
- **Cheyne-Stokes respirations** are respirations that are characterized by a rhythmic increasing and then decreasing depth of respirations, followed by periods of apnea. The Cheyne-Stokes respiratory pattern is frequently associated with respiratory center damage or heart failure.
- **Apnea** is the cessation of breathing. This pattern of increasing and then decreasing depth of respirations, alternated with periods of apnea, is continuously repeated.

Altered Breath Sounds

The nurse should also carefully auscultate the patient's breath sounds. Alterations in breath sounds can occur as a result of a lack of airflow through the air passages, narrowing of airways, and presence of fluid in the airways. The nurse can detect these problems through auscultation of the breath sounds. By carefully assessing the patient's breath sounds, the nurse can gather data about the patient's pulmonary and cardiac status and detect early changes in the patient's condition. The nurse should be able to auscultate breath sounds throughout all areas of the lungs.

Normal Breath Sounds

Normal breath sounds are identified as vesicular, bronchial, and bronchovesicular.

- **Vesicular breath sounds** are auscultated over all the lung fields with the exception of major bronchi. Vesicular breath sounds are quiet, soft, and low pitched.
- **Bronchial breath sounds**, which are loud and high pitched, are located over the trachea.
- **Bronchovesicular breath sounds** are of medium pitch and intensity, and are heard over the first and second intercostal spaces, close to the sternal border, and also between the scapulae.

Adventitious Breath Sounds

Adventitious breath sounds are abnormal lung sounds that can develop as a result of respiratory or cardiac problems. Abnormal lung sounds include crackles, rhonchi, wheezes, and pleural friction rub.

- **Crackles** are fine, high-pitched sounds present upon inspiration. The presence of crackles indicates fluid in small airways or the collapse of small airways. For example, the presence of crackles can indicate the development of atelectasis, pneumonia, or congestive heart failure.
- **Rhonchi** are heard upon expiration, and they are low-pitched sounds that indicate a larger airway obstruction with fluid. Rhonchi are commonly present in chronic obstructive pulmonary disease and pneumonia.
- **Wheezes** occur upon inspiration or expiration, and they are high pitched and musical in nature. The presence of wheezing indicates that air is moving through narrowed airways. Common causes of wheezing include asthma, chronic obstructive pulmonary disease, and the presence of a foreign body. Any condition that causes bronchospasms can cause wheezing. One example of a condition that can produce sudden bronchospasms and wheezing is laryngeal edema that develops as a result of an anaphylactic reaction.
- **Pleural friction rubs** are harsh, grating, rubbing sounds that can be heard upon inspiration or expiration. Pleural friction rubs are caused by inflamed pleura rubbing together as the patient breathes. Inflamed pleura are usually caused by the presence of an infection.
- **Diminished or absent** breath sounds indicate that air is not moving freely through the lungs. This can occur when areas of the lung have collapsed, as in atelectasis or pneumothorax, or when secretions have accumulated and consolidated within the lungs, thus blocking airflow.

Altered Skin Color and Temperature

The patient's skin color is can be altered by respiratory disorders. Skin color indicates the adequacy of tissue oxygenation. The following are examples of altered skin color:

- **Cyanosis**, a bluish discoloration of the skin, is indicative of decreased oxygenation of tissues. Cyanosis can be most easily noted in the oral mucous membranes, lips, and nail beds. If the patient is dark skinned, cyanosis is most likely to be noticed in the conjunctivae or lips. Cyanosis is a late sign of hypoxia and, furthermore, cannot be considered a reliable indication of the presence of hypoxia due to variations that occur depending upon the patient's hemoglobin levels.
- **Clubbing of the fingernails** indicates chronic tissue hypoxia.
- A patient who is hypoxic may also be **pale**.
- A patient who has an increased carbon dioxide level due to carbon dioxide retention may have a **ruddy (red)** complexion.

Skin temperature should also be assessed. Respiratory disorders that are caused by infection can lead to a fever. The patient's skin will appear flushed and feel warm to touch.

Altered Physical Appearance

The nurse should also assess the patient's general appearance to detect evidence of respiratory distress.

Pursed-Lip Breathing

Pursed-lip breathing, in which the patient prolongs the expiratory phase of respiration by exhaling through pursed lips, is indicative of chronic obstructive pulmonary disease or asthma. Pursed-lip breathing can also be taught to patients to prolong expiration and decrease dyspnea.

Nasal Flaring

Nasal flaring may be present in acute respiratory distress. The use of neck and shoulder **accessory muscles** and the **retraction of intercostal muscles** (muscles between the ribs) upon inspiration indicate severe respiratory distress.

Orthopneic Position

The **orthopneic position**, in which the patient leans forward with the arms supported, indicates that the patient is experiencing respiratory distress. This is a common position in patients with chronic obstructive pulmonary disease or an exacerbation of asthma.

Splinting

In some patients, the nurse may observe **splinting**, in which the patient guards against taking an inspiration of normal depth. In patients who have an abdominal or chest surgical incision or pleurisy, splinting allows the patient to decrease the pain that occurs when taking a deep breath. However, splinting is a potentially harmful activity as it also leads to hypoventilation and a decreased expansion of the alveoli. This can result in such respiratory complications as atelectasis, and ultimately pneumonia.

This example of splinting, in which the patient guards against taking deep breaths, should not be confused with the appropriate nursing technique, *also* referred to as splinting, in which the nurse assists or teaches the patient to gently, but firmly, support an incision with a blanket to enable the patient to cough and deep breathe with less pain.

Barrel Chest and Chest Expansion

When assessing the respiratory system, the nurse should note the diameter of the thorax. A **barrel chest**, which is an increase in the anteroposterior (AP) diameter of the chest, is caused by overexpansion, or hyperinflation, of the lungs. Normally, the chest has an AP to lateral diameter ratio of 1:2. With a barrel chest, the AP to lateral diameter ratio can change to 2:1. A barrel chest typically develops in emphysema. **Chest expansion** should be inspected and found to be bilaterally symmetrical. Chest expansion that is asymmetrical most likely indicates a decreased expansion of the lungs on the side that is smaller.

Tracheal Deviation

The trachea should be assessed for **tracheal deviation**. The trachea normally lies in a midline position; deviation to either side indicates that structures within the chest cavity have shifted in position. One gradual cause of tracheal deviation is the growth of a tumor. Another more acute and sudden cause is a **tension pneumothorax**, in which air enters into the chest cavity and has no avenue for exit. This will lead to a tracheal deviation away from the side of the pneumothorax. *A tension pneumothorax is a medical emergency.*

Alterations in Behavior

Because of a lack of oxygen to the brain, patients who have respiratory problems may also experience behavioral changes. The earliest indication of hypoxia is frequently a subtle change in behavior. The patient may appear anxious, irritable, or restless. The patient could also experience difficulty with memory or with speaking. Confusion can develop. When patients develop unexplained alterations in behavior such as restlessness, anxiety, or confusion, the nurse's priority action should be to first check the oxygen saturation levels of the patient.

Alterations in Comfort

When caring for a patient with respiratory problems, the nurse should carefully assess the patient for pain or discomfort related to breathing. Chest pain may be pulmonary or cardiac in origin. Careful assessment by the nurse can help determine the origin of the pain. For example, sharp chest pain that increases upon inspiration could be **pleuritic** pain. Midsternal chest pain that is described as "crushing" and radiating into the neck is likely to be cardiac in origin. Other alterations in comfort that the patient with a respiratory problem may experience include difficulty breathing, difficulty eating, fatigue, and difficulty sleeping.

Chapter 3 Study Questions

1.   Describe the altered breathing patterns of Cheyne-Stokes respirations and
      Kussmaul's respirations. Identify one potential etiology for each respiratory
      pattern.

2.   Identify and describe normal breath sounds.

3.   Describe crackles, rhonchi, and wheezes.

4.   When assessing a child with asthma, the nurse notes the presence of intercostal retraction and the use of accessory muscles. What do these assessments indicate about the patient's respiratory status?

5.   The nurse is assessing the chest diameter of a patient with emphysema. What would be an expected assessment finding?

6.   What clinical manifestations are typically the earliest indicators of the development of hypoxia?

Answers to Chapter 3 Study Questions

1. Kussmaul's respirations are rapid, deep respirations (hyperventilation) that are caused by metabolic acidosis. The respiratory system attempts to compensate for the body's state of acidosis by increasing the respiratory rate to increase carbon dioxide elimination. Cheyne-Stokes respirations are characterized by a rhythmic increasing and then decreasing depth of respirations followed by periods of apnea. This type of respiratory pattern is frequently associated with cardiac failure or respiratory center damage.

2. Normal breath sounds are identified as vesicular, bronchial, and bronchovesicular. Vesicular breath sounds are auscultated over all the lung fields with the exception of major bronchi. Vesicular breath sounds are quiet, soft, and low pitched. Bronchial breath sounds, which are loud and high pitched, are located over the trachea. Bronchovesicular breath sounds are of medium pitch and intensity, and are heard over the first and second intercostal spaces, close to the sternal border, and also between the scapulae.

3. Crackles are fine, high-pitched sounds present upon inspiration. The presence of crackles indicates fluid in small airways or collapse of small airways. For example, the presence of crackles can indicate the development of atelectasis, pneumonia, or congestive heart failure. Rhonchi, heard upon expiration, are low-pitched sounds that indicate a larger airway obstruction with fluid. Rhonchi are commonly present in chronic obstructive pulmonary disease and pneumonia. Wheezes occur upon inspiration or expiration, and they are high pitched and musical in nature. The presence of wheezing indicates that air is moving through narrowed airways. Common causes of wheezing include asthma, chronic obstructive pulmonary disease, and the presence of a foreign body. Any condition that causes bronchospasms can cause wheezing.

4. The use of neck and shoulder accessory muscles and the retraction of intercostal muscles (muscles between the ribs) upon inspiration indicate that the patient is in severe respiratory distress.

5. A barrel chest develops in emphysema. A barrel chest, which is an increase in the anteroposterior diameter of the chest, is caused by overexpansion of the lungs.

6. The earliest indication of hypoxia is frequently a subtle change in behavior. The patient may appear anxious, irritable, or restless. The patient could also experience difficulty with memory or with speaking. Confusion can develop. When patients develop unexplained alterations in behavior such as restlessness, anxiety, or confusion, the nurse's priority action should be to first check the oxygen saturation levels of the patient.

Chapter 4: Laboratory and Diagnostic Tests for Respiratory Disorders

Key Terms

Arterial blood gases
Bronchoscopy
Computed tomography (CT)
Hematocrit
Hemoglobin
Lung biopsy
Lung scan
Pulmonary function tests
Pulse oximetry
Sputum studies
 Culture and sensitivity
 Cytology
 Acid-fast smear
Thoracentesis
Thoracoscopy
Throat culture

Introduction

This chapter discusses the laboratory and diagnostic tests that are used to diagnose and monitor respiratory problems. Included are patient instructions and nursing interventions related to the tests.

Laboratory Tests for Respiratory Disorders

Laboratory tests are used primarily for respiratory disorders to determine oxygen saturation, the oxygen-carrying capacity of the patient's blood supply, and to detect the presence of infection or abnormal cells. Blood tests are also used to assess the therapeutic drug levels of medications used to treat respiratory problems. Common laboratory tests for respiratory disorders are described below.

Hemoglobin and Hematocrit

The analysis of a hemoglobin and hematocrit blood test provides data that indicate the number of red blood cells available to carry hemoglobin, and the amount of hemoglobin available to carry oxygen to body tissues.

- Specifically, a **hemoglobin** blood test measures the amount of hemoglobin available to carry oxygen. **Normal hemoglobin values** for males are 13.5–17.5 g/dL; for females, 11.5–15.5 g/dL.
- A **hematocrit** blood test measures the proportion of red blood cells to plasma, or red blood cell mass. **Normal hematocrit values** for males are 40 to 52 percent; for females, 36 to 48 percent.

Arterial Blood Gases

Arterial blood gases (ABGs) measure the blood pH, as well as oxygen and carbon dioxide levels in arterial blood. ABGs are used to determine the acid-base balance of the patient's body and the need for and effectiveness of oxygen therapy. ABGs are also used to determine the effectiveness of mechanical ventilation and can be obtained from an arterial puncture, usually radial. (Pressure must be applied for five minutes following puncture, or longer if the patient has been receiving anticoagulants.) ABGs can also be obtained from an indwelling arterial catheter. Table 4.1 summarizes normal ABG values.

Table 4.1 Normal Values for Arterial Blood Gases (Arterial Sample)	
pH	7.35–7.45
$PaCO_2$	35–45 mm Hg
PaO_2	80–100 mm Hg
HCO_3^-	22–26 mEq/L
O_2 saturation	95–100%
Base excess/deficit	+ or – 2

Pulse Oximetry

Pulse oximetry is a noninvasive method used to measure the oxygen saturation level of hemoglobin. The sensor is usually attached to the patient's finger or earlobe. Normal pulse oximetry readings reflect normal oxygen saturation readings of 95 to 100 percent.

Sputum Specimen

A **sputum specimen** can be collected to identify organisms through **culture and sensitivity**. Sputum can also be examined for **cytology** to determine if abnormal cells indicative of a malignancy are present. An **acid-fast smear** can be collected to determine the presence of acid-fast bacilli that are present in tuberculosis. If collecting sputum for an acid-fast smear, three consecutive morning specimens will be required.

When collecting a sputum specimen, the nurse should instruct the patient to cough deeply and expectorate sputum from the lungs, not from the throat. It is best to obtain the specimen in the early morning, as secretions accumulate during the night. Sputum is expectorated into a sterile container. If the patient has a tracheostomy, is intubated, or is otherwise incapable of producing a sputum specimen, the patient may be suctioned to obtain the specimen. A special sputum container or "trap" is connected to the suction catheter to facilitate collection of the sputum.

Throat Culture

A **throat culture** may be obtained to identify organisms in an upper or lower respiratory infection. A sterile swab is used to swab the throat and then placed in a special culture tube. The nurse should be careful to touch only the throat with the culture swab, so as to not contaminate the swab with normal oral cavity microorganisms. A tongue depressor can be used to help avoid swab contact with the tongue.

Drug Levels

After prescription, various respiratory **drug levels** may be drawn to determine if the therapeutic levels of drugs are being administered. For example, patients who are receiving the bronchodilator **theophylline** will have a theophylline drug level drawn. Therapeutic theophylline levels are 10–20 mcg/ml. If the actual drug level were higher than this, the nurse would assess the patient for side effects of the drug and notify the physician prior to administering the next dose of theophylline. If the level is lower than the therapeutic level, the drug dosage may need to be adjusted in order to be effective in controlling symptoms.

Diagnostic Tests for Pulmonary Disorders

A variety of noninvasive and invasive diagnostic tests are used to visualize the structures of the lungs, evaluate pulmonary functioning, biopsy lung tissue, administer therapeutic interventions, and evaluate the patient's response to treatment. Common pulmonary diagnostic procedures and associated nursing interventions are described below.

Chest X ray

A **chest X ray** is used to identify pathophysiological changes in lung tissue and structure. It is usually taken in posteroanterior (front to back) and lateral (side) positions. No specific nursing care is associated with a chest X ray. The patient should be asked to remove any metal (jewelry) that is around the neck.

Computed Tomography (CT)

A **computed tomography (CT)** scan of the lungs is a noninvasive imaging diagnostic test that displays a cross-sectional view of the lungs. This computerized test is much more specific in visualizing lung tissue, and may detect lesions that a chest X ray does not. A CT scan may be conducted with or without the use of radiopaque contrast media. If a contrast medium is used, the patient will be placed on NPO prior to the test. The nurse should assess the patient for iodine sensitivity to avoid allergic reactions. The nurse should also inform the patient about the warm, flushed feeling that may occur when the medium is injected and that a salty taste may be experienced.

Lung Scans

Lung scans are used to identify abnormalities in lung perfusion, lung functioning, and gas exchange. They are frequently used in the diagnosis of pulmonary emboli, lung cancer, inflammatory conditions, and other pulmonary disorders. Lung scans require the use of a radioactive agent.

Magnetic Resonance Imaging (MRI)

Magnetic resonance imaging (MRI) produces cross-sectional views of the body and is useful for detecting lesions of the chest wall and cardiac abnormalities. (In general, however, CT scans are better for detecting most lung abnormalities.) Patients must remove all metal objects prior to undergoing an MRI. The MRI may interfere with the functioning of cardiac pacemakers. Any individual who has a ferromagnetic prosthetic device in place should not undergo an MRI because the test could cause the prosthetic device to shift.

Pulmonary Function Tests

Pulmonary function tests are used to evaluate pulmonary functioning and the effectiveness of prescribed respiratory treatment. These tests evaluate the status of the patient's ventilatory functioning and lung volumes. A **spirometer** is used to measure air movement in the lungs. The tests should not be conducted immediately after a meal, and a rest period should be provided immediately following the procedure, as the tests require the patients to breathe as deeply and forcefully as they are able and can be tiring. Patients are asked not to use bronchodilators for approximately six hours before procedure.

Endoscopy

Endoscopic procedures can be used to directly visualize the lungs and other structures.

- A **bronchoscopy** is used to directly visualize the larynx, trachea, and bronchi. A biopsy may be performed and specimen cells collected for cytology during the procedure.
- A **laryngoscopy** is performed to visualize the larynx, biopsy a tumor, or remove a foreign object.

Preoperative Nursing Care

Preoperative nursing care prior to an endoscopic procedure includes the following:

- Ensure that the patient is NPO for six to twelve hours prior to the procedure.
- A consent form must be signed by the patient.
- A preoperative medication is administered to decrease secretions and provide sedation. This preoperative medication may be intramuscular or intravenous.
- Dentures are removed.
- A local anesthetic is usually sprayed or swabbed onto the throat to aid in the passage of the scope.

Postoperative Nursing Care

Postoperatively, nursing care includes the following:

- Keep the patient NPO until the cough and gag reflexes return.
- The patient should be monitored for respiratory distress, laryngeal spasm, hemoptysis, pneumothorax, hypotension, and hypoxia.
- Nursing assessments include monitoring the respiratory rate and rhythm, as well as auscultating breath sounds.
- If the patient has had a biopsy, the sputum may contain streaks of blood.
- The individual is positioned in a lateral (side-lying) position or in a semi-Fowler's position during the recovery phase.

Thoracoscopy

A **thoracoscopy** is a surgical procedure performed to visualize the pleural cavity and other structures of the thoracic cavity. This is frequently done to diagnose the etiology (cause) of pleural effusion or inflammation, or to stage malignant tumors. A small incision is made in an intercostal space and an endoscope is inserted. It may be done with a local or general anesthetic, depending upon the patient and the extent of the surgery.

Preoperative Nursing Care

Preoperatively, nursing care of a patient undergoing a thoracoscopy includes the following:

- The nurse ensures that the patient is NPO for eight hours prior to the thoracoscopy.
- The nurse reviews the procedure with the patient to answer any questions the patient may have and verifies that a consent form has been signed.
- An intravenous line is usually started for administration of fluids and medications during the procedure.
- A chest tube may be inserted during the procedure to remove fluid and air during the postoperative phase.

Postoperative Nursing Care

Postoperative nursing care of the patient who has had a thoracoscopy includes the following:

- Monitoring vital signs.
- Assessing the patient for signs of respiratory distress.
- Monitoring the chest tube drainage system. (Nursing care of a patient with a chest tube drainage system is addressed in chapter 5.)

- Pain medication should be administered as necessary to relieve the patient's discomfort.
- Coughing and deep breathing are encouraged to help re-expand the lung and prevent respiratory complications.

Lung Biopsy

A **lung biopsy** is performed to obtain a tissue specimen for laboratory analysis. The procedure may be done either transbronchially through a bronchoscope or through a percutaneous needle biopsy, in which a needle is inserted into the pleura to obtain the specimen. Nursing care is the same as for a bronchoscopy or a thoracoscopy. Following the biopsy, the nurse should closely assess the patient for shortness of breath, bleeding, and infection. If a pneumothorax develops following the percutaneous needle biopsy, a chest tube may be inserted to re-expand the lung.

Thoracentesis

In a **thoracentesis**, pleural fluid is removed from the pleural space by inserting a needle through the chest wall into the pleural space. This procedure may also be used to instill medication into the pleural space. During this procedure, the patient is positioned upright with their elbows and head supported on a bedside table. A chest X ray will be done following the procedure to rule out a pneumothorax. The patient is monitored for respiratory distress, hemoptysis, coughing, and tachycardia following the procedure.

Chapter 4 Study Questions

1.   What is the significance of hemoglobin and hematocrit levels to a patient's respiratory status?

2.   What would be the purpose of obtaining arterial blood gases on a patient with respiratory problems?

3.   The nurse is collecting a sputum specimen for an acid-fast smear. For accurate results, when should the nurse collect the sputum?

4.   A patient is scheduled to have a bronchoscopy for the biopsy of a suspicious lesion. What preoperative care should the nurse anticipate for this patient?

5.   What nursing assessments would be appropriate for a patient following a bronchoscopy?

6.   A patient is scheduled to have a thoracentesis to remove pleural fluid. How
        should the nurse position the patient in preparation for the thoracentesis?

7.   What postoperative patient care should the nurse anticipate following a
        thoracentesis?

Answers to Chapter 4 Study Questions

1. The analysis of a hemoglobin and hematocrit blood test provides data that indicate the number of red blood cells available to carry hemoglobin and the amount of hemoglobin available to carry oxygen to body tissues. A decrease in hemoglobin and/or hematocrit levels can affect the oxygenation of body tissues.

2. ABGs measure the blood pH, as well as oxygen and carbon dioxide levels in arterial blood, and are used to determine the acid-base balance of the patient's body and the need for and effectiveness of oxygen therapy. ABGs are also used to determine the effectiveness of mechanical ventilation.

3. When collecting sputum for an acid-fast smear, three consecutive morning specimens will be required. To collect a sputum specimen, the nurse should instruct the patient to cough deeply and expectorate sputum from the lungs, not from the throat. It is best to obtain the specimen in the early morning, as secretions collect during the night. Sputum is expectorated into a sterile container.

4. Preoperative nursing care prior to a bronchoscopy procedure includes ensuring that the patient is NPO for six to twelve hours prior to the procedure. A preoperative medication is administered to decrease secretions and provide sedation. This preoperative medication may be intramuscular or intravenous. Dentures are removed. A local anesthetic is usually sprayed or swabbed onto the throat to aid in the passage of the scope. A consent form must be signed prior to the procedure.

5. Postoperatively, nursing care includes keeping the patient NPO until the cough and gag reflexes return. The patient should be monitored for respiratory distress, laryngeal spasm, hemoptysis, pneumothorax, hypotension, and hypoxia. Nursing assessments include monitoring the respiratory rate and rhythm, as well as auscultating breath sounds. If the patient has had a biopsy, the sputum may contain streaks of blood. The individual is positioned in a lateral (side-lying) position or in a semi-Fowler's position during the recovery phase.

6. In preparation for the thoracentesis, the patient is positioned upright with elbows and head supported on a bedside table.

7. A chest X ray will be done following the thoracentesis to rule out a pneumothorax. The patient is monitored for respiratory distress, hemoptysis, coughing, and tachycardia following the procedure.

Chapter 5: Therapeutic Interventions for Respiratory Disorders

Key Terms

Chest tubes
Incentive spirometry
Mechanical ventilators
Medications
    Antihistamines
    Antitussives
    Bronchodilators
    Decongestants
    Expectorants
    Mucolytic agents
Oxygen administration
    Nasal cannula
    Oxygen hood
    Oxygen mask
    Oxygen tent

Introduction

This chapter discusses the therapeutic interventions commonly used in the treatment of patients with respiratory disorders and the nursing care associated with these interventions. Pharmacological treatment will be covered, as well as dietary modifications and therapeutic devices.

Medications Commonly Used to Treat Respiratory Disorders

Antihistamines

Antihistamines are used to relieve allergic symptoms, especially in allergic rhinitis. Antihistamines block the action of histamine, which is released as part of the inflammatory process. The use of antihistamines can help relieve sneezing and rhinorrhea. Some commonly prescribed antihistamines include the following:

- **Fexofenadine (Allegra)**
- **Loratidine (Claritin)**
- **Diphenhydramine (Benadryl)**

Side effects of the newer antihistamines, such as fexofenadine and loratidine, are minimal. There are fewer sedative side effects associated with these drugs than with the first-generation antihistamines. Common side effects include drowsiness, fatigue, and GI distress (nausea). Elderly patients are more likely to experience drowsiness, dizziness, and syncope. The nurse should encourage patients to take antihistamines with food to decrease the likelihood of GI distress. Patients should also be told to avoid alcohol while taking the drug and not to drive until the patient's response to the drug has been determined. The patient may notice a dry mouth as a result of taking an antihistamine. This can be counteracted by encouraging the patient to drink fluids and suck on sugarless lozenges.

Diphenhydramine (Benadryl) has fewer GI side effects than the other antihistamines, but is much more likely to cause sedation. Patients should be strongly cautioned about driving while taking this drug.

Antitussives

Antitussives are used to suppress the cough reflex. They are used to suppress persistent, nonproductive coughs that are uncomfortable to the patient. Some commonly prescribed antitussives are the following:

- **Dextromethorphan (Benylin, Pertussin)**
- **Codeine**
- **Hydrocodone bitartrate (Hycodan)**

Antitussives are contraindicated in the treatment of the chronic coughs associated with emphysema and asthma. Patients should understand the importance of having a persistent cough investigated by a health-care provider; antitussives should not be taken if the source of the cough has not been diagnosed. Individuals with hepatic impairment should use antitussives with caution.

Side effects are rare with antitussives. The most common side effects are drowsiness, dizziness, restlessness, nausea, and vomiting. Patients should be warned to avoid alcohol when taking antitussives, as both substances are CNS depressants. The nurse should also caution the patient to avoid driving or operating machinery because of the potential sedative effect of the drug.

Bronchodilators

Bronchodilators are used to dilate the bronchial airways and facilitate respiration. Commonly prescribed bronchodilators include **methylxanthine derivatives** and **beta-2 agonists** (adrenergic agents). These drugs can be administered orally, intravenously, and through metered dose inhalers.

Some commonly prescribed bronchodilators are the following:

- **Theophylline (Slo-Phyllin)**—methylxanthine derivative
- **Albuterol (Proventil)**—beta-2 agonist
- **Metaproterenol (Alupent)**—beta-2 agonist

These medications can cause systemic side effects and should be administered with caution.

Theophylline

Theophylline directly acts upon bronchial smooth muscle, causing it to relax. It also decreases bronchial swelling by inhibiting the release of histamine. Theophylline is contraindicated for use with patients who have peptic ulcers and status asthmaticus. The drug should be used cautiously in patients with hypertension or cardiac, renal, or hepatic disease.

The side effects of theophylline are numerous and are associated with the blood level of the drug. The nurse should carefully monitor theophylline drug levels prior to administering the drug. If the drug blood level is kept at 10–20 mcg/mL, side effects will usually be minimal. When serum blood levels reach 20–25 mcg/mL, the patient may experience headache, irritability, nausea, vomiting, and diarrhea. If the blood level exceeds 30 mcg/mL, the patient can develop hypotension, arrhythmias, convulsions, and circulatory failure. The nurse should keep in mind that patient response to blood levels can vary.

Drug interactions are numerous with theophylline. In particular, rifampin, cimetidine, oral contraceptives, macrolide antibiotics (such as erythromycin) and quinoline antibiotics (such as ciprofloxacin) can increase the effect of theophylline and lead to toxicity. The nurse should carefully review the patient's prescribed medications prior to administration of theophylline.

Other factors, such as smoking and diet, can also affect theophylline's action. Smoking decreases the blood level of the drug. Caffeine can increase the effect of the drug. A low-carbohydrate, high-protein diet and charcoal broiled beef will increase elimination of the theophylline, while a high-carbohydrate, low-protein diet will decrease elimination.

The nurse should instruct the patient to take the drug as prescribed. If a dose is missed, the patient should not double the next dose—this can lead to side effects. The patient should also be instructed to report any side effects.

Albuterol and Metaproterenol

Albuterol and other beta-2 agonists act by dilating the bronchi and increasing the respiratory rate and depth. The side effects of albuterol include tachycardia, hypertension, and decreased renal and GI blood flow. The systemic side effects of beta-2 agonists can be minimized by administering the medications via a metered-dose inhaler. Beta-2 agonists are the drugs of choice for acute respiratory distress because of their rapid onset of action.

Decongestants

Decongestants are used to decrease nasal congestion. They are typically prescribed to treat upper respiratory disorders such as the common cold, allergic rhinitis, and sinusitis.

These respiratory disorders are caused by inflammation. Decongestants may be taken orally, or topically using nasal spray or drops. A prototype decongestant is **pseudoephedrine (Sudafed)**.

Pseudoephedrine has a sympathomimetic action and causes vasoconstriction of the nasal mucous membranes, thus decreasing congestion. Sinus drainage is promoted with the shrinkage of mucous membranes.

Because of the sympathomimetic action of the drug, there are a variety of side effects. Restlessness, anxiety, insomnia, and tremors are common side effects. More serious side effects include convulsions, delusions, and hallucinations. The cardiovascular system can also be affected. Side effects related to the cardiovascular system include tachycardia, palpitations, arrhythmias, and hypertension. Patients who have hypertension or coronary artery disease should not take pseudoephedrine. It should be used cautiously with other chronic illnesses, such as diabetes, benign prostatic hypertrophy, glaucoma, and thyrotoxicocis.

Pseudoephedrine interacts with numerous drugs, most importantly MAOIs, guanethidine, furazolidone, and methyldopa. Hypertension may develop if pseudoephedrine is administered with these drugs.

Patients should be instructed to take this drug as prescribed to avoid overdosage. The nurse should also caution the patient not to take over-the-counter (OTC) drugs with pseudoephedrine, as many OTC drugs also contain pseudoephedrine. It is recommended that this drug not be taken for more than four days. Patients using nasal sprays or drops can experience nasal **rebound congestion** if the sprays or drops are overused.

Expectorants

Expectorants are used to help liquefy and thin respiratory secretions so that patients can more easily cough them up. A prototype drug for expectorants is **guaifenesin (Robitussin)**.

Guaifenesin decreases the adhesiveness of respiratory fluids and makes them less viscous. The decreased viscosity of the fluids promotes a more productive cough. Eventually, a more productive cough will lead to a decreased amount of coughing.

The most common side effects associated with guaifenesin are GI symptoms, including nausea, vomiting, and anorexia. A headache or dizziness may also be experienced.

Patients should be encouraged to drink a full glass of water with each dose of medication. Small, frequent meals may help decrease the GI symptoms. The patient should avoid alcohol while taking this drug. If the cough does not begin to resolve within one week, the patient should see a health-care provider.

Mucolytic Agents

Mucolytic agents break down and facilitate the removal of tenacious secretions from the respiratory tract. Mucolytic agents are administered via a nebulizer. They may also be instilled directly into the trachea via a tracheostomy or endotracheal tube. A commonly used mucolytic agent is **acetylcysteine (Mucomyst)**.

Acetylcysteine breaks down the viscosity and the tenacity of sputum, making it easier for the patient to cough up the secretions. Coughing up the secretions should help clear the patient's airway and ease breathing.

The most common side effects include difficulty breathing, bronchospasm, and bronchoconstriction. The drug should be used with caution in patients who have asthma. Some patients may experience nausea.

The nurse should advise the patient that a disagreeable odor will be noted at the beginning of the treatment. The treatment is usually followed by clapping and postural drainage to help facilitate removal of secretions. The nurse should also instruct the patient in how to maximize the effect of the drug by increasing fluid intake, coughing and deep breathing at regular intervals, and maintaining a humidified environment.

Therapeutic Devices for Respiratory Disorders

There are a variety of therapeutic devices that the nurse uses to support the nursing care provided to patients with respiratory disorders. This section will cover oxygen therapy, incentive spirometry, chest tubes, mechanical ventilators, and the nursing interventions associated with these devices.

Oxygen Therapy

Oxygen therapy is a key component of the treatment of patients who have a respiratory disorder. Oxygen is considered to be a medication and should be administered with the same precautions that a nurse takes in administering other medications. Oxygen is administered as prescribed by the physician; however, in the event of an emergency, the nurse may initiate oxygen therapy without an order.

It is important that the nurse assess the effect of oxygen therapy on the patient. It is possible to administer too much oxygen, leading to **oxygen toxicity**. Administering too high a concentration (over 50 to 60 percent) of oxygen for a prolonged period of time, usually over forty-eight hours, causes oxygen toxicity. Oxygen toxicity leads to lung tissue damage and pulmonary edema. Signs and symptoms of oxygen toxicity include dyspnea, restlessness, lethargy, paresthesia, substernal chest discomfort, and increasing respiratory discomfort. It is important to only use the amount of oxygen necessary to achieve a satisfactory oxygen saturation level.

Administering Oxygen

Oxygen is administered using several different methods. The **nasal cannula** is one of the most common ways of delivering oxygen therapy. A nasal cannula is used for delivering low to moderate flow rates of oxygen (1–6 liters/minute). Oxygen concentration increases about 4 percent for each increase in liter/minute. The cannula is inserted into the patient's nares, allowing the patient to talk, eat, and move around with relative ease without interrupting the oxygen flow. The nasal cannula, however, does not insure the delivery of a precise amount of oxygen, which is very dependent upon the rate and depth of respiration. A patient who is a mouth breather, for example, will receive less oxygen than the patient who breathes through the nose. Some disadvantages of the nasal cannula are that the cannula can become easily dislodged from the patient's nares, thus decreasing the delivery of oxygen, and nasal mucosal drying and irritation can occur.

Oxygen masks can also be used to deliver oxygen. Masks come in different forms, with each form having a specific use. The **simple oxygen mask** is used to administer low to moderate concentrations of oxygen. Usual flow rates for the simple oxygen mask are 6–8 liters/minute. It is important to keep the flow rate on a simple oxygen mask on at least 6 liters/minute to prevent rebreathing of accumulated, exhaled carbon dioxide. **Partial rebreathing** and **nonrebreathing masks** are used to deliver moderate to high concentrations of oxygen. The flow rates for the partial rebreathing mask are typically 8–11 liters/minute. Flow rate for the nonrebreathing mask is 8–12 liters/minute. Flow rates should be high enough that the bags that are attached to the partial and nonrebreathing masks remain inflated at all times.

These masks can be difficult to fit to the patient's face and are uncomfortable for some patients. Patients may complain of feeling claustrophobic with the mask in place. Skin breakdown can also occur if the mask fits too tightly to the face. It is difficult to achieve a controlled delivery of oxygen with the use of these masks. The masks must be removed for the patient to eat or drink.

The **Venturi mask** is considered to be the most reliable method of delivering a prescribed oxygen concentration. A dial on the mask end piece regulates the precise concentration of oxygen. A Venturi mask allows the patient to receive a continuous mix of room air and fixed concentration of oxygen. A perforated cuff allows carbon dioxide to leave the mask. Because of the high airflow and oxygen flow that is maintained within the mask, a constant concentration of oxygen is provided, regardless of respiratory rate or depth. As with the other masks, a Venturi mask must be removed for the patient to eat or drink.

Oxygen hoods or **tents** are used to administer oxygen to infants and young children who do not tolerate the use of a cannula or mask. The hood is used for infants, while the tent is used for children who are beyond early infancy. Both the hood and tent provide increased humidity as well as increased oxygen concentrations. The oxygen hood should not be positioned to rub against the infant's head, neck, or shoulders. The oxygen tent may be frightening to some children. It is important for the child to not feel isolated. It helps if family members are nearby and can be seen through the tent. A favorite toy can be placed in the tent with the child for comfort and distraction. The temperature within the tent can become warm due to the enclosure. The nurse should periodically check the temperature. Also, moisture may gather on the enclosure, so the nurse should check to be sure the child remains warm and dry. A major disadvantage of the oxygen tent is that it is difficult to keep the oxygen concentrations maintained. Frequent opening of the tent will deplete the oxygen levels. Nursing care should be planned to minimize disruption of oxygen concentration levels.

Caution should be used when administering oxygen. Oxygen supports combustion, so any device that may start a fire should not be used around oxygen. Smoking is strictly prohibited. Oxygen should be humidified to decrease the drying effect and the water level in the humidifier bottle should be checked frequently so that it does not run dry. A water-soluble lubricant can be applied to the nose to decrease irritation. The nurse should frequently check the flow rate settings to insure that the flow rate being administered is the prescribed rate.

Incentive Spirometry

Incentive spirometry is used to help promote expansion of the alveoli and prevent the development of atelectasis. It is most frequently ordered for use with postoperative patients, especially those patients who have had thoracic and abdominal surgery, and patients who are immobilized. The spirometer provides patients with a visual measurement of how deeply they are breathing to expand the lungs.

The nurse should assist the patient to use the incentive spirometer correctly. The ideal position for the patient to be in when using the spirometer is a semi-Fowler's or sitting position. The patient should be encouraged to take a few normal breaths before using the spirometer. The patient then places the mouthpiece in the mouth and inhales slowly and deeply, holding the breath at the end of the inspiration for approximately three seconds. The patient then slowly exhales. Patients should be encouraged to perform this exercise every hour during the waking hours, about ten times each time. Coughing is encouraged after the deep breathing exercises are completed. The nurse should help the patient set a realistic goal of the volume of air to inspire.

Chest Tubes

Chest tubes are inserted following thoracic surgery and for treatment of a chest trauma that may result in a pneumothorax or hemothorax. The chest tube is inserted to remove air, fluid, blood, or even purulent material from the intrapleural space. Insertion of a chest tube into the pleural space will facilitate the removal of these substances and promote the re-expansion of the lung. To summarize, the major purposes for insertion of a chest tube, or tubes, are the following:

- To promote removal of air and fluid from the pleural space
- To reestablish normal negative pressure in the pleural space, thus promoting re-expansion of the lung
- To prevent the development of a tension pneumothorax (discussed in chapter 7).

In the past, the equipment used to establish a **closed chest tube drainage system** was typically a one-, two-, or three-glass bottle drainage system. Today, there are many commercial drainage systems on the market (such as Pleur-evac, Thora-Seal, or Atrium) that have almost completely replaced the three-glass bottle system with a single, disposable, plastic unit. It is important, however, to understand the basic principles of the closed chest tube drainage system, and it is easiest to explain and understand today's commercial systems by using the three-bottle system as an illustrative example.

Single-Bottle System

In a **single-bottle system**, the end of the chest drainage tube is submerged below water. This underwater seal allows air and fluid to drain from the pleural space into the bottle, while preventing air from re-entering. As the fluid level within the bottle increases, it can become more difficult for the air and fluid to drain from the pleural space. Gentle suction can be applied to aid in removal of air and fluid. The amount of suction added is usually 10–20 cm H_2O. Suction is typically provided by a wall suction unit, where the nurse controls the amount of suction by adjusting a gauge on the wall unit.

Two-Bottle System

A **two-bottle system** consists of the underwater seal bottle described in the single-bottle system, as well as an additional bottle that is used to collect fluid. The first bottle in the system is used to collect fluid, and the second bottle is used to create an underwater seal. With this set-up, the underwater seal fluid level remains unaffected by the amount of drainage coming from the pleural space. Again, in this system, as in the single-bottle system, the effectiveness of the drainage system depends upon gravity or suction being applied to the system. Suction is added to the underwater seal bottle by attaching the suction connection to the vent stem on the underwater seal bottle. The amount of suction applied and how it is regulated is the same as described in the single-bottle system.

Three-Bottle System

The **three-bottle system** has an additional third bottle that is used to control the amount of suction that is applied to the drainage system. The level to which the venting tube is submerged in the water controls the amount of water suction that is applied to the patient. For example, if the tube is submerged to twenty centimeters below the surface of the water, twenty centimeters of water suction will be applied to the patient. Wall suction is applied to the system to create negative pressure, but the amount of suction provided is controlled by the water in the third bottle. Constant bubbling will be noted in this third bottle, which means the system is functioning correctly. There is an outside vent to room air in the third bottle.

Commercial Drainage System

Commercial drainage systems combine the three separate bottles into one plastic, disposable unit. This provides several advantages over the old system. First of all, the system is unbreakable and self-contained. Sterility is easier to maintain. Secondly, with the exception of the connection to the patient's chest tube, there are no connections that can become loose. It is also easier to manage this system, as it is lightweight and the patient can ambulate more easily.

The commercial systems operate upon the same principles of the three-bottle system. The device consists of three chambers. The chest tube is attached to the first chamber of the system with the use of a one-way valve that prevents reflux of fluid. Water is placed into the second chamber to act as an underwater seal. This seal causes fluid and air to be drained from the pleural space into the first chamber. The air escapes through an air vent in the second chamber out into the atmosphere and cannot re-enter the patient's pleural space. The air vent *must not be clamped* or the air will not be able to escape.

The water level of the second chamber will fluctuate with the patient's respirations: the level will move up with inspiration and down with expiration. Suction can be applied to the second chamber to help increase drainage. Usual amounts of suction are 10–20 cm H_2O, but can range to up to 40 cm H_2O. Suction amounts of over 50 cm H_2O can create lung tissue damage.

The third chamber of the device is the suction control chamber. If suction is applied to the second chamber, the water in the third chamber will continuously bubble, indicating that the system is working. The suction gauge should be regulated to produce slow, steady bubbling in the third chamber. It is not the suction gauge that controls the amount of suctioning applied to the patient; instead, it is the amount of water level that is in the third chamber. The more water, the more suction created. A vent to room air is located in the third chamber.

Nursing Care of the Patient with a Chest Tube

Nursing care of the patient with a chest tube includes the following actions:

- Using sterile water, set up the closed drainage system following the manufacturer's directions. Fill the suction control chamber to the level prescribed by the physician.
- Attach the patient's chest tube securely to the collection chamber of the drainage system. Secure the connection with adhesive tape.
- Turn on the suction machine, adjusting the suction so that the water in the suction control chamber bubbles slowly and steadily. Ensure that the tubes do not hang in dependent loops between the bed and the drainage system, as this can affect the removal of air and fluid from the pleural space.
- Mark the starting drainage level with tape on the outside of the drainage system. Monitor the increase in drainage at regular intervals (hourly, every eight hours, daily, etc.). As the drainage increases, mark the level on the tape with the date and time. The amount of drainage that is to be anticipated from a chest tube depends upon the nature of the patient's problem. A pneumothorax may produce only a scant amount of fluid, as mostly air is removed from the pleural space. In a postsurgical patient, if the drainage is bright red or approaches 200 cc/hour, notify the surgeon, as this could indicate hemorrhage. In the immediate postoperative phase, the nurse can anticipate some bloody drainage initially. This drainage will gradually change into serous drainage. The amount of drainage will decrease gradually during the first twenty-four hours following the surgery.

- Check the tubing frequently for loops or kinks. The patient should not be allowed to lie on the tubing. The patient may assume any position that is comfortable; frequently that is a semi-Fowler's position. The nurse should encourage the patient to change position frequently.
- Patients with chest tubes can get out of bed to sit in a chair or ambulate. It is important that the drainage device be kept upright at all times and not be raised above the level of the waist. Suction may be discontinued during ambulation if ordered by the physician.
- Administer analgesics as necessary to promote patient comfort. Adequate pain control is essential so that the patient can deep breathe and cough at regular intervals. These activities will help re-expand the lung, remove airway secretions, and facilitate drainage of fluid and air from the pleural space.
- Milking and stripping of chest tubes is no longer routinely recommended due to the increased pressure that occurs during these activities that can be damaging to lung tissue. If the nurse's assessment indicates that chest tube drainage is obstructed by clots or tissues, a gentle squeezing of the tube may be initiated. The nurse should stabilize the tube close to the chest with one hand, while the other hand moves carefully down the tube towards the drainage device.
- The nurse should routinely assess the functioning of the drainage system, making note of the following conditions:
    1. Fluctuation (**tidaling**) of the fluid in the water seal chamber should occur with the patient's respirations. Tidaling will stop if the lung has re-expanded (can be verified by chest X ray) or if tubing is obstructed. Asking the patient to change position or cough may cause tidaling to start again. Notify the physician if tidaling is not reestablished. Fluctuation may be minimal when suction is applied.
    2. The nurse should observe for bubbling in the water seal compartment. Intermittent bubbling can be considered normal as air is removed from the pleural space. However, continuous bubbling in the water seal chamber indicates the presence of an air leak. The system should be investigated closely for the location of the air leak—the insertion site at the chest, loose tubing connections, or a puncture in the tubing or drainage system are likely places for the nurse to troubleshoot and repair if possible. Petrolatum gauze can be applied to air leaks at the chest tube insertion site. Loose connections can be re-taped. If the air leak cannot be repaired, the system may need to be replaced. If an external source for the air leak cannot be found, it is possible that a large amount of air is escaping from the pleura. The physician should be notified immediately.
    3. If the bubbling in the suction control chamber stops, the system is not operating correctly (i.e., suction apparatus is broken or power source has been interrupted) or there is an air leak into the suctioning apparatus. The nurse should inspect the system for an air leak or malfunctioning equipment and repair promptly.
    4. Chest tubes should not be clamped unless specifically ordered by the physician, because clamping the tube can trap air in the lung and precipitate a lung collapse. If the chest tube becomes disconnected, it is best to simply

reattach the tubes instead of clamping the tube. Clamping may be necessary, however, in order to help determine the location of a persistent air leak.

5. A liter of sterile water should be kept at the bedside. If the chest tube drainage system should become cracked, the chest tube can be submerged into the bottle of sterile water to maintain a water seal until the system is replaced.

6. The nurse should assess the patient frequently for signs and symptoms of respiratory distress. This includes vital sign changes such as tachypnea, tachycardia, or hypotension; chest pain or pressure; dyspnea; diminished or absent lung sounds; or tracheal deviation. These signs and symptoms could be indications of a developing tension pneumothorax.

- Upon removal of the chest tube, a small piece of petrolatum gauze and a gauze pad will be immediately applied and taped securely over the chest tube opening to create an airtight bandage. The patient is asked to take a deep breath and hold it while the tube is being removed in order to keep air from being introduced into the pleural space. The nurse should administer pain medication about thirty minutes prior to the removal of the tube to decrease the discomfort of the procedure.

Mechanical Ventilators

Mechanical ventilation is used when patients are not able to sustain adequate ventilation under their own efforts. Examples of clinical conditions that may require a patient to be placed on mechanical ventilation includes postoperative thoracic surgery, acute respiratory failure, drug overdose, neuromuscular disorders that impair the respiratory system, trauma, shock, or multisystem organ failure. While many patients on ventilators are cared for in intensive care units, more and more ventilated patients can be found on medical-surgical units, skilled long-term care facilities, and in the home setting.

A patient is typically considered to be a candidate for mechanical ventilation if one or more of the following conditions develop:

- A continuous decline in oxygenation (Pa O_2 < 50 mm Hg)
- A continuous increase in $PaCO_2$ levels with acidosis (pH < 7.35)
- Respiratory rate of 35 breaths/minute
- Decreasing vital capacity

Mechanical ventilators can be **pressure-cycled**, **time-cycled**, or **volume-cycled ventilators**. All of these ventilators are positive-pressure ventilators that exert positive pressure upon the airway, thus inflating the lungs. The most commonly used type of positive-pressure ventilator is the volume-cycled ventilator.

- A **pressure-cycled ventilator** delivers a flow of air to the lungs during inspiration until a preset pressure is reached. Upon reaching the preset pressure, the ventilator cycles off and begins exhalation. This type of ventilator can deliver an inconsistent amount of air, as the amount of air delivered is dependent upon airway resistance and compliance. These ventilators are for short-term use only in adults. An IPPB machine is a common example of a pressure-cycled ventilator.

- A **time-cycled** ventilator delivers an inspiration for a preset time interval. This type of ventilator is used with newborns and infants.
- A **volume-cycled** ventilator delivers a preset volume of air with each inspiration. When the present volume of air has been delivered, the ventilator cycles off and exhalation begins. This type of ventilator delivers a consistent amount of air to the patient without regard to airway resistance or compliance.

When a patient is placed on a ventilator, the physician will prescribe the settings that are to be established for the ventilator, including the respiratory rate, mode, use of positive-end expiratory pressure (PEEP), tidal volume, concentration of inspired oxygen, and the inspiratory/expiratory ratio. It is the nurse's responsibility to ensure that the prescribed settings are maintained, monitor the functioning of the equipment, and note the patient's response to the therapy. Usually, a flow sheet is maintained to record hourly checks of the ventilator settings. In particular, the nurse should assess and monitor the following aspects of the ventilator settings and equipment:

- Control mode
- Settings for respiratory rate, tidal volume, and fraction of inspired oxygen (FiO_2)
- Inspiratory pressure reading
- Inspiratory/expiratory ratio
- Minute volume
- Use of PEEP
- Sigh setting
- Sensitivity of ventilator triggering
- Periodic (hourly) checks of ventilator alarms to ensure proper functioning
- Assess humidifier water level; empty accumulated condensation from tubing

Another important aspect of nursing care for a patient on a ventilator is to carefully monitor the patient's response to the ventilation. Specific nursing interventions related to the patient's respiratory status include the following:

- Auscultating lung sounds and respiratory pattern every one to two hours. It is important to assess that the endotracheal (ET) tube is correctly positioned and ventilating both lungs.
- Suctioning the patient as needed with hyperoxygenation before and after each suctioning episode; maintaining sterile technique when suctioning.
- Maintaining humidification of system to thin secretions.
- Turning and positioning the patient every two hours.
- Monitoring ABGs and pulse oximeter.
- Providing oral hygiene every two hours to prevent stomatitis and respiratory infection.

- Assessing for development of respiratory infection, noting WBC count and differential and color and odor of sputum.
- Monitoring patient for complications related to mechanical ventilation: pneumothorax, cardiovascular compromise, accidental extubation, improper position of endotracheal tube.
- Being prepared to manually ventilate the patient with an AMBU bag in the case of ventilator malfunction.

Being intubated and placed on a ventilator can be a frightening experience for a patient. The nurse should strive to decrease the patient's anxiety by carefully explaining all aspects of the patient's care, even if the patient is nonresponsive. Remind family members that it is important to talk to the patient, even though the patient may be sedated or comatose. For the patient who is conscious, it is important to establish a method of communication so that the patient can communicate with others. A writing board may be a helpful tool. Medication may also be administered PRN to help decrease anxiety.

The patient will be weaned from the ventilator when the patient's condition stabilizes and the patient is able to sustain adequate ventilation efforts. When a patient is weaned, the ventilatory support is gradually decreased while the patient regains responsibility for maintaining spontaneous breathing. ABGs will be closely monitored to ensure that the patient is capable of maintaining ventilation without ventilatory support. Once the patient has demonstrated this ability, the ET tube will be removed. Usually, the patient is placed on supplemental oxygen immediately after extubation.

Chapter 5 Study Questions

1. Fexofenadine (Allegra) has been prescribed to treat a patient's allergic symptoms. What information about the drug's side effects should the nurse include in the patient education plan?

2. A patient who is receiving theophylline tells the nurse that he has a headache and is feeling nauseated. How should the nurse interpret this information?

3. The nurse is developing a patient education plan for a patient who is taking theophylline. What information should the nurse include about dietary interference with the effectiveness of theophylline?

4. The nurse is administering oxygen to a patient with pneumonia. What signs and symptoms would indicate the patient has developed oxygen toxicity?

5.   Describe the disadvantages of oxygen masks.

6.   The nurse is caring for a four-year-old child who is receiving oxygen therapy in a tent. What nursing actions are appropriate for caring for the child in the tent?

7.   Develop a teaching plan for instructing a patient on how to correctly use an incentive spirometer.

8.   Identify the three major purposes for inserting a chest tube.

9.   Describe the basic operating principles of a commercial chest tube drainage
      system.

10.   The nurse is caring for a patient who is in the immediate postoperative phase of
      thoracic surgery. Chest tubes have been inserted. The nurse notes that in the last
      hour the patient has had 250 cc of bright red drainage from the tube. How should
      the nurse interpret this finding?

11.   The nurse notes fluctuations of the fluid level in the water seal chamber of the
      closed chest tube drainage system. How should the nurse evaluate this finding?

12.   The nurse notices continuous bubbling in the water seal chamber of a closed chest tube drainage system and suspects an air leak. What nursing actions should the nurse implement at this time?

13.   The nurse is assisting in the removal of a patient's chest tube. How should the wound be dressed following removal of the tube?

14.   What criteria indicate that a patient may be a candidate for mechanical ventilation?

15.   Identify specific nursing interventions related to maintaining the respiratory status of a patient on mechanical ventilation.

Answers to Chapter 5 Study Questions

1.   Common side effects include drowsiness, fatigue, and GI distress (nausea). Elderly patients are more likely to experience drowsiness, dizziness, and syncope. The nurse should encourage patients to take antihistamines with food to decrease the likelihood of GI distress. Patients should also be told to avoid alcohol while taking the drug, and not to drive until the patient's response to the drug has been determined. The patient may notice a dry mouth as a result of taking an antihistamine. This can be counteracted by encouraging the patient to drink fluids and suck on sugarless lozenges.

2.   The headache and nausea indicate the patient is experiencing side effects related to the administration of theophylline. The nurse should carefully monitor theophylline drug levels prior to administering the drug. If the drug blood level is kept at 10–20 mcg/mL, side effects will usually be minimal. When serum blood levels reach 20–25 mcg/mL, the patient may experience headache, irritability, nausea, vomiting, and diarrhea. If the blood level exceeds 30 mcg/mL, the patient can develop hypotension, arrhythmias, convulsions, and circulatory failure. The nurse should keep in mind that patient response to blood levels can vary.

3.   Factors such as smoking and diet can affect theophylline's action. Smoking decreases the blood level of the drug. Caffeine can increase the effect of the drug. A low-carbohydrate, high-protein diet and charcoal broiled beef will increase elimination of the theophylline, while a high-carbohydrate, low-protein diet will decrease elimination.

4.   It is possible to administer too much oxygen, leading to oxygen toxicity. Administering too high a concentration (over 50 to 60 percent) of oxygen for a prolonged period of time, usually over forty-eight hours, causes oxygen toxicity. Oxygen toxicity leads to lung tissue damage and pulmonary edema. Signs and symptoms of oxygen toxicity include dyspnea, restlessness, lethargy, paresthesia, substernal chest discomfort, and increasing respiratory discomfort. It is important to only use the amount of oxygen necessary to achieve a satisfactory oxygen saturation level.

5.   Masks can be difficult to fit to the patient's face and are uncomfortable for some patients. Patients may complain of feeling claustrophobic with the mask in place. Skin breakdown can also occur if the mask fits too tightly to the face. It is difficult to achieve a controlled delivery of oxygen with the use of these masks. The masks must be removed for the patient to eat or drink.

6.   The oxygen tent may be frightening to some children. It is important for the child to not feel isolated. It helps if family members are nearby and can be seen through the tent. A favorite toy can be placed in the tent with the child for comfort and distraction. The temperature within the tent can become warm due to the enclosure. The nurse should periodically check the temperature. Also,

moisture may gather on the enclosure, so the nurse should check to be sure the child remains warm and dry. A major disadvantage of the oxygen tent is that it is difficult to keep the oxygen concentrations maintained. Frequent opening of the tent will deplete the oxygen levels. Nursing care should be planned to minimize disruption of oxygen concentration levels.

7. The ideal position for the patient to be in when using the spirometer is a semi-Fowler's or sitting position. The patient should be encouraged to take a few normal breaths before using the spirometer. The patient then places the mouthpiece in the mouth and inhales slowly and deeply, holding the breath at the end of the inspiration for approximately three seconds. The patient then slowly exhales. Patients should be encouraged to perform this exercise every hour during the waking hours, about ten times each time. Coughing is encouraged after the deep breathing exercises are completed.

8. The major purposes for insertion of a chest tube, or tubes, are to 1) promote removal of air and fluid from the pleural space; 2) reestablish normal negative pressure in the pleural space, thus promoting re-expansion of the lung; and 3) prevent the development of a tension pneumothorax.

9. The commercial systems operate upon the same principles of the three-bottle system. The device consists of three chambers. The chest tube is attached to the first chamber of the system with the use of a one-way valve that prevents reflux of fluid. Water is placed into the second chamber to act as an underwater seal. This seal causes fluid and air to be drained from the pleural space into the first chamber. The air escapes through an air vent in the second chamber out into the atmosphere and cannot re-enter the patient's pleural space. The air vent must not be clamped or the air will not be able to escape. The water level of the second chamber will fluctuate with the patient's respirations: the level will move up with inspiration and down with expiration. Suction can be applied to the second chamber to help increase drainage. Usual amounts of suction are 10–20 cm H_2O, but can range to up to 40 cm H_2O. Suction amounts of over 50 cm H_2O can create lung tissue damage. The third chamber of the device is the suction control chamber. If suction is applied to the second chamber, the water in the third chamber will continuously bubble, indicating that the system is working. The suction gauge should be regulated to produce slow, steady bubbling in the third chamber. It is not the suction gauge that controls the amount of suctioning applied to the patient; instead, it is the amount of water level that is in the third chamber. The more water, the more suction created. A vent to room air is located in the third chamber.

10. In a postsurgical patient, if the drainage is bright red or approaches 200 cc/hour, notify the surgeon, as this could indicate hemorrhage.

11. Fluctuation (tidaling) of the fluid in the water seal chamber should occur with the patient's respirations. Tidaling will stop if the lung has re-expanded (can be

verified by chest X ray) or if tubing is obstructed. Asking the patient to change position or cough may cause tidaling to start again. Notify the physician if tidaling is not reestablished. Fluctuation may be minimal when suction is applied.

12.   The system should be investigated closely for the location of the air leak—the insertion site at the chest, loose tubing connections, or a puncture in the tubing or drainage system are likely places for the nurse to troubleshoot and repair if possible. Petrolatum gauze can be applied to air leaks at the chest tube insertion site. Loose connections can be re-taped. If the air leak cannot be repaired, the system may need to be replaced. If an external source for the air leak cannot be found, it is possible that a large amount of air is escaping from the pleura. The physician should be notified immediately.

13.   Upon removal of the chest tube, a small piece of petrolatum gauze and a gauze pad will be immediately applied and taped securely over the chest tube opening to create an airtight bandage. The patient is asked to take a deep breath and hold it while the tube is being removed in order to keep air from being introduced into the pleural space. The nurse should administer pain medication about thirty minutes prior to the removal of the tube to decrease the discomfort of the procedure.

14.   A patient is typically considered to be a candidate for mechanical ventilation if one or more of the following conditions develop: 1) a continuous decline in oxygenation (Pa O_2 < 50 mm Hg); 2) a continuous increase in $PaCO_2$ levels with acidosis (pH < 7.35); 3) respiratory rate of 35 breaths/minute; and 4) decreasing vital capacity.

15.   Specific nursing interventions related to the patient's respiratory status include the following:

- Auscultating lung sounds and respiratory pattern every one to two hours. It is important to assess that the endotracheal (ET) tube is correctly positioned and ventilating both lungs.
- Suctioning the patient as needed with hyperoxygenation before and after each suctioning episode; maintaining sterile technique when suctioning.
- Maintaining humidification of system to thin secretions.
- Turning and positioning the patient every two hours.
- Monitoring ABGs and pulse oximeter.
- Providing oral hygiene every two hours to prevent stomatitis and respiratory infection.
- Assessing for development of respiratory infection, noting WBC count and differential and color and odor of sputum.

- Monitoring patient for complications related to mechanical ventilation: pneumothorax, cardiovascular compromise, accidental extubation, improper position of endotracheal tube.
- Being prepared to manually ventilate the patient with an AMBU bag in the case of ventilator malfunction.

Chapter 6: Nursing Care for Upper Respiratory Tract Disorders

Key Terms

Acute epiglottitis
Acute laryngitis
Acute laryngotracheobronchitis
Croup syndrome
Laryngeal cancer
Laryngeal obstruction
Laryngectomy
Sleep apnea
Tonsillitis
Tonsillectomy
Tracheostomy

Introduction

This chapter discusses the nursing care of patients who have an upper respiratory tract disorder. Upper respiratory disorders can interfere with the patient's intake and supply of oxygen. Upper respiratory disorders can be relatively minor, for example, the common cold. Upper respiratory disorders may also be life threatening if they lead to airway obstruction. The disorders that are specifically covered in this chapter are croup syndrome, tonsillitis, sleep apnea, laryngeal obstruction, and laryngeal cancer. Care of the patient with a laryngectomy is also addressed.

Croup

Croup syndrome is a childhood disorder caused by acute respiratory infections that have affected the larynx, trachea, and/or bronchi. Croup can lead to significant airway problems in infants and small children due to the small diameter of their airways. Croup can be mild or life threatening.

Pathophysiology

Croup is actually a syndrome and can be caused by any upper respiratory infection that affects the larynx, trachea, and/or bronchi. The characteristic symptoms include a "barking" cough, inspiratory stridor, hoarseness, and respiratory distress that are caused by swelling of the larynx. The respiratory distress can range from mild to life threatening. The three forms of croup are acute laryngotracheobronchitis (LTB), acute epiglottitis, and acute laryngitis.

Acute Laryngotracheobronchitis (LTB)

The most common form of croup syndrome is **acute laryngotracheobronchitis (LTB)**. LTB usually occurs in children who are less than five years old. Inflammation in the larynx and trachea causes swelling and obstruction of the airway, as well as difficulty moving air through the narrowed passage. As the child has increasing difficulty inhaling sufficient amounts of air, symptoms of hypoxia develop. If the child is not capable of eliminating adequate amounts of carbon dioxide, respiratory acidosis can develop. Eventually, if the respiratory acidosis is not corrected, respiratory failure will occur.

Acute Epiglottitis

Acute epiglottitis can occur at any age, but is most likely to occur between the ages of two to five years. The supraglottic region of the airway becomes obstructed as a result of inflammation that is most commonly caused by the *Haemophilus influenzae* organism. Respiratory distress can develop very rapidly.

Acute Laryngitis

Acute laryngitis is most common in older children and teenagers, and is typically caused by a virus infection. Accompanying clinical manifestations are mild in comparison to epiglottitis and laryngotracheobronchitis.

Clinical Manifestations

Acute Laryngotracheobronchitis (LTB)

LTB has the following clinical manifestations:

- Children with LTB have typically had an upper respiratory infection for a few days preceding the croup.
- They may have a low-grade fever.
- The "barking" cough develops along with inspiratory stridor.
- Respirations will be increased and labored.
- Suprasternal retractions can also be noted.
- If the condition is severe enough to significantly impede the flow of oxygen into the lungs, the child will develop signs of hypoxia. Restlessness and anxiety will be present. As the hypoxia increases, cyanosis will be evident and respiratory failure can result.

Acute Epiglottitis

Acute epiglottitis has the following clinical manifestations:

- The onset of acute epiglottitis is sudden, frequently preceded by a sore throat, and rapidly progresses to extreme respiratory distress.
- The child will lean forward and sit upright in the **tripod position**, with the mouth open, chin thrust out, and the tongue protruding.
- Drooling saliva is prominent due to excessive secretions and difficulty swallowing.

- The child will be anxious, very restless, and irritable.
- Cyanosis can develop.
- Substernal and suprasternal retraction may be apparent.
- The throat will appear reddened and inflamed.
- The epiglottis will be edematous and cherry red. **Note:** If acute epiglottitis is suspected, the epiglottis should only be examined if the equipment for immediate intubation is readily available. The use of a tongue depressor or throat culture swab can precipitate further airway obstruction.

Acute Laryngitis

In **acute laryngitis** the predominant complaint is hoarseness. The patient may also complain of upper respiratory symptoms such as nasal congestion and drainage, and a sore throat. Fever, muscle aches, headache, and malaise are other common complaints.

Medical Management

Acute Laryngotracheobronchitis (LTB)

The goal of medical management in LTB is to maintain an open airway and decrease respiratory distress. If the child has mild croup, they will be managed at home. Cool mist humidifiers are used to provide moisture and decrease inflammation, ultimately providing relief from the cough.

If the child needs to be hospitalized, an oxygen tent will be used to provide humidified air and oxygen. Nebulized epinephrine may be used to decrease swelling in cases of more serious breathing difficulty. Corticosteroids are also used for their anti-inflammatory effect, which causes a decrease in edema and provides respiratory relief.

Acute Epiglottitis

The child who has acute epiglottitis requires emergency medical care to maintain an open airway. Respiratory obstruction can move rapidly to respiratory failure and death. Immediate endotracheal intubation may be necessary and should always be anticipated, with intubation equipment readily available. Intravenous antibiotic therapy will be administered; most children improve after approximately twenty-four hours of therapy. Corticosteroids may also be administered.

Acute Laryngitis

Care of the patient with acute laryngitis is symptomatic. The disease is usually self-limiting. Patients will be encouraged to increase fluid intake and use humidified air.

Nursing Care of the Child with Croup

Nursing care is similar for LTB and epiglottitis. Frequent assessment of the respiratory status of the child with croup is a necessity. The nurse should be particularly alert for early signs of respiratory distress and airway obstruction. Increased restlessness, increased respiratory rate and pulse, flaring nostrils, and retraction of the accessory muscles are indications of increasing airway obstruction and demand prompt action by the nurse. Pulse oximetry and ABGs will be monitored. Intubation equipment should be readily available for emergency intervention.

An appropriate **nursing diagnosis** for the patient with croup is impaired gas exchange related to airway obstruction. The **goal** of nursing care is to prevent airway obstruction and relieve respiratory distress.

Nursing measures include the following:

- Encourage the infant or child to rest.
- Adequate fluid intake is also important and should be encouraged in those children who have mild croup.
- Intravenous fluids will be administered to those who are more seriously ill and cannot take fluids.
- The nurse should encourage the family to be present and involved in the child's care, as their involvement can help decrease anxiety and relieve some respiratory distress. Parents may need to hold and comfort the child to help decrease anxiety.
- The child should be placed in any position that promotes ease of breathing; usually the child will prefer to sit upright.

Upon discharge, the nurse should teach the parents to continue to provide humidified air in the home environment and encourage fluid intake, as well as a good nutritional diet. The infant or child should not be subjected to cigarette smoke. The parents should be instructed to watch the child closely for increased difficulty breathing, increased coughing, or temperature, and to seek health care promptly if signs and symptoms of respiratory distress return.

Tonsillitis

Tonsillitis is an acute infection of the tonsils. The most common cause of tonsillitis is Group A streptococci. Common clinical manifestations of tonsillitis include sore throat and fever. The patient may also complain of difficulty swallowing due to the sore throat. Tonsillitis is frequently accompanied by adenoiditis (inflamed adenoids). Otitis media can also develop as the infection spreads to the ears.

Tonsillitis is diagnosed by a thorough history and physical. A **throat culture** is taken to determine the causative organism. Antibiotics, most commonly penicillin, are prescribed. For recurrent episodes of tonsillitis, a **tonsillectomy** may be performed. Most tonsillectomies are performed on children; however, adults may also require a tonsillectomy with repeated infections.

Most tonsillectomies are performed as outpatient surgery. Therefore, nursing care is focused on the immediate postoperative period and patient education. Immediately following surgery the nurse closely monitors the patient for hemorrhage. The nurse should report vomiting of large amounts of bright-red or brown (coffee-ground emesis) blood to the surgeon. The patient is monitored for restlessness and tachycardia, as these signs and symptoms may indicate bleeding is occurring. Hemorrhage is most likely to occur in the first twelve to twenty-four hours following surgery, but can occur up to ten days following surgery. The nurse uses a light to directly visualize the back of the throat to detect bleeding. Frequent swallowing, especially while sleeping, can also be an indication of active bleeding. Activity will be limited to minimize the likelihood of bleeding. Analgesics are administered to promote comfort. Decreasing throat pain following surgery will help improve the patient's appetite and fluid intake.

Additional discharge teaching includes care of the throat following surgery. The patient is cautioned to avoid coughing, clearing the throat, or blowing the nose, as these activities can irritate the surgical area. Patients should report any signs of bleeding. The patient is taught to use warm saline solution to rinse out the mouth—gargling is avoided. Liquids or a semi-liquid diet is recommended for the first one to two days after surgery to prevent irritation of the throat, followed by a soft diet. Liquids should be tepid. Hot and cold beverages are avoided, as are acidic or spicy foods. Milk products may be given in limited amounts as they increase mucus production and throat clearing in some individuals.

Sleep Apnea

Sleep apnea is an obstructive respiratory disorder that occurs during sleep. Obstructive sleep apnea occurs most commonly in males, especially those who are overweight and older. Cigarette smoking and alcohol intake are additional risk factors. Individuals who have sleep apnea are at an increased of stroke and myocardial infarction and have a higher incidence of hypertension.

Individuals who have sleep apnea experience loud snoring episodes with periods of apnea that last at least ten seconds. There are five or more episodes of apnea per hour, ending with the patient awakening with a loud gasp, after which breathing resumes. The cycle is usually repeated throughout the night, sometimes up to several hundred times. When individuals wake up in the morning they can complain of a headache, sore throat, and feeling excessively tired. They may have difficulty concentrating.

Obstructive sleep apnea is due to relaxation of tonic dilator muscles of the upper airway during sleep. This relaxation promotes the collapse of small airways in the upper airway. The apneic episode can stress the cardiac and respiratory systems. Sleep apnea is diagnosed with a **sleep test** that demonstrates the occurrence of apneic episodes.

Patients diagnosed with sleep apnea are advised to lose weight, quit smoking, and avoid alcohol. The most common treatment is to place patients on **continuous positive airway pressure** (CPAP) while they sleep to prevent airway collapse. Patients usually report a dramatic improvement in the quality of their sleep with the use of CPAP. Surgery may also be performed to decrease the obstruction. The nurse's role in care of the patient with sleep apnea is to provide patient teaching and ensure the patient understands self-care activities associated with the disorder.

Laryngeal Obstruction

As in the child, laryngeal obstruction in the adult can be a life-threatening event. The obstruction can be the result of inflammation of the larynx that leads to edema, or it can be due to obstruction by a foreign body. Allergic reactions are a frequent cause of obstruction in adults.

Laryngeal obstruction is a medical emergency. If it is caused by edema from an allergic reaction, epinephrine will be administered to decrease swelling. Corticosteroids may also be used. If the larynx is obstructed by a foreign body, the Heimlich maneuver should be attempted to dislodge it. Immediate tracheostomy may be necessary when emergency efforts are not successful at opening the airway.

Cancer of the Larynx

Laryngeal cancer typically occurs in middle age, most often in men. Risk factors include smoking, especially in combination with alcohol. Inhalation of toxins can also lead to cancer of the larynx.

Pathophysiology

A malignant tumor can develop in three different areas in the larynx. Most commonly tumors will occur in the glottic area around the vocal cords. Other regions include the supraglottic area and the subglottis.

Clinical Manifestations

Hoarseness is the most common initial symptom of laryngeal cancer in the glottic area, due to the vocal cords being affected. Other signs and symptoms can include pain, difficulty swallowing, and a feeling of a lump in the throat. Dyspnea can also develop.

Medical Management

Cancer of the larynx is diagnosed through a laryngoscopy. Treatment will depend upon size and location of the tumor. Surgery, radiation therapy, and chemotherapy are all treatment options. These treatment options are frequently used in combination with each other. Surgical treatment includes a **laryngectomy**, in which the larynx is removed and a permanent airway opening is created in the neck. The patient also has permanent voice loss.

Nursing Process: Assessment

The nurse should assess the patient for hoarseness, pain, and difficulty swallowing. Any respiratory distress, which may be present in more advanced cases, is also noted. If the patient is scheduled for a laryngectomy, the nurse should assess the patient's knowledge of the procedure and any fears and concerns related to the surgery. The nurse will plan a means of communication following surgery with the patient so that the patient may be able to communicate his or her needs.

Nursing Process: Diagnosis and Planning

Based upon an analysis of the gathered data, the following **nursing diagnoses** may be appropriate for the patient with laryngeal cancer who has a laryngectomy:

- Anxiety related to diagnosis of cancer and anticipated surgical procedure
- Impaired verbal communication related to laryngectomy
- Ineffective airway clearance related to creation of alternate airway
- Body image disturbance related to potentially disfiguring neck surgery
- Ineffective management of therapeutic regimen related to lack of knowledge regarding laryngectomy care
- Altered nutrition, less than body requirements related to difficulty swallowing

Primary goals for the patient with a laryngectomy due to laryngeal cancer include the following:

- Reduction of anxiety
- Maintenance of a patent airway
- Ability to communicate effectively
- Adequate nutrition and fluid intake
- Improved body image
- Knowledge of self-care management of laryngectomy
- Avoidance of complications: respiratory distress, wound or respiratory infection, hemorrhage

Nursing Process: Implementation

Following a laryngectomy, nursing interventions will be directed towards maintaining a patent airway, controlling secretions, assisting the patient with an alternate means of communication, decreasing patient anxiety, and promoting adequate nutritional intake. Other priority nursing interventions include promoting a positive body image, teaching the patient how to care for the tracheostomy, and monitoring the patient for complications.

Maintaining a Patent Airway

Maintaining a patent airway is a priority nursing intervention. Immediately postoperatively, it is common for the patient to experience a significant amount of airway secretions. The patient may find this frightening as they try to breathe and cough up the secretions. Remember that the airway is now located at the stoma that has been created in the patient's neck; no longer can the patient breathe through the nose. It is important that the nurse maintain a calm and reassuring manner while helping the patient to deep breathe, cough, and expectorate the secretions. The nurse should also reassure the patient that the amount of secretions will decrease daily as healing occurs. The patient should be positioned in a semi-Fowler's or Fowler's position to facilitate breathing and removal of secretions. Early ambulation will be encouraged to help prevent respiratory complications such as atelectasis or pneumonia.

It is important that the nurse remain alert to any signs or symptoms that may be indicative of respiratory distress: restlessness, anxiety, tachypnea, difficulty breathing, inability to cough up secretions, tachycardia, or change in mental status. If the patient cannot cough up the secretions enough to clear the airway, the nurse may gently suction the stoma. Care must be taken to not traumatize the sutures with the suction catheter. Humidified air will also help keep the secretions moist and easier to expectorate.

Wound Care

Wound care is another priority nursing measure. A small wound drain will usually be inserted in surgery to help remove fluid from the surgical area and promote wound healing. The physician will remove the drain when the fluid collection is less than 50 cc per twenty-four-hour period.

Because of the copious secretions present in the early postoperative period, it is difficult to keep the wound area clean and dry. It is important, however, to keep the incision and the skin around the stoma clean and dry to prevent infection and skin breakdown. The nurse should gently cleanse the skin at least once a shift with normal saline (or other prescribed solution) and pat the area dry.

Establishing Alternate Means of Communication

Helping the patient establish an alternate means of communication is another important aspect of patient care following a laryngectomy. Following the removal of the larynx, the patient will not be able to produce normal voice sounds. This loss is permanent. Prior to surgery, the nurse should work with the patient to establish a means of communication to be used in the immediate postoperative period. Hand signs, communication boards, and Magic Slates are some suggested means of communication. The patient may become impatient and frustrated with attempts at communication as an adjustment is made to voice loss.

A speech therapist will begin to work with the patient as soon as the surgeon approves. This usually occurs about one week following surgery. There are three techniques that may be used to reestablish speech: esophageal speech, artificial larynx, and tracheoesophageal puncture (TEP).

- **Esophageal speech** is produced by belching air. It is seldom used, as it is difficult for the patient to learn to make intelligible sounds.
- The **artificial**, or **electrical**, **larynx** is capable of producing sounds when the patient articulates words. While easy to use, the disadvantage is that the words may be difficult to distinguish and sound mechanical.
- The **tracheoesophageal puncture** (**TEP**) is the most common procedure used today. A valve that is placed in the stoma is used to move air from the trachea into the esophagus and out the mouth to form speech. The sounds produced with the TEP are more normal than the other methods, and there is a high (80 to 90 percent) success rate with patients relearning to speak with it.

Nutritional Status

The patient's nutritional status is another area of concern. The patient may not be able to eat or drink for up to ten to fourteen days postoperatively. Edema around the surgical area must subside and secretions decrease before the patient will be able to swallow effectively. During this time period, the patient will receive nutrients and fluids through intravenous infusions, total parenteral nutrition (TPN), or enteral feedings through a small gauge feeding tube.

When the patient is allowed to eat, oral intake will be resumed with foods that are easily swallowed. Thick liquids are the easiest for the patient to swallow; other foods will be introduced as the patient is able to tolerate them. Because air no longer moves through the nose to stimulate the olfactory senses, smell and taste will be affected for a period of time following surgery. This change is usually temporary. It is important that the patient receive good oral hygiene prior to and after each meal. This will help stimulate the patient's appetite and decrease the likelihood of oral infections.

Discharge

Upon discharge to the home setting, the nurse should ensure that the patient is prepared to safely provide self-care. The patient should be instructed on how to care for the stoma, how to suction secretions when needed, and the importance of humidifying the air in the home environment. Other safety issues should also be addressed. Swimming is not allowed. The patient may shower as long as the stoma is protected from the flow of water. The stoma should also be protected from sprays, powders, cut hair, and any other substance that may be an irritant to the airways. The patient can usually resume all normal activities. If the patient is scheduled to receive radiation therapy as additional treatment for the cancer, the nurse will also emphasize the importance of frequent oral hygiene to prevent drying and irritation of the oral mucosa.

Self-Esteem and Body Image

Because of the potentially disfiguring nature of neck surgery and the creation of a permanent stoma, patients may experience a loss of self-esteem and a disturbance in body image. The nurse should encourage the patient to express fears and concerns. Patients and their significant others may benefit from a referral to a support group. Active involvement in self-care activities can also help the patient regain self-esteem.

Nursing Process: Evaluation

The effectiveness of nursing interventions can be measured by the patient's achievement of the following **expected outcomes**:

- Expresses relief of anxiety
- Maintains a patent airway
- Expresses understanding of self-care activities
- Develops effective communication techniques
- Maintains adequate nutrition and fluid intake
- Exhibits positive body image and self-esteem
- Avoids development of complications

Chapter 6 Study Questions

1.　　Describe the pathophysiology of croup.

2.　　What are the characteristic symptoms of croup?

3.　　A nurse is caring for a three-year-old child who has croup. What would be a priority nursing assessment for this child?

4.　　Describe the medical management that the nurse can anticipate for the treatment of croup.

5.　　Describe the signs of increasing airway obstruction in a child with croup that would demand immediate intervention by the nurse.

6.   What nursing measures would be appropriate for the nurse to implement when caring for a child with croup?

7.   What is the most common initial symptom of laryngeal cancer?

8.   Identify three potential nursing diagnoses that would be appropriate for the patient with laryngeal cancer who has had a laryngectomy.

9.   A nurse is caring for a patient who is immediately post-op with a laryngectomy. In what position should the nurse place the patient to help maintain a patent airway?

10.   What would be an appropriate means of communication for a patient to use immediately following a laryngectomy?

11.   Briefly describe three techniques that may be used to reestablish speech in a
        patient who has had a laryngectomy.

12.   A nurse is assisting a patient to eat following a laryngectomy. What would be the
        easiest foods for the patient to swallow when first resuming eating?

13.   Briefly describe the discharge instructions that would be appropriate for a nurse to
        give a patient with a laryngectomy upon his discharge home.

Answers to Chapter 6 Study Questions

1. Croup is actually a syndrome and can be caused by any upper respiratory infection that affects the larynx, trachea, and/or bronchi. The most common cause of croup is acute laryngotracheobronchitis (LTB). Inflammation in the larynx and trachea causes swelling and obstruction of the airway, as well as difficulty moving air through the narrowed passage.

2. The characteristic symptoms of croup include a "barking" cough, inspiratory stridor, and respiratory distress that are caused by swelling of the larynx. The respiratory distress ranges from mild to life threatening. Children with LTB and croup have typically had an upper respiratory infection for a few days preceding the croup. They may have a low-grade fever. Suprasternal retractions can also be noted. If the condition is severe enough to significantly impede the flow of oxygen into the lungs, the child will develop signs of hypoxia. Restlessness and anxiety will be present. As the hypoxia increases, cyanosis will be evident and respiratory failure can result.

3. Frequent assessment of the respiratory status of the child with croup is a necessity. The nurse should be particularly alert for early signs of respiratory distress and airway obstruction.

4. The goal of medical management is to maintain an open airway. If the child has mild croup, they will be managed at home. Cool mist humidifiers are used to provide moisture and decrease inflammation, ultimately providing relief from the cough. If the child needs to be hospitalized, an oxygen tent will be used to provide humidified air and oxygen. Nebulized epinephrine may be used to decrease swelling in cases of more serious breathing difficulty. Corticosteroids are also used for their anti-inflammatory effect, which causes a decrease in edema and provides respiratory relief.

5. Increased restlessness, increased respiratory rate and pulse, flaring nostrils, and retraction of the accessory muscles are indications of increasing airway obstruction and demand prompt action by the nurse. Intubation equipment should be readily available for emergency intervention.

6. Nursing measures include encouraging the infant or child to rest. Adequate fluid intake is also important and should be encouraged in those children who have mild croup. Intravenous fluids will be administered to those who are more seriously ill and cannot take fluids. The nurse should encourage the family to be present and involved in the child's care, as their involvement can help decrease anxiety and relieve some respiratory distress.

7. Hoarseness is the most common initial symptom of laryngeal cancer.

8.   Any three of the following nursing diagnoses would be potential nursing diagnoses for a patient with a laryngectomy: anxiety related to diagnosis of cancer and anticipated surgical procedure; impaired verbal communication related to laryngectomy; ineffective airway clearance related to creation of alternate airway; body image disturbance related to potentially disfiguring neck surgery; ineffective management of therapeutic regimen related to lack of knowledge regarding laryngectomy care; and altered nutrition, less than body requirements related to difficulty swallowing.

9.   The patient should be positioned in a semi-Fowler's or Fowler's position to facilitate breathing and removal of secretions.

10.   Prior to surgery, the nurse should work with the patient to establish a means of communication to be used in the immediate postoperative period (e.g., hand signs, communication boards, and Magic Slates). The patient may become impatient and frustrated with attempts at communication as an adjustment is made to voice loss.

11.   There are three techniques that may be used to reestablish speech: esophageal speech, artificial larynx, and tracheoesophageal puncture (TEP). Esophageal speech is produced by belching air. It is seldom used, as it is difficult for the patient to learn to make intelligible sounds. The artificial, or electrical, larynx is capable of producing sounds when the patient articulates words. While easy to use, the disadvantage is that the words may be difficult to distinguish and sound mechanical. The TEP is the most common procedure used today. A valve that is placed in the stoma is used to move air from the trachea into the esophagus and out the mouth to form speech.

12.   When the patient is allowed to eat, oral intake will be resumed with foods that are easily swallowed. Thick liquids are the easiest for the patient to swallow; other foods will be introduced as the patient is able to tolerate them.

13.   The patient should be instructed on how to care for the stoma, how to suction secretions when needed, and the importance of humidifying the air in the home environment. Other safety issues should also be addressed. Swimming is not allowed. The patient may shower as long as the stoma is protected from the flow of water. The stoma should also be protected from sprays, powders, cut hair, and any other substance that may be an irritant to the airways. The patient can usually resume all normal activities. If the patient is scheduled to receive radiation therapy as additional treatment for the cancer, the nurse will also emphasize the importance of frequent oral hygiene to prevent drying and irritation of the oral mucosa.

Chapter 7: Nursing Care for Lower Respiratory Tract Disorders

Key Terms

Acute respiratory failure
Adult respiratory distress syndrome (ARDS)
Asthma
Chronic obstructive pulmonary disease (COPD)
    Chronic bronchitis
    Emphysema
Flail chest
Hemopneumothorax
Hemothorax
Orthopnea
Pneumothorax
    Closed (simple or spontaneous)
    Open
    Tension
Pneumonia
    Community-acquired
    Hospital-acquired
    Immunosuppressed host
    Aspiration
Pulmonary embolus
Respiratory syncytial virus (RSV)
Status asthmaticus
Tuberculosis
    Acid-fast bacillus smear
    Ghon's tubercle
    Mantoux test

Introduction

This chapter discusses the nursing care of patients who have a lower respiratory tract disorder. Lower respiratory disorders may produce an alteration in the intake and supply of oxygen or oxygen absorption. They may be acute in onset or of a chronic nature. Many of these disorders can be life threatening. Chronic respiratory disorders also impact the patient's quality of life. The specific lower respiratory disorders covered in this chapter include asthma, chronic obstructive pulmonary disease, respiratory syncytial virus, pneumonia, pneumothorax, flail chest, pulmonary embolus, and acute respiratory failure.

Asthma

Asthma is a chronic, inflammatory disorder of the airways. Asthma can develop at any age. It is the most common chronic childhood disease. The most frequent predisposing factor to the development of asthma is an allergy to an airway irritant. Common airway irritants include animal dander, mold, dust, and pollens. Other irritants and asthma triggers include polluted air, smoke, cold or hot weather changes, stress, or physical exertion.

Pathophysiology

Asthma is characterized by the presence of airway inflammation that causes hyperresponsiveness of the airways, airway edema, and the production of thick mucus. These pathophysiological changes lead to a narrowed airway diameter that obstructs the flow of air throughout the lungs. The changes can occur suddenly, triggering an asthma attack in the patient. These acute exacerbations vary in intensity, and may last only minutes or for days. In some patients, the asthma exacerbations can be severe and life threatening if the patient does not seek prompt medical attention. Because the pathophysiological changes are reversible, the patient may be free of breathing problems between attacks.

Clinical Manifestations

The most common clinical manifestations of asthma are a cough, wheezing, and dyspnea. These symptoms may occur suddenly or may develop over a matter of days. The cough can be nonproductive or productive of mucus. Wheezing is heard upon expiration as air is pushed through the narrowed airways. Wheezing may be present upon inspiration as well. The patient will complain of a feeling of chest tightness and dyspnea. The patient must work hard to move air out of the lungs and, as a result, expiration becomes prolonged. As the attack continues, hypoxemia can develop.

A severe, continuous asthma attack is referred to as **status asthmaticus**. This condition is life threatening and is considered to be a medical emergency. In status asthmaticus, the patient exhibits labored breathing, prolonged expiration, and wheezing. However, as the attack worsens, the wheezing will disappear. *This is an ominous sign and a dire indication that the patient has stopped moving air in and out of the lungs. Respiratory failure and death is imminent if prompt medical intervention is not implemented.*

Diagnostic Tests

Common diagnostic tests for asthma include pulmonary function studies, ABGs, and pulse oximetry. During an asthma attack, pulmonary function studies will indicate a decreased **forced expiratory volume** (FEV) and decreased **forced vital capacity** (FVC). ABGs and pulse oximetry will indicate hypoxemia. Because of the patient's rapid breathing, **hypocapnia** (decreased carbon dioxide levels) may develop, leading to respiratory alkalosis. If the patient has a severe asthma attack, severe hypoxemia and respiratory acidosis may develop. Between asthma attacks, pulmonary function and other diagnostic tests are likely to be normal.

Medical Management

Asthma is treated with pharmacological therapy. Medications are used to provide long-term control of the asthma symptoms, as well as prompt relief from exacerbations. Long-term treatment of asthma is achieved through the use of anti-inflammatory drugs administered through **metered-dose inhalers** (MDI). The drug of choice is **corticosteroids**. Commonly administered inhaled corticosteroids include **beclomethasone (Vanceril); triamcinolone acetonide (Azmacort); flunisolide (Aerobid)** and **fluticasone (Flovent)**. A side effect of corticosteroid inhalers is the development of thrush. The patient should be instructed to rinse the mouth out after each use of the inhaler and is encouraged to use a spacer to administer the drug and minimize contact of the drug with the oral mucosa.

Other drugs commonly used for long-term therapy include **long-acting beta-2 adrenergic agonists** and **bronchodilators**, such as methylxanthines. These drugs can be used in combination with the inhaled corticosteroids, and may be given orally or inhaled. When using these drugs together, it is recommended that the patient use the inhaled bronchodilators first, and then the corticosteroid inhaler. By dilating the airways first with the bronchodilators, the corticosteroid will be more effective. **Leukotriene inhibitors** are a relatively new category of anti-inflammatory medications that are being used in long-term treatment of asthma and can be used in combination with the above-mentioned drugs.

For acute symptoms of an asthma attack, **short-acting beta-2 adrenergic agonists** are the drugs of choice for their rapid onset of action. Examples of these drugs include **albuterol (Proventil); metaproterenol (Alupent); and terbutaline (Brethaire)**.

It is recommended that individuals monitor their peak flow readings daily. This helps individuals to gauge the effectiveness of their asthma control.

Nursing Process: Assessment

Depending upon the degree of respiratory distress the patient is experiencing, the nurse may need to defer aspects of the data-gathering process until the patient's condition is stable. During an acute attack, the nurse focuses assessment on the patient's respiratory status and implements immediate intervention to improve ventilation and gas exchange.

Subjective assessment data that is gathered by the nurse includes information about the patient's history of asthma and any known precipitating factors. The nurse should also gather information about the patient's self-care activities and compliance with the prescribed medication regimen.

Objective assessment data that is gathered includes assessment of vital signs, including the presence of tachypnea, tachycardia, and **pulsus paradoxus**, which is a diminished pulse upon inspiration. Pulsus paradoxus, which is caused by air trapping within the lungs and obstructed venous return, is best detected by confirming a drop in systolic blood pressure (6 to 8 mm Hg) during inspiration. The patient will likely be anxious or apprehensive. The nurse should assess for any changes in the patient's sensorium.

Inspection of the patient may reveal dyspnea, use of accessory muscles, prolonged expiration, use of the orthopneic position (forward leaning), and cyanosis. Percussion reveals hyperresonance and decreased excursion of the diaphragm. Inspiratory and expiratory wheezing and rhonchi can be heard upon auscultation. However, the nurse should note that as the patient becomes fatigued or develops status asthmaticus, there will be only faint or absent breath sounds. This is a critical finding that indicates the patient is approaching respiratory failure and is a medical emergency.

The nurse will evaluate ABG findings that will typically reveal mild hypoxemia and respiratory alkalosis in a mild to moderate asthma attack, and severe hypoxemia and respiratory acidosis in a severe attack.

Nursing Process: Nursing Diagnosis and Planning

Based upon an analysis of the gathered data, the following **nursing diagnoses** may be appropriate for the patient with asthma:

- Ineffective breathing pattern related to bronchospasm
- Ineffective airway clearance related to bronchospasm, increased secretions, and fatigue
- Impaired gas exchange related to ventilation/perfusion mismatch
- Anxiety related to difficulty breathing and oxygen deprivation
- Ineffective management of treatment regimen related to lack of knowledge about asthma and pharmacological therapy

Primary goals for the patient with asthma include the following:

- Maintenance of a patent airway
- Restoration of normal breathing pattern
- Improved gas exchange
- Reduction in anxiety and fear
- Knowledge of self-care program and treatment regimen
- Avoidance of complications: status asthmaticus and respiratory failure

Nursing Process: Implementation

The initial care of the client will depend upon the severity of the respiratory symptoms. In an acute attack, the first step is to assess the patient's airway and initiate interventions to maintain a patent airway.

It is important that the nurse be calming and reassuring to help decrease the patient's anxiety. The patient should not be left alone. Place the patient in a high-Fowler's position to aid breathing. The patient should be encouraged to breathe through the nose and exhale through pursed lips. Supplemental oxygen is initiated.

The nurse should promptly administer inhaled beta-2 adrenergics to relieve the bronchospasms and evaluate the patient's response. Corticosteroids may also be administered for their anti-inflammatory effect. IV fluids will be initiated to administer IV medications, such as theophylline, and to also replace any fluid losses. If the underlying cause of the asthma attack is determined to be a respiratory infection, the nurse can anticipate beginning intravenous antibiotic therapy. In a severe attack, the nurse should anticipate the need for intubation and have the appropriate equipment nearby.

Patient Teaching

Patient teaching is an important aspect of nursing care for the patient with asthma. The nurse should cover the following information in the patient teaching plan:

- Avoiding respiratory infections
- Avoiding precipitating factors for an asthma attack
- Stopping smoking and/or avoiding tobacco smoke
- Using a metered-dose inhaler correctly (see instructions below)
- Using a peak flow meter to monitor respiratory functioning
- Taking medication correctly and regularly as prescribed
- Knowing when to seek health-care assistance

Patient Instructions for Use of a Metered-Dose Inhaler (MDI):

1. Hold the inhaler upright and shake.
2. Sit upright and breathe out slowly.
3. Hold inhaler one to two inches from mouth or use a spacer device. If using a spacer, put lips around the mouthpiece.
4. Inhale slowly while pushing down on the inhaler cartridge to deliver medication. Inhalation should be slow and deep, lasting around five seconds.
5. Hold breath for about ten seconds after completing inhalation.
6. If taking more than one puff of medication, allow one to two minutes to elapse between puffs.
7. If using a corticosteroid inhaler, rinse mouth with water following each use to prevent the development of oral thrush.

Nursing Process: Evaluation

The effectiveness of nursing interventions in the care of the patient with asthma can be measured by the patient's achievement of the following **expected outcomes:**

- Maintains a patent airway
- Demonstrates effective airway clearance
- Improves breathing pattern

- Exhibits evidence of improved gas exchange
- Demonstrates a decrease in anxiety
- Demonstrates knowledge of treatment regimen and effectively manages self-care activities
- Avoids development of complications: status asthmaticus and respiratory failure

Chronic Obstructive Pulmonary Disease

Chronic obstructive pulmonary disease (COPD) is a common disease in the United States, currently ranked as the fourth leading cause of death. COPD is a chronic, progressive disease, typically developing in middle-aged individuals. The incidence of the disease increases with age. COPD consists of **chronic bronchitis** and **emphysema** and is characterized by airflow obstruction. Primary risk factors for the development of COPD include smoking, secondhand smoke, air pollution, and occupational exposure to pollutants. It has also been determined that in some cases there is a genetic abnormality that leads to the development of COPD. COPD is more common in males and whites.

Pathophysiology

Two respiratory disorders, chronic bronchitis and emphysema, are classified as COPD. While the pathophysiology of these two disorders differs, the medical management and nursing interventions for chronic bronchitis and emphysema are similar.

Chronic Bronchitis

Chronic bronchitis is caused by inhaling irritants into the lungs. Cigarette smoke is the most common inhaled irritant and is believed to be a primary cause of chronic bronchitis. Other causes are thought to be air pollution and occupational exposure to irritants. Chronic bronchitis can also be caused by a bacterial or viral infection.

In chronic bronchitis, the mucus-secreting glands in the small airways of the lungs hypertrophy due to chronic irritation and begin to secrete excessive mucus. Chronic inflammation of the small airways also develops, further contributing to excess mucus production. Due to the excess mucus secretions and impaired ciliary action, bacteria proliferate in the airways and the individual is predisposed to the development of infection. Because of the chronic inflammation of the bronchial walls and the resulting edema and mucus production, airway obstruction develops and completely blocks small airways. Airway obstruction can lead to the development of atelectasis. Bronchospasms and increased airway resistance also develops.

Because of these pathophysiological changes, the oxygen and carbon dioxide exchange at the alveolar-capillary level is affected. A ventilation/perfusion (V/Q) mismatch develops because a decreased amount of oxygenated blood reaches the alveoli. Eventually, the patient develops hypoxemia, hypercapnia, and respiratory acidosis. Hypercapnia and hypoxia lead to pulmonary vascular vasoconstriction and increased pulmonary vascular resistance. Over a period of time, the patient can develop right-sided ventricular heart failure (**cor pulmonale**) due to increased pressure in the right ventricle from pumping against the increased pulmonary vascular resistance.

Emphysema

The cause of **emphysema** is unknown. However, it is believed to be due to the destruction of connective tissue in the lungs by protease and elastase enzymes. **Alpha$_1$-antitrypsin (AAT)** is a globulin that serves as an enzyme inhibitor, thus protecting connective tissue from the destructive effects of the enzymes. Cigarette smoking blocks the inhibitory functions of AAT and is a common predisposing factor to the development of emphysema. However, some individuals have a genetic AAT deficiency that leads to the development of emphysema.

In emphysema, the alveolar walls lose their elasticity, enlarge, and are eventually destroyed. There are essentially two forms of emphysema: **centrilobular** and **panlobular**.

- In **centrilobular emphysema (CLE)** there is selective enlargement and destruction of the respiratory bronchioles. CLE tends to occur in the upper portion of the lungs.
- In **panlobular emphysema (PLE)** there is more widespread enlargement and destruction of the alveoli, usually occurring in the lower portion of the lungs. PLE tends to occur more commonly in individuals with an AAT deficiency.

A patient can have both types of emphysema.

The pathophysiological changes that occur in the lungs due to emphysema include increased lung compliance due to loss of elastic recoil, causing the lungs to become overdistended. In addition, there is an increased airway resistance due to collapse of small airways, especially during expiration. The collapse of airways leads to air trapping, causing further lung overdistension. The overdistension of the lungs applies pressure to the diaphragm, decreasing diaphragmatic excursion (movement). As the diaphragm becomes fixed in position, its ventilatory effectiveness is decreased. Destruction of the alveolar and bronchiole walls affects the alveolar-capillary membrane surface and eventually results in decreased diffusion of oxygen and carbon dioxide.

Clinical Manifestations

Early clinical manifestations of **chronic bronchitis** include the following:

- A productive cough upon awakening. The sputum is typically grayish white, unless the patient has a respiratory infection, in which case it can be yellow.
- The patient develops a gradually increasing dyspnea, eventually using accessory muscles to breathe.
- It becomes difficult for the patient to walk.
- Cyanosis, or a blue-tinged, dusky skin color, is a common sign, along with a bloated appearance, distended neck veins, and ankle (pedal) edema.

- In the later stages of the disease, the patient can develop the complications of right-sided heart failure and respiratory failure.

In **emphysema**, clinical manifestations include the following:

- The first noticeable symptom is usually **dyspnea upon exertion (DOE)**. As the disease progresses, the dyspnea becomes more constant.
- The patient can also develop **orthopnea**, in which the patient cannot assume a recumbent position without developing dyspnea. Patients may report requiring two or more pillows to elevate the head when sleeping to decrease dyspnea; many may report sleeping upright in a recliner. When awake, the patient may assume an **orthopneic position**, in which the patient sits forward with the forearms propped up on an over-bed table to ease breathing.
- The patient is usually thin in appearance with a **barrel chest**. A barrel chest, which is an increased anteroposterior diameter of the chest, is the result of hyperinflation of the lungs.
- Unlike chronic bronchitis, there is little to no sputum production with emphysema.
- Patients are likely to develop pursed-lip breathing, which helps decrease airway collapse and prolong expiration. Accessory muscle breathing can also be present.

Diagnostic Tests

The tests used to diagnose chronic bronchitis and emphysema are the same for both diseases. Pulmonary function tests, chest X rays, sputum for culture and sensitivity, arterial blood gas studies, and complete blood counts may be used to diagnose COPD.

In the patient with **chronic bronchitis**, the following may occur:

- Pulmonary function studies will demonstrate a decreased vital capacity (VC) and forced expiratory volume (FEV). In addition, the residual volume (RV) will be increased, as will the total lung capacity (TLC).
- ABGs may demonstrate hypoxemia and slight hypercapnia and show that the patient is in respiratory acidosis.
- Hemoglobin and hematocrit values may be increased due to chronic hypoxemia.
- The chest X ray may reveal a flattened diaphragm and an enlarged heart.

In the patient with **emphysema**, the following may occur:

- Pulmonary function tests will demonstrate a decreased forced expiratory volume (FEV) and vital capacity (VC). There will be an increase in the total lung capacity (TLC), functional reserve capacity (FRC), and residual volume (RV) due to air trapping.
- In the early stages of emphysema, the patient is likely to develop a mild hypoxemia and respiratory alkalosis.

- In the latter stages of the disease, ABGs may demonstrate hypoxemia and hypercapnia, as well as respiratory acidosis.
- CBC findings may include an increased hemoglobin and hematocrit.
- Chest X rays will reveal a flattened diaphragm and hyperinflated lungs.

Medical Management

Medical management of chronic bronchitis and emphysema is similar. Pharmacological therapy may include the use of **bronchodilators, anticholinergic agents, corticosteroids**, and **antibiotics**.

- **Bronchodilators** are used to improve airflow and help facilitate removal of secretions. Bronchodilators may be administered either orally, through a nebulizer, or with a metered-dose inhaler (MDI). MDI is the preferred method, as there are less systemic side effects with this route of administration.
- An **anticholinergic agent**, ipratropium bromide (Atrovent), is an effective bronchodilating agent that is administered as a MDI. Because of Atrovent's slow onset of action, it is not appropriate for use as a PRN medication, but instead is recommended to be taken on a regularly scheduled basis.
- **Corticosteroids** may be prescribed for short-term therapy to treat exacerbations of symptoms. Oral prednisone or inhaled (MDI) corticosteroids are the most common forms of corticosteroids prescribed. MDI is the preferred route. The lowest effective dose should be administered. Long-term use of corticosteroids is controversial, but may be effective in some patients. It is important that patients receiving corticosteroids via a MDI be taught how to use a spacer and rinse their mouth following each use of the inhaler to avoid thrush.
- **Antibiotics** are administered during acute exacerbations of COPD and at the first sign of a respiratory infection. It is important that a respiratory infection be treated as soon as it is detected to prevent respiratory complications. Antibiotics are not administered prophylactically.
- In patients with an AAT deficiency, **AAT replacement therapy** may be administered intravenously every one to four weeks. Administering AAT may preserve pulmonary function and slow the progression of emphysema. The long-term effects of AAT replacement therapy have not been determined.
- Additional pharmacological therapy may include **digitalis** and **diuretics** if the patient has developed the complication of heart failure.

Oxygen therapy is usually required in patients with COPD who cannot maintain a PaO_2 above 55 mm Hg or an oxygen saturation level of greater than 85 percent when at rest, or those patients who cannot carry out their activities of daily living without becoming dyspneic. *When administering oxygen to patients with COPD, it is important that the oxygen flow rate be kept at a low rate, usually 1 to 2 L of oxygen per nasal cannula.*

Many patients with COPD develop a chronic excess of carbon dioxide; as a result, their stimulus to breathe becomes their low PaO_2 levels. Administering a high flow rate of oxygen can raise the low PaO_2 level and remove the patient's stimulus to breathe, causing respiratory failure to develop.

Chest physiotherapy, such as postural drainage and percussion, may also be ordered to help mobilize and remove sputum from the lungs.

Nursing Process: Assessment

Subjective data that the nurse will gather from the patient with COPD will include smoking history, history of respiratory infections, and family history of respiratory problems. Gathering information about the patient's occupation, living environment, and possible exposure to respiratory irritants is part of the assessment. The nurse will also want to gather data about the patient's self-treatment of his or her condition, and how the symptoms have impacted the activities of daily living and quality of life.

Assessing the onset, character, and duration of dyspnea, and cough and sputum production is also important. In the patient with chronic bronchitis, a productive cough, especially in the morning, is usually present; in the patient with emphysema, a cough is usually mild or even absent with only scant sputum production.

Vital signs may reveal tachypnea, tachycardia, and an elevated temperature if an infection is present. Inspection of the patient may reveal the use of accessory muscle breathing, orthopneic posture, and, in the patient with emphysema, a barrel chest, pursed-lip breathing, and prolonged expiration. A patient with chronic bronchitis may have clubbing of the fingers.

Upon auscultating the lungs, the nurse may hear inspiratory crackles and inspiratory and expiratory rhonchi. Patients with emphysema typically have diminished breath and heart sounds due to the barrel chest and hyperinflation of the lungs. Chest percussion in the patient with emphysema indicates hyperresonance, flattened diaphragm, and decreased diaphragmatic excursion.

The presence of dyspnea can also affect the patient's sleep patterns and lead to fatigue and activity intolerance. Nutritional needs may not be met due to the patient's inability to eat as a result of the dyspnea and fatigue. Excessive sputum production can lead to anorexia. The nurse should complete a thorough assessment of the patient's energy levels and nutritional intake.

Nursing Process: Nursing Diagnosis and Planning

Based upon an analysis of the gathered data, the following **nursing diagnoses** may be appropriate for the patient with COPD:

- Impaired gas exchange related to altered ventilation/perfusion ratio
- Ineffective airway clearance related to excess sputum production, decreased energy, and ineffective cough
- Ineffective breathing pattern due to airway obstruction and fatigue

- Altered nutrition, less than body requirements related to dyspnea, fatigue, and excess sputum production
- Activity intolerance related to hypoxemia
- Sleep pattern disturbance related to orthopnea
- Fear and anxiety related to chronic, potentially debilitating disease
- Potential for the development of respiratory infection related to decreased pulmonary defenses
- Ineffective therapeutic management related to lack of knowledge about disease and treatment

Primary goals for the patient with COPD include the following:

- Maintenance of a patent airway
- Improved gas exchange
- Conservation of energy
- Improved sleep pattern
- Adequate nutritional intake
- Reduction in anxiety and fear
- Demonstration of self-care activities
- Avoidance of complications: infection and respiratory failure

Nursing Process: Implementation

Priority nursing interventions are focused on helping the patient with COPD improve gas exchange and breathing efficiency as well as maintain a patent airway. The nurse should closely monitor the patient's ABGs to determine the efficiency of the patient's breathing and the degree of gas exchange taking place at the alveolar-capillary membrane. Rapidly changing ABG values can indicate that the patient's condition is worsening, and respiratory failure may be imminent. The patient should also be frequently assessed for signs and symptoms of hypoxemia and hypercapnia, which can include headache, altered mental status, irritability, increasing drowsiness, and the development of tachycardia and arrhythmias.

The nurse carefully administers oxygen therapy at the prescribed rate and monitors the patient's response. Since oxygen is drying to mucous membranes, a water-soluble lubricant should be applied to the inside of the nares to prevent dryness. Petroleum jelly should never be used because of its oil-based property and the potential for it to be inhaled into the lungs. The water level in the humidifier bottle should be checked periodically to make sure that it does not run dry. It is important that the nurse also instruct the patient about necessary safety precautions regarding the use of oxygen in the home, such as avoiding smoking, keeping oxygen away from sources of gas and kerosene, and keeping a fire extinguisher nearby. It is also important for the nurse to explain the benefits of using the oxygen continuously, and not just when the patient is experiencing dyspnea.

In addition to monitoring the patient's ABGs and administering oxygen, the nurse also assists the patient in improving the efficiency of his or her breathing patterns. There are several breathing techniques and positions that can help the patient breathe more comfortably.

- **Pursed-lip breathing** is a technique that helps the patient slow down the respiratory rate and prolong the expiratory phase of the respiratory cycle. It also helps prevent the airways from collapsing and decreases air trapping.
- The nurse should also encourage the patient to assume a **forward-leaning position** when exhaling. This position helps the patient remove more air from the lungs during the exhalation period.
- Teaching the patient to do **abdominal breathing** will allow the diaphragm to elevate more and improve breathing efficiency.

The patient should also be taught how to cough effectively. **Huff coughing** is recommended to help move secretions and minimize bronchospasms. The patient is taught to inhale slowly through the nose, lean forward, and exhale slowly through pursed lips to open the airway and begin to move secretions. This step should be repeated several times. Then the patient takes a slow, deep breath through the nose, and when exhaling, coughs with short, repeated coughs. Encouraging an adequate fluid intake will help liquefy secretions.

Patients with COPD usually have nutritional problems due to dyspnea, fatigue, excessive sputum production, and anorexia. The nurse should work closely with the patient to help the patient choose foods that are high calorie and high protein. Vitamin supplements are also recommended. Smaller, more frequent meals that are easily chewed are likely to be better tolerated than larger meals. Good oral hygiene prior to each meal is essential to improving the appetite and decreasing anorexia.

Because of the dyspnea and hypoxemia, patients with COPD may experience activity intolerance. In order to improve the patient's activity tolerance, the nurse should provide a relaxed, unrushed environment and allow the patient to perform activities at his or her own pace. Helping the patient to balance periods of activity with periods of rest is also important. After a period of an acute exacerbation of symptoms, activities should be gradually resumed. During periods of rest or sleep, the patient should be assisted to assume a position of comfort. Usually the patient's preferred position is semi-Fowler's or high-Fowler's position.

Patient Teaching

Patient and family education is especially important in helping the patient with COPD cope with the illness and avoid complications. The single greatest complication of COPD is respiratory infection. To decrease the chances of acquiring a respiratory complication, the patient should be instructed to receive influenza and pneumonia vaccines as recommended, avoid people with upper respiratory infections, avoid large crowds, and contact the health-care provider at the first sign of a possible infection.

Patients should also be instructed to avoid inhaled irritants and temperature extremes, and to maintain a healthy lifestyle to decrease their susceptibility to infection. Cigarette smoke must be avoided in the environment. Air conditioners and HEPA filters can be used to help filter particulate matter from the air.

The nurse should also stress the importance of taking medications as prescribed. The patient should be knowledgeable about how to administer the drugs and what side effects to report to the health-care provider. The nurse should have the patient demonstrate all breathing exercises to ensure the patient is performing them correctly. The patient should also be comfortable with operating any required respiratory equipment in the home environment.

Many patients with COPD are fearful and anxious when they are breathless. The nurse should allow them time to express their concerns, and discuss measures they can take to improve their breathing. Having a ready list of identified community resources and emergency contacts can help decrease the patient's anxiety. Also, helping the individual locate community support groups can be helpful to the patient and family.

Nursing Process: Evaluation

The effectiveness of nursing interventions can be measured by the patient's achievement of the following **expected outcomes**:

- Maintains a patent airway
- Improves breathing pattern
- Exhibits evidence of normal gas exchange
- Maintains adequate nutritional intake
- Conserves energy and participates in activity as tolerated
- Minimized sleep pattern disturbances
- Avoids development of complications: respiratory infection and respiratory failure
- Demonstrates appropriate self-care activities

Respiratory Syncytial Virus (RSV)

Respiratory syncytial virus (RSV) is an acute viral infection that primarily affects the bronchioles causing **bronchiolitis**. It is common in children under the age of two, and it occurs most frequently during the winter and spring seasons. It is easily transmitted by hand contact to the eyes and nose.

RSV begins as an upper respiratory infection, with the child gradually developing respiratory distress as the bronchioles become involved. The bronchiole tissue becomes edematous, with exudate developing and filling the bronchiole airways. Obstruction develops in the small airways due to the collection of exudate and areas of hyperinflation (obstructive emphysema) develop as air enters the lungs and becomes trapped in the narrowed airways. Areas of atelectasis also develop.

The child develops increasing respiratory distress as the obstruction worsens. Assessment of the respiratory system will reveal coughing, wheezing, tachypnea, dyspnea, and retractions. Auscultation of the lungs will reveal crackles and diminished breath sounds. The child may be cyanotic due to poor air exchange; apneic episodes can also occur, especially in infants whose airways are easily occluded.

Chest X rays will indicate areas of hyperinflation and possibly consolidation. Arterial blood gases may indicate hypercapnia and respiratory acidosis as a result of the altered air exchange and airtrapping. RSV can be positively diagnosed through an **enzyme-linked immunosorbent assay (ELISA)**. A rapid **immunofluorescent antibody (IFA)** can also be performed to confirm the diagnosis.

RSV is treated symptomatically with most children being treated at home. Rest, increased fluid intake, and a humidified environment are key to the treatment. A child who is experiencing serious respiratory distress or has another underlying chronic health problem is hospitalized. Oxygen therapy via tent or hood will be provided. IV fluids will be administered to ensure adequate fluid intake.

Pharmacological therapy does not play a prominent role in most cases of RSV. However, **ribavirin**, which is an antiviral medication, may be used. It is administered by aerosol through a mask, hood, or tent. It can also be administered through ventilator tubing if the child requires intubation. The use of the drug is still considered to be controversial. Children with chronic health conditions who are considered to be high risk for development of RSV may be considered candidates for prophylactic therapy to prevent RSV. These children may either receive **RSV immune globulin** or **palivizumab**, a monoclonal antibody.

Nursing care of children with RSV focuses on infection control and preventing the spread of the infection. **Hand washing** is essential, as is avoiding contact with nasal or conjunctival secretions. Children with RSV are kept isolated from other children or are assigned rooms with other RSV-infected children. The nurse closely monitors the respiratory status of the patient, as prompt intervention is required if air exchange worsens.

Pneumonia

Pneumonia is an inflammation of lung tissue caused by microorganisms. The microorganisms that cause pneumonia are varied and can be a bacteria, virus, fungus, or parasite.

Pneumonia is a very common disease, currently ranking as the sixth leading cause of death in the United States. It is the most common cause of death among infectious diseases in the United States. Pneumonia is commonly classified as community-acquired, hospital-acquired, immunocompromised host, or aspiration pneumonia.

- **Community-acquired pneumonia (CAP)** develops within the community or within the first forty-eight hours of hospitalization. Patients with CAP may be treated as outpatients or in the hospital, depending upon the severity of their symptoms. Microorganisms that commonly cause CAP include Legionella, *Pseudomonas aeruginosa*, and streptococcal pneumoniae. Mycoplasma pneumonia is another type of CAP.
- **Hospital-acquired pneumonia (HAP)**, or nosocomial pneumonia, develops in a patient after more than forty-eight hours in the hospital. HAP is considered to be the most dangerous form of nosocomial infection that can be acquired, and is estimated to account for 15 percent of all infections acquired in the hospital.
- **Immunocompromised host pneumonia** is increasing in occurrence. The patient, or host, is immunocompromised and unable to resist the invading microorganism. The patient may be immunocompromised from chemotherapy, the use of other immunosuppressive drugs (such as corticosteroids), a genetic immune disorder, AIDS, or malnutrition. Examples of microorganisms that cause pneumonia in the immunocompromised host include *Pneumocystis carinii*, Klebsiella, *Escherichia coli*, and *Pseudomonas aeruginosa*.
- **Aspiration pneumonia** results from the entry of a substance into the lower respiratory tract. The most common cause of aspiration pneumonia is the introduction of bacteria from the upper respiratory tract into the lower airways. Organisms causing aspiration pneumonia include *Staphylococcus aureus*, *Streptococcus pneumoniae*, and *Haemophilus influenzae*. The reflux of gastric contents is another common cause of aspiration pneumonia.

Risk Factors for Pneumonia

It is important for nurses to recognize patients who are high risk for developing pneumonia. Any patient who is immunocompromised, either by disease or through treatment with immunosuppressive drugs, will be at a high risk for developing pneumonia. Elderly individuals and any patient who has a chronic illness, such as chronic obstructive pulmonary disease, congestive heart failure, AIDS, cancer, or degenerative neurological disorders, are also at high risk for developing pneumonia. Patients who smoke are also predisposed to developing pneumonia. Other patients at risk include those who are unconscious, have a depressed cough reflex, or who have been placed under a general anesthetic, as these patients are prone to respiratory depression. Patients who are intubated or require suctioning are also at risk for developing pneumonia through the introduction of microorganisms into the respiratory tract.

It is important that the nurse monitor the patient closely for signs and symptoms of developing pneumonia. It is also essential that the nurse teach the patient and caregivers in the home what signs and symptoms to report so that early treatment for pneumonia can be implemented.

Any patient that is considered a high risk for pneumonia should be strongly encouraged to seek medical advice about receiving a vaccination against pneumococcal infection. Pneumonia vaccines are thought to provide immunity for about ten years. High-risk patients are also encouraged to receive annual influenza vaccinations, as influenza can predispose a patient to pneumonia. Patients who are considered to be at high risk and encouraged to receive vaccination against pneumococcal infection include individuals who meet the following conditions:

- Are sixty-five years of age or older
- Have a chronic illness
- Live in an environment that promotes risk of disease (crowded living conditions, poor sanitation, etc.)
- Are immunocompromised

Pathophysiology

Pneumonia interferes with lung ventilation and diffusion. Organisms enter the lower airways of the lungs and create an inflammatory response within the alveoli. The inflammatory response causes **exudate** (secretions) to develop within the alveoli; the presence of the exudate disrupts the diffusion of oxygen and carbon dioxide across the alveolar-capillary membrane, as the gases cannot diffuse through the exudate. White blood cells migrate to the alveoli in response to the inflammation and fill up the alveoli. Mucosal edema also develops, and combined with the exudate, leads to blockage of the alveoli and bronchi, causing hypoventilation.

Because of the hypoventilation, a ventilation/perfusion mismatch develops in the affected areas of the lungs. Blood circulating through the hypoventilated areas of the lungs leaves the lungs without being adequately oxygenated. The patient eventually develops hypoxemia due to the inadequate oxygenation of the blood.

Depending upon the severity of the pneumonia, fluid can collect in the lungs beyond the level of the alveoli. If a lobe of the lung is significantly affected by the inflammatory process and filled with fluid, the patient is said to have **lobar pneumonia**. In lobar pneumonia, areas of consolidation, in which the lung tissue is completely solidified by fluid, develop and completely obstruct airflow. If the area of pneumonia is "patchy" and located in various different areas of the bronchi and surrounding tissue, the patient is said to have **bronchopneumonia**. It is more common for patients to develop bronchopneumonia, instead of lobar pneumonia.

Clinical Manifestations

The clinical manifestations of pneumonia can vary significantly from patient to patient, depending upon the virulence of the organism causing the illness. A patient with bacterial pneumonia may exhibit a more acute and sudden onset of symptoms, while a patient with viral pneumonia may have a more gradual onset. It is not possible to determine the organism responsible for the pneumonia based upon the patient's signs and symptoms alone. Diagnostic tests such as a sputum culture and blood culture must be obtained to determine the organism.

Common clinical manifestations include the sudden onset of chills, rapid increase in fever ranging from 101° to 105° Fahrenheit, and chest pain. The chest pain is pleuritic (sharp, stabbing) in nature and increases when the patient breathes deeply and coughs. The patient usually experiences dyspnea and tachypnea, and in severe cases of pneumonia, can exhibit cyanosis.

Patients can also develop a more gradual onset of symptoms beginning with an upper respiratory tract infection. The patient may experience a headache, low-grade fever, myalgia (joint pain), and pleuritic chest pain.

Other common signs and symptoms of pneumonia include diaphoresis, anorexia, and fatigue. Sputum may be present and may be purulent, blood-tinged, or rust-colored. Breath sounds upon auscultation can include crackles. Breath sounds can be diminished or absent over areas of consolidation.

Elderly patients who develop pneumonia may have subtle signs and symptoms, such as generalized weakness and deterioration, anorexia, tachycardia, tachypnea, and confusion. It is possible for the elderly patient to develop pneumonia without demonstrating a fever, cough, sputum production, or chest pain. It is important for the nurse to be vigilant in monitoring the elderly patient, especially those with an underlying chronic illness, as the signs and symptoms of pneumonia can be easily obscured in the elderly.

Diagnostic Tests

The diagnosis of pneumonia is made by chest X ray, blood culture tests, and sputum examination. The chest X ray may show patchy areas of infiltrate or consolidation. The patient's history may reveal that the patient has had a recent upper respiratory tract infection.

Medical Management

Bacterial pneumonia is treated by the administration of **antibiotics** that are given either intravenously or orally. The antibiotic will be selected based upon the results of culture and sensitivity tests conducted on sputum or blood specimens. Antibiotics that are commonly administered for the treatment of pneumonia include penicillin G, clindamycin, the cephalosporins, and erythromycin. If the patient has viral pneumonia, the treatment will be primarily supportive, as antibiotics are not effective for treating viruses.

With the exception of antibiotic therapy, treatment for the patient with bacterial or viral pneumonia is the same. Other medications that may be prescribed for the patient includes **antipyretics** to treat fever and headache; **antihistamines** and **decongestants** to decrease nasal congestion; and **antitussives** to relieve cough. **Oxygen** will be administered if the patient develops hypoxemia.

It is important for the patient with pneumonia to receive adequate hydration to offset any insensible fluid loss that results from fever and tachypnea. Adequate fluid intake is also important for decreasing sputum tenacity and helping the patient to mobilize and expectorate secretions. In addition, warm, moist inhalations may be used to moisten the patient's airways, decrease bronchial irritation, and loosen secretions. During the acute phase of the illness, the patient will be placed on bed rest to conserve oxygen consumption and energy.

There are several potential complications of pneumonia, especially if it is not treated promptly. The patient can develop **atelectasis**, which is caused by an accumulation of lung secretions that eventually block the airways and cause collapse of the alveoli. **Pleural effusion**, which is an accumulation of fluid in the pleural space, can also develop. The pleural effusion may be an indication of the development of **empyema**, or purulent fluid, in the pleural space. Severe complications of pneumonia include **hypotension** and **shock**, and **respiratory failure**. A patient who is critically ill may require hemodynamic monitoring and mechanical ventilation.

Nursing Process: Assessment

It is important that the nurse closely monitor all hospitalized patients for the development of pneumonia, especially elderly patients, immobilized patients or those on bed rest, postoperative patients, and those patients who are considered to be at high risk for developing pneumonia. The nurse should keep in mind that the initial indications of pneumonia can be subtle, such as a change in mental status or fatigue. The nurse should carefully assess the patient for the following:

- Changes in lung sounds upon auscultation (crackles, diminished breath sounds)
- Shortness of breath or tachypnea
- Use of respiratory accessory muscles
- Elevated temperature
- Change in pulse rate
- Presence of cough, including frequency and severity
- Chest pain (noting location, type, causative factors, severity)
- Presence of secretions, including amount, color, odor, tenacity
- Signs of fluid volume deficit

Nursing Process: Nursing Diagnosis and Planning

Based upon an analysis of the gathered data, the following **nursing diagnoses** may be appropriate for the patient with pneumonia:

- Ineffective airway clearance related to the presence of copious secretions
- Impaired gas exchange related to the presence of pulmonary secretions
- Fatigue related to altered respiratory status and decreased oxygenation
- Altered nutrition, less than body requirements related to dyspnea and fatigue
- Potential for fluid volume deficit related to fluid loss from fever and dyspnea

Primary goals for the patient with pneumonia include the following:

- Maintenance of a patent airway
- Improved gas exchange
- Conservation of energy
- Adequate nutrition and fluid intake
- Avoidance of complications: atelectasis, pleural effusion, shock, respiratory failure

Nursing Process: Implementation

Maintaining a patent airway and ensuring adequate gas exchange are priority nursing interventions in the patient with pneumonia. The nurse should do the following:

- Encourage the patient to cough and deep breathe at frequent intervals to help move secretions out of the lungs.
- If the patient is experiencing pleuritic chest pain, the nurse should help the patient splint the chest wall by placing his or her hands, or a folded blanket, on the rib cage to provide support during the coughing and deep breathing process.
- Warm, humidified air can be used to help loosen secretions and aid expectoration of sputum.
- The nurse should also ensure that the patient has a fluid intake of 2 to 3 L/day to thin secretions.
- Chest percussion and postural drainage may also be used to loosen and mobilize pulmonary secretions.
- If the patient is not able to cough up secretions, the nurse may need to use nasotracheal suctioning to assist in the removal of secretions.
- The nurse may also administer oxygen to maintain adequate oxygenation levels. Pulse oximetry and ABG levels will be used to determine the effectiveness of oxygen therapy.

It is important for the nurse to encourage the patient to conserve energy and rest during the acute phase of the illness. The patient is usually on bed rest during this time and will require assistance with completing the activities of daily living. Frequent position changes will help mobilize secretions and help prevent skin breakdown in the patient who is confined to bed. The patient should be placed in a comfortable position to promote ease of breathing. A semi-Fowler's position is usually most comfortable for the patient. As the patient's condition improves, activity will be gradually resumed, with the nurse closely monitoring the patient for signs of respiratory distress and fatigue.

The patient may experience anorexia and difficulty eating due to shortness of breath and fatigue. The nurse should ensure an adequate intake of fluids and observe the patient closely for any indication of fluid and electrolyte imbalances. Intravenous fluids with electrolytes are frequently administered to maintain the patient's fluid and electrolyte balance. The patient may best tolerate a liquid diet during the acute phase of the illness, with the diet progressing as the patient's condition improves. A diet high in carbohydrates, vitamins, and protein is appropriate for the patient with pneumonia.

Patient Teaching

As the patient prepares for discharge, it is important for the nurse to provide patient teaching that will enable the patient to continue to recover at home and prevent complications. The patient will most likely continue to experience fatigue for some time after discharge, and should be encouraged to pace resumption of activity and schedule periodic rest periods. Smoking should be avoided, including secondhand smoke. Alcohol should also be avoided. A well-balanced, nutritional diet should be eaten, and adequate fluid intake is encouraged.

The nurse should stress the necessity of taking all medications as prescribed. Follow-up chest X rays and office visits are usually required to monitor recovery. Prescribed breathing exercises should be implemented faithfully to help prevent recurrence of respiratory infection. The patient and family members are also carefully instructed in the signs and symptoms of potential complications, and informed of when to notify health care providers. The nurse should encourage the patient to obtain influenza and pneumonia vaccines as recommended.

Nursing Process: Evaluation

The effectiveness of nursing interventions can be measured by the patient's achievement of the following **expected outcomes**:

- Maintains a patent airway
- Exhibits evidence of normal gas exchange
- Maintains adequate fluid and nutrition intake
- Conserves energy and resumes activity as tolerated
- Avoids development of complications
- Demonstrates appropriate self-care activities

Tuberculosis

Tuberculosis (TB) is an infectious disorder that primarily affects the lungs. The incidence of TB is increasing around the world. Poverty, poor quality housing, overcrowded living conditions, lack of adequate health care, and poor nutrition are risk factors associated with TB. TB is the leading cause of death among infectious diseases globally.

Risk factors for TB transmission are numerous. TB is spread by airborne transmission from individual to individual. This is why close, crowded living quarters support the transmission of the disease between people. Risk factors in addition to the ones listed above include the following:

- Exposure to immunocompromised individuals and individuals with chronic illness/conditions
- Living in institutions such as nursing homes, long-term care facilities, prisons
- Emigration from Africa, Latin America, Asia, the Caribbean where TB rates are high
- Health-care workers

Pathophysiology

TB is caused by *Mycobacterium tuberculosis*, an acid-fast aerobic rod that is inhaled by a susceptible individual. The bacteria lodge in the alveoli and begin to multiply, spreading throughout the lungs. The bacteria can also be spread to other organs, such as bones, kidneys, lymph glands, via the bloodstream and lymph system. In response to the bacterial invasion, an inflammatory reaction is initiated to destroy the bacteria. Phagocytes, including macrophages and neutrophils, surround and lyse the bacteria.

Granulomas, which are deposits of live and dead bacilli, are surrounded by the macrophages during this process. The macrophages "wall-off" the granulomas, effectively sealing them to prevent further spread of the organism. These granulomas, or small nodules, are called **primary nodules**. Inside this wall, the blood supply of the granuloma is gradually compressed by fibrotic tissue and a necrotic, cheesy mass develops at the center of the nodule. This process is called **caseation necrosis**. This cheesy material can liquefy and be coughed up by the patient, leaving cavities in lung tissue.

In other cases the cheesy material calcifies and a scar forms. When calcification develops, the bacteria in the tubercle become dormant and the disease is no longer active. The calcified tubercle is known as a **Ghon tubercle**. Later, the disease can be reactivated in individuals whenever their immune system becomes compromised. Physical or emotional stress may precipitate reactivation. When the disease is reactivated, the tubercle ulcerates and releases the bacteria into the bronchi where it then becomes airborne and is spread to others. The tubercle can then heal, reseal, and form further scar tissue.

Because of the ulceration and inflammatory process that occurs in TB, lung tissue becomes inflamed, exudate accumulates in the alveoli, and bronchopneumonia can develop.

Clinical Manifestations

The clinical manifestations of TB can be subtle. Common signs and symptoms include cough, hemoptysis, fatigue, and night sweats. A low-grade fever and weight loss also occur. The cough may be nonproductive or could be productive of mucopurulent sputum. An elderly patient may have atypical clinical manifestations and display anorexia, fever, weight loss, or altered mental status.

Diagnostic Tests

TB is diagnosed through a complete history and physical that reveals the clinical manifestations listed above. These findings are confirmed by a positive tuberculin skin test, chest X ray that demonstrates calcified nodules or cavities, and a positive acid-fast bacillus smear containing mycobacterium or a positive sputum culture.

Tuberculin Skin Testing

The tuberculin skin test that is used to diagnose TB is the **Mantoux test.** The Mantoux test is an intradermal injection of tubercle bacillus extract, purified protein derivative (PPD). A reaction forty-eight to seventy-two hours following administration of the tuberculin extract indicates that the individual has been exposed to the bacillus. The nurse inspects the injection site for both redness (erythema) and induration. Redness alone does not indicate the patient has experienced a reaction; induration must be present as well. The induration is measured and size is documented.

The size of the induration reaction indicates the significance of the finding. If the induration is 0–4 mm it is not considered to be significant. If the size of the induration is over 5 mm, it may be significant. If the size is 10 mm or more, it is considered to be significant. A significant finding does not mean the patient actually has active TB; it means that the individual has been exposed to TB and may possibly develop active TB if treatment is not received.

There are some exceptions to the above interpretation of the findings. Individuals who have been vaccinated with the bacille Calmette-Guérin (BCG) vaccine will always have a positive response to the Mantoux test. The BCG vaccine is given in some European and Latin countries to help create resistance to TB. Individuals who are immunocompromised will not be able to mount an immune response; therefore, they will not have a reaction even if they are infected with the bacteria. The elderly may also have a delayed reaction and require a second skin test to determine exposure.

Medical Management

TB is curable when treated. TB is treated with **antituberculosis drugs** for six to twelve months. The term **chemotherapy** is also used to refer to the drug therapy prescribed for the treatment of TB.

Multiple drugs are used for treatment of TB to decrease the likelihood of drug resistance. First line antituberculosis drugs include: **isoniazid (INH)**, **rifampin**, **pyrazinamide**, and **streptomycin** or **ethambutol.** The first four drugs are administered in combination with either streptomycin or ethambutol for at least eight weeks. The streptomycin or ethambutol will be dropped before the eight weeks are up if the organism is sensitive to the other drugs. The remaining three drugs will continue to be administered for another eight weeks, with the pyrazinamide being dropped after that time. The INH and the rifampin will continue to be administered for another four to twelve months.

The patient is considered to be noninfectious after they have been on drug therapy for fourteen to twenty-one days.

Drugs can also be administered prophylactically. **INH** will be administered for six to twelve months as a prophylactic or preventive therapy to high-risk individuals. High-risk individuals include, in part, the following:

- HIV patients with a positive Mantoux skin test of 5 mm or more
- Individuals who live with someone diagnosed with active TB
- Individuals who have converted from negative to positive Mantoux skin test
- Intravenous drug users with Mantoux skin test of 10 mm or more

Side effects of antituberculosis drugs can be significant and require monitoring during the therapy. Table 7.1 identifies the most common side effects associated with antituberculosis drugs.

Table 7.1 Side Effects of Common Antituberculosis Drugs		
Drug	**Common side effects**	**Comments**
Rifampin	Hepatitis; nausea, vomiting	Monitor liver enzymes
Isoniazid (INH)	Peripheral neuritis, hepatitis	Monitor liver enzymes; administer pyridoxine to prevent peripheral neuritis
Pyrazinamide	Hepatomegaly; hyperuricemia	Monitor liver enzymes and uric acid levels
Streptomycin	Nephrotoxicity; deafness r/t to 8th cranial nerve damage	Monitor BUN, creatinine, and for hearing loss
Ethambutol	Skin rash; optic neuritis	Monitor vision

Nursing Process: Assessment

Nursing assessment will focus on obtaining a complete history and physical, noting clinical manifestations such as cough, sputum production, weight loss, night sweats, and low-grade fever. A thorough respiratory assessment is indicated. The nurse should note the presence of adventitious breath sounds that might indicate the development of bronchopneumonia. In addition, the nurse will want to collect information about the patient's living conditions and possible contacts with other individuals who are at high risk for contracting TB. It will be important for any close contacts of the patient to also be screened for TB. The nurse should also assess the patient's understanding of TB and the importance of completing the prescribed antituberculosis drug regimen.

Nursing Process: Planning and Nursing Diagnoses

Based upon an analysis of the gathered data, the following **nursing diagnoses** may be appropriate for the patient with TB:

- Knowledge deficit about TB and treatment regimen related to lack of previous experience with disease
- Ineffective management of therapeutic regimen related to lack of understanding and/or experience with drug therapy
- Ineffective airway clearance related to increased bronchial secretions and fatigue
- Activity intolerance related to fatigue
- Altered nutrition, less than body requirements related to fatigue and chronic illness

Primary goals for the patient with TB include:

- Increased knowledge about TB and treatment regimen
- Effective management of therapeutic regimen, including completion of drug therapy as prescribed
- Maintenance of patent airway
- Increased tolerance of activity
- Maintenance of normal nutrition
- Avoid complications related to side effects of drug therapy

Nursing Process: Implementation

Priority nursing interventions when caring for patients with TB include promoting adherence to the prescribed drug therapy and maintaining follow-up appointments with health-care professionals. It is essential that the nurse educate the patient on the importance of completing the prescribed therapy in order to prevent further progression and transmission of the disease. Directly observed therapy, during which the patient is observed taking his or her daily medications, may be implemented to assure adherence to the regimen. It is also important for the nurse to emphasize the importance of maintaining follow-up appointments so that the patient can be monitored for possible side effects from the antituberculosis drugs.

The patient also needs to be instructed on how to avoid transmission of the disease to others. The nurse should instruct the patient on how to properly use tissues and dispose of them to avoid droplet spread. The patient should cover the mouth when coughing, laughing, or sneezing. Hand washing should also be emphasized.

Because TB is a chronic illness, the patient may become debilitated and suffer from malnutrition. Because of the accompanying fatigue and cough, the patient will best tolerate small, frequent feedings. High-calorie, well-balanced meals are offered and liquid nutritional supplements may also be needed to meet nutritional requirements. Fluid intake is encouraged to help liquefy sputum.

Nursing Process: Evaluation

The effectiveness of nursing interventions can be measured by the patient's achievement of the following **expected outcomes**:

- Maintains a patent airway
- Maintains adequate fluid and nutritional intake
- Increases activity tolerance to participate appropriately in activities of daily living
- Verbalizes an understanding of TB and treatment regimen
- Adheres to treatment regimen
- Demonstrates appropriate self-care activities
- Avoids development of complications from disease and side effects of drug therapy

Pneumothorax

Pneumothorax (collapsed lung) develops when the parietal or visceral pleura of the lungs have been punctured, allowing atmospheric air to enter the pleural space. Under normal physiological conditions, the pleural space has negative atmospheric pressure. This negative pressure maintains lung inflation. When the pleura are no longer intact and atmospheric air enters the pleural space, the lung will collapse. The degree of collapse will depend upon the extent of the damage to the pleura and how much air enters the pleural space. The lungs may collapse partially or totally.

Pathophysiology

There are three types of pneumothorax—simple, traumatic, and tension pneumothorax.

Simple Pneumothorax

A **closed (simple or spontaneous) pneumothorax** develops when air enters the pleural space through an opening in the parietal or visceral pleura. Chronic lung problems, such as emphysema or a bronchopleural fistula, can lead to the development of a pneumothorax. Patients with chronic lung disease can develop air blebs on the lungs that rupture and lead to a pneumothorax. A spontaneous pneumothorax can also occur suddenly in otherwise healthy appearing individuals, usually young males. The rupture of a bleb, or blister, on the lung's surface allows air to enter the pleural space, and causes the pneumothorax.

Traumatic Pneumothorax

A **traumatic pneumothorax** is caused by a laceration or puncture of the lung itself that allows air to leave the lung and enter the pleural space. Penetrating chest wounds (stab wounds, gunshot wounds), rib fractures, motor vehicle accidents, and invasive surgical procedures are all examples of events that can lead to the development of a traumatic pneumothorax. In the event of major chest trauma, it is common for a **hemothorax** to develop as well. A hemothorax is the development of blood in the pleural space. If air and blood are both present, this is referred to as a **hemopneumothorax**.

A traumatic pneumothorax can also be an **open pneumothorax**. If the chest wound is large enough, air will move freely in and out of the wound with each respiration. This condition is also commonly called a **sucking chest wound**. An open pneumothorax can lead to a shift in the heart and great vessels **(mediastinal)** flutter towards the uninjured side with each breath the patient takes. This creates serious circulatory problems for the patient.

Tension Pneumothorax

While an open pneumothorax is a serious clinical condition, a tension pneumothorax is even more serious. A **tension pneumothorax** can develop when air is drawn into the pleural space through a small puncture in the chest wall or a lacerated lung. A closed pneumothorax can also develop into a tension pneumothorax. Regardless of the underlying cause, the pathophysiology is the same. The air that enters into the pleural space becomes trapped and cannot escape through the opening. Each time the patient takes a breath, more air is drawn into the lungs, increasing the intrathoracic pressure. The lung collapses and the heart, great vessels, and the trachea shift toward the unaffected side. This is called **mediastinal shift**. Respirations and circulation are greatly compromised. *A tension pneumothorax is a medical emergency and requires immediate intervention.*

Clinical Manifestations

The signs and symptoms associated with a pneumothorax will depend upon the size and type of the pneumothorax.

- Chest pain will be sharp and sudden in nature.
- The patient may display little to no respiratory distress in a small, closed pneumothorax, or in the case of a large pneumothorax, the patient may display acute respiratory distress.
- The patient may be anxious and restless.
- Tachypnea, dyspnea, air hunger, use of accessory muscles, and cyanosis can develop.
- Inspection of the chest wall may reveal decreased movement on the affected side of the chest.
- Percussion of the chest wall would reveal a tympanic (hyperresonance) sound and auscultation of the lungs would indicate diminished or absent breath sounds.
- Hypotension can develop.

In the case of a **tension pneumothorax**, respiratory distress is acute. Signs and symptoms include the following:

- Air hunger, restlessness and agitation, cyanosis, hypotension, and tachycardia.
- The patient will be profusely diaphoretic.

- The trachea will be deviated from the midline toward the unaffected side.
- Jugular venous distention can occur.
- Diminished heart sounds, shock, and subcutaneous emphysema (air leakage into surrounding tissue—produces a "crackling" sound when the skin is lightly compressed) can develop, along with ineffective ventilation.

In an **open pneumothorax**, in addition to the above signs and symptoms, there will be a "sucking" sound at the site of the opening with each respiration. The trachea will deviate toward the unaffected side with each inspiration, and shift back to midline with each expiration.

Diagnostic Tests

A pneumothorax is diagnosed through the clinical signs and symptoms presented by the patient. A chest X ray can verify the diagnosis. The degree of pneumothorax is usually expressed by percentage, for example, 100 percent (complete pneumothorax), 20 percent (partial pneumothorax), etc. By using percentages, the clinician can more easily track treatment progress as the lung re-expands.

If the client's respiratory distress is too acute to allow for X ray examination, the physician will forego the X ray and immediately insert an 18-gauge needle (an emergency thoracentesis) or chest tube into the second or third intercostal space to remove air.

Medical Management

The goal of the medical management of a pneumothorax is to remove the air (or blood) from the pleural space so that the lung can be allowed to re-expand. The severity of the pneumothorax will dictate the medical management. For a small, asymptomatic pneumothorax, the patient may be observed on an outpatient basis. For more serious cases, hospitalization is required.

For a simple pneumothorax, a chest tube will be inserted into the second intercostal space. If a hemothorax is also present, a second chest tube will be inserted posteriorly around the fourth or fifth intercostal space to drain off the fluid. (Remember, air rises to the top of the thoracic cavity, while fluid will settle towards the bottom.) After the tube(s) are inserted, gentle suction is applied to help remove the air and fluid. As the fluid is removed, the pleural space is decompressed and the lung can re-expand.

Additionally, supplemental oxygen will be provided for the patient. If an open "sucking" chest wound is present, it must be immediately covered with an airtight dressing to prevent the development of a tension pneumothorax. In an emergency, anything that can serve as a covering may be used—do not waste any time looking for a sterile dressing. However, the ideal dressing is a piece of sterile, petrolatum gauze.

Nursing Care for a Patient with a Pneumothorax

When caring for a patient with a pneumothorax, the goal of nursing care is to support respiratory ventilation and provide adequate oxygenation. The nurse should be prepared to assist the physician with a thoracentesis for the insertion of chest tubes. (Thoracentesis is discussed in chapter 4.)

The nurse should place the patient with a pneumothorax in a semi-Fowler's position to support respiration and administer oxygen. The patient's activity level will be confined to bed rest during the acute stage of the pneumothorax. The nurse should closely monitor the respiratory and cardiovascular status, including vital signs, lung sounds, and cardiac sounds. Physical inspection of the patient for chest wall expansion, tracheal deviation, and jugular vein distention are important assessments.

When caring for a patient with a **tension pneumothorax**, the nurse must appreciate that this is a life-threatening event and move quickly to intervene. It is essential that a needle or tube be inserted promptly to relieve the accumulation of air. If the nurse observes any signs or symptoms that indicate a tension pneumothorax is developing, immediate preparation for an emergency thoracentesis must be undertaken. In addition to the above nursing assessments, the nurse should closely observe for cardiac arrhythmias and subcutaneous emphysema.

If caring for a patient with an **open pneumothorax**, the nurse should also be prepared to cover the wound with an airtight, nonporous dressing and secure it with several strips of wide tape. After the opening has been covered, it is essential to monitor the patient closely for the development of a tension pneumothorax, which is even more serious than an open pneumothorax. If a tension pneumothorax develops, the dressing must be immediately removed.

Upon re-expansion of the lung (confirmed by chest X ray), the chest tube will be removed. Discharge teaching is the same for all patients, regardless of the type of pneumothorax experienced. Discharge teaching should include instructing the patient in what signs to report: chest pain and increased dyspnea. The patient is instructed to avoid strenuous activity, holding his or her breath, or any activity that increases the respiratory rate and depth. Gradual resumption of normal activity is recommended.

Flail Chest

A **flail chest** develops as a result of chest trauma, most commonly occurring as the result of impact with a steering wheel in a motor vehicle accident. The traumatic impact causes multiple adjacent ribs to fracture in two or more areas. The ribs are thus "free floating" and can no longer support the chest wall. With each breath the patient takes, the ribs move in and out and the mediastinum shifts. For example, as the patient breathes in, the ribs move in, pushing the mediastinum toward the unaffected side. When the patient exhales, the ribs move out and the mediastinum shifts back toward the affected side. There is decreased ventilation and increased dead space within the lungs. Respiratory distress develops, with the extent of the distress dependent upon the size of the rib segments involved. The patient develops hypoxemia and can also develop respiratory acidosis due to carbon dioxide retention.

Assessment of the patient's respiratory status will reveal asymmetrical chest movement and severe chest pain. Respirations will be rapid and shallow with dyspnea. Cyanosis may be evident. Breath sounds will be decreased. The patient will be anxious and restless. The patient should also be closely assessed for a tension pneumothorax.

Treatment and nursing care will depend upon the extent of the injury. For severe injuries the patient will require mechanical ventilation. For milder injuries, airway clearance is promoted by deep breathing, coughing, and positioning the patient on the affected side to provide support to the rib segments. The nurse splints the chest with his or her hands when coughing and deep breathing. Suctioning may be required. Pain control is essential in all cases to promote comfort and adequate lung expansion. The nurse monitors the patient's respiratory status closely by assessing lung sounds, chest expansion, arterial blood gas analysis, and pulse oximetry. Emphasis will be placed on preventing such complications as pneumonia and ARDS.

Pulmonary Embolus

Pulmonary embolus (PE) is the occlusion of a pulmonary artery by a clot. The clot is carried through the blood stream until it lodges in a pulmonary vessel, thus obstructing circulation. The seriousness of the condition depends upon the size of the vessel that the clot lodges in. PE can be fatal if enough lung tissue is denied its blood supply by the obstruction.

Typically, clots develop for one of three reasons:

1. Damage to the blood vessel walls
2. Stasis of blood
3. Blood hypercoagulability

Clots most frequently originate from deep vein thrombosis (DVT). Other risk factors for the development of PE include surgery (especially in the pelvic region or orthopedic), immobility, obesity, myocardial infarction, congestive heart failure, and fractures. Pregnancy and the use of estrogen therapy can also predispose an individual to PE.

Pathophysiology

The emboli move through the bloodstream from their site of origination until they become lodged in a pulmonary vessel. Blood flow to the area supplied by the vessel is obstructed and perfusion is decreased. The patient is able to ventilate the lung, but because of the decreased tissue perfusion, a ventilation/perfusion mismatch develops. This causes the development of hypoxemia.

If a large enough vessel is occluded, pulmonary vascular resistance can increase, leading to the development of atelectasis and eventually a decrease in cardiac output. Increased vascular resistance is due to the release of chemical agents such as histamine, prostaglandins, catecholamines, and serotonin. Right-sided heart failure can eventually develop as a result of increased cardiac workload caused by the increased pulmonary vascular resistance.

Clinical Manifestations

Clinical manifestations of PE vary, depending upon the size and number of emboli and the size of the vessel(s) obstructed. In some cases, PE results in instant death. The onset of symptoms is usually sudden.

If the embolus is relatively small, symptoms will be mild. The patient may develop tachypnea, a cough, and pleuritic chest pain. There may be some slight hemoptysis and a low-grade temperature. An elevated white blood count (WBC) may be noted due to inflammation. Upon auscultation of breath sounds, crackles may be heard.

In a larger embolus, the patient will most likely develop dyspnea and severe, sharp chest pain. The patient will be diaphoretic and anxious. Coughing will be more pronounced, as will hemoptysis. The patient may develop shock.

Diagnostic Tests

Diagnosis of PE is usually made based upon symptoms and the results of diagnostic tests. One noninvasive test that is usually used first in diagnosing PE is the ventilation-perfusion lung scan. However, the pulmonary angiogram is the most useful diagnostic tool, as it can clearly identify the area of obstruction.

A test used to measure the patient's respiratory status is ABGs, which may demonstrate hypoxemia and hypocapnia. Respiratory alkalosis can also develop.

Medical Management

Anticoagulant Therapy

Anticoagulant therapy is the major component of medical management in approximately 95 percent of the cases of PE. Intravenous heparin infusions are administered. Usually the patient receives a bolus (around 5000 u) of heparin followed by continuous IV infusions. Heparin serves to prevent the further expansion of the already existing emboli and helps prevent the development of additional emboli. Anticoagulant therapy does not "dissolve" the existing clot.

Following initial treatment with heparin infusions, the patient may require long-term anticoagulant therapy. Warfarin (Coumadin) will be used to provide this long-term therapy. Typically, the patient will be started on warfarin therapy while still receiving heparin. The heparin will be gradually tapered off, while the warfarin dosage is gradually increased to therapeutic levels. It takes two to three days of warfarin administration before therapeutic levels are reached in the bloodstream.

During heparin administration, the patient's partial thromboplastin time (PTT) is closely monitored with a goal of achieving and maintaining a therapeutic range of 1.5 to 2 times the control. When warfarin therapy is introduced, the prothrombin time (PT) will be monitored with a goal of achieving an international normalized ratio (INR) of 2:3. Patients are likely to be maintained on warfarin treatment for three to six months following the incident of PE.

Thrombolytic Therapy

In the care of a patient who is hemodynamically unstable as a result of the PE, **thrombolytic therapy** may be implemented. A thrombolytic agent is capable of dissolving the embolus and may serve to restore the patient's hemodynamic status. This option is not available for patients who have developed PE as a result of surgical intervention, as it can promote postoperative hemorrhage at the surgical site.

Surgical Management

If anticoagulant therapy is not effective or feasible, **surgical management** may be attempted. A **pulmonary embolectomy** is performed, in which the clot is removed from the pulmonary vessel either through a thoracotomy or a special embolectomy catheter. The mortality rate is high for this procedure.

In patients who experience reoccurring PE, a filter may be inserted in the vena cava near the renal arteries. This filter will allow blood flow to continue uninterrupted, but will filter out any clots.

In addition to anticoagulant therapy, the patient will be placed on oxygen; if the respiratory status is severely compromised, the patient may need to be intubated and mechanically ventilated. Intravenous fluids may need to be administered to treat hypotension. Analgesics, typically morphine, are administered to relieve pain and anxiety.

Nursing Process: Assessment

A priority nursing assessment for PE is to first assess which patients are at high risk (as previously identified) for the development of PE. These patients should be monitored closely for initial signs and symptoms that might indicate the development of PE.

The majority of PEs occur as a result of **deep vein thrombosis (DVT)**. The nurse should be particularly vigilant in assessing for signs and symptoms of DVT in those patients who are at high risk for developing DVT. Immobility, surgery, obesity, trauma, and use of estrogen therapy are common causes of DVT. Of those patients who develop DVT, approximately 50 percent will develop PE. Clinical manifestations of DVT include the following:

- Local pain or tenderness
- Edema (swelling) in the affected leg
- Warmth and redness
- Low-grade temperature
- Palpable firm vein
- Positive **Homans' sign** (Homans' sign is calf tenderness when the foot is dorsiflexed. The majority of patients with DVT *do not* demonstrate a positive Homans' sign.)

When assessing for the development of PE, the nurse should assess the patient closely for anxiety, a sense of foreboding, dyspnea, and chest palpitations. Substernal chest pain, hemoptysis, pleuritic chest pain, cough, and diaphoresis are other signs and symptoms for which the nurse should be alert.

The nurse should frequently assess the patient's vital signs and lung sounds. Auscultation of lung sounds may indicate decreased breath sounds or crackles. The nurse should evaluate the patient's ABG values, especially looking for the development of hypoxemia and respiratory alkalosis.

When the patient is receiving anticoagulant therapy, the nurse should closely monitor PTT, PT, and INR laboratory values. The nurse should also assess for signs of abnormal bleeding related to anticoagulant therapy.

Nursing Process: Nursing Diagnosis and Planning

Based upon an analysis of the gathered data, the following **nursing diagnoses** may be appropriate for the patient with pulmonary embolus:

- Impaired gas exchange related to ventilation/perfusion mismatch
- Anxiety related to respiratory distress and pain
- Chest pain related to ischemia and inflammation of lung tissue
- Knowledge deficit regarding the disease process and treatment regimen

Primary goals for the patient with pulmonary embolus include the following:

- Improved gas exchange
- Reduction of anxiety
- Relief from chest pain
- Adherence to prescribed therapeutic regimen
- Avoidance of complications: right cardiac failure and cardiogenic shock

Nursing Process: Implementation

A key responsibility of the nurse is to prevent the formation of a thrombus in the first place so that PE does not develop. Important **preventive activities** include the following:

- Encourage patients to ambulate early and avoid bed rest as much as possible.
- Have patients perform leg exercises hourly to stimulate peripheral circulation.
- Use antiembolism stockings or sequential compression devices on patients with limited mobility.
- Instruct patient to avoid prolonged sitting or standing, as well as to avoid restrictive clothing and crossing the legs.
- Administer low-dose prophylactic heparin as ordered.
- Carefully monitor patients for the development of DVT, so that early intervention can begin if detected. Treatment for DVT consists of anticoagulant therapy, leg elevation, analgesics, and the application of warm, moist packs.

If the patient does develop a PE, the nurse will focus attention on promoting gas exchange, tissue perfusion, and comfort. Specific nursing actions that will help achieve these goals include the following:

- Placing the patient in a semi-Fowler's position (head elevated 30° to 40°)
- Administering oxygen; monitoring SaO_2 with pulse oximetry
- Administering opioid analgesics to decrease chest pain, promote rest
- Encouraging deep breathing and incentive spirometry
- Maintaining calm environment
- Encouraging activity within prescribed limitations

Another key nursing responsibility is the safe administration of anticoagulant therapy. The nurse should monitor the IV heparin infusion closely, keeping in mind that IV infusion pumps can malfunction and deliver erroneous amounts of fluid and medication. Close monitoring of the PTT value by the nurse is essential. If the PTT climbs above therapeutic range, the heparin dosage must be adjusted promptly. When warfarin treatment is initiated, the nurse will closely monitor the PT and INR as well.

The nurse should assess the patient closely for signs of bleeding. Blood in the stool, hematuria, easy bruising, and bleeding gums are some examples of where abnormal bleeding can be detected. If ABGs are drawn, the puncture site will need to have pressure applied after each stick for ten minutes.

Upon discharge, the patient will need to be instructed in how to safely take anticoagulant drugs, as warfarin will continue to be administered for three to six months following the PE. The patient should also be told what signs and symptoms require immediate attention from a health care provider, including apprehension, chest pain, dyspnea, cough, and hemoptysis. These could indicate a return of the PE. Patients should be instructed to avoid prolonged sitting and standing, and avoid constrictive clothing. They should not smoke. The importance of maintaining follow-up appointments must be emphasized.

Nursing Process: Evaluation

The effectiveness of nursing interventions can be measured by the patient's achievement of the following **expected outcomes**:

- Exhibits evidence of normal gas exchange
- Expresses relief from chest pain
- Demonstrates relief from anxiety
- Avoids development of complications
- Demonstrates appropriate self-care activities

Acute Respiratory Failure

Acute respiratory failure (ARF) can result from a number of respiratory and nonrespiratory disorders. Examples of respiratory disorders that can lead to ARF include COPD, asthma, pulmonary embolus, severe respiratory infection, pulmonary edema, adult respiratory distress syndrome (ARDS), and chest trauma. Examples of nonrespiratory disorders that can lead to ARF include neurological disorders that affect the respiratory muscles or cause paralysis of the diaphragm (such as multiple sclerosis, myasthenia gravis, Guillain-Barré syndrome), central nervous system disturbances (drug overdose, head injury), and prolonged mechanical ventilation.

Pathophysiology

ARF is defined as any rapid change in respiration that leads to the development of hypoxemia and/or hypercapnia. The physiological criteria that are used to define ARF include a sudden onset of the following:

- PaO_2 of 50 mm Hg or less (on room air)
- $PaCO_2$ of 50 mm Hg or more
- pH of 7.35 or less

In respiratory failure, there is either an alteration in the gas exchange process in the lungs where oxygen is not able to be diffused into the blood and carbon dioxide eliminated, or there is an alteration in the ventilation function of the lungs that leads to a decreased ability to move oxygen into the lungs and carbon dioxide out of the lungs. In either case, the outcome is the same: arterial oxygen levels fall, with tissues becoming hypoxic, and carbon dioxide levels rise, leading to a drop in pH and the development of **respiratory acidosis**.

It is possible for a patient who has compensated chronic respiratory failure (as in COPD) to suddenly develop acute respiratory failure. This is referred to as **acute on chronic respiratory failure**. A common cause is the onset of a respiratory infection with an underlying chronic lung condition. Due to the infection, the patient is no longer able to compensate for the altered pulmonary function. When this happens, severe hypoxemia and pH acidosis will develop; the PaCO$_2$ is already elevated due to the underlying chronic disorder, so it is not as relevant in determining the patient's respiratory status.

Clinical Manifestations

The clinical manifestations exhibited by the patient in ARF are the result of the development of hypercapnia, hypoxemia, and respiratory acidosis. These signs and symptoms include headache, irritability, altered mental status including confusion, increasing lethargy, and asterixis (flapping tremor). The patient may become comatose. Other signs and symptoms can include tachycardia, hypotension, cyanosis (a late sign), and arrhythmias. There may be an alteration in the patient's respiratory pattern; depending upon the underlying cause of the ARF, tachypnea, bradypnea, or apnea may develop.

Diagnostic Tests

Diagnostic tests usually include ABGs, chest X rays, and bedside pulmonary spirometry. Vital capacity will be decreased. Sputum for culture and sensitivity may be obtained to check for an underlying respiratory infection.

Medical Management

The primary goals of the medical management of ARF are to identify and treat the underlying cause, and to provide support for adequate respiratory functioning. Mechanical ventilation will need to be immediately provided for those patients who are experiencing severe ARF.

Treatment of ARF includes administration of oxygen therapy, intubation and the use of mechanical ventilation as indicated by the patient's condition, and treatment for the underlying cause and any developing complications.

Nursing Process: Assessment

Assessment of a patient in ARF includes a thorough assessment of the patient's respiratory status and an evaluation of the blood gas analysis. If the patient is in severe respiratory distress, the nurse must intervene promptly to provide respiratory support; therefore, aspects of the assessment may need to be delayed. Assessment findings will vary depending upon the underlying cause of the ARF.

The nurse should note the patient's general appearance and mental status. The patient may be anxious, apprehensive, agitated and confused, or lethargic and somnolent. A respiratory rate of less than 8 breaths/minute indicates hypoventilation; a respiratory rate of more than 35 breaths/minute will cause rapid fatigue and cannot be sustained by the patient. Tachycardia and hypotension are common findings.

Nursing Process: Nursing Diagnosis and Planning

Based upon an analysis of the gathered data, the following **nursing diagnoses** may be appropriate for the patient with acute respiratory failure:

- Impaired gas exchange related to ventilation/perfusion imbalance
- Ineffective breathing pattern related to fatigue
- Ineffective airway clearance related to increased secretions, obstruction, and/or fatigue
- Decreased cardiac output related to increased pulmonary vascular resistance
- Anxiety related to difficulty breathing

Primary **goals** for the patient with acute respiratory failure include the following:

- Maintenance of a patent airway
- Restoration of normal breathing pattern
- Improved gas exchange
- Restoration of normal cardiac output
- Reduction in anxiety and fear

Nursing Process: Implementation

Nursing interventions are focused primarily on promoting effective gas exchange and airway clearance. If the patient is placed on mechanical ventilation, it is the nurse's responsibility to effectively maintain the ventilation and evaluate the patient's response to the therapy. (Care of the patient who is on mechanical ventilation is covered in chapter 5.)

In addition, the nurse will implement nursing care that will help prevent the hazards of immobility, including promoting circulation, maintaining skin integrity, maintaining fluid and electrolyte balance, and providing adequate nutritional intake. Promoting the patient's comfort and decreasing anxiety are other important nursing interventions. Additional nursing interventions are dependent upon the underlying cause of the ARF.

Nursing Process: Evaluation

The effectiveness of nursing interventions can be measured by the patient's achievement of the following **expected outcomes**:

- Demonstrates improved ventilation
- Improves breathing pattern
- Demonstrates effective airway clearance
- Exhibits signs of adequate cardiac output
- Expresses relief from anxiety
- Avoids complications related to decreased tissue perfusion, intubation, and immobility

Adult Respiratory Distress Syndrome (ARDS)

Adult respiratory distress syndrome (ARDS) occurs in critically ill adults. It has a high mortality rate. ARDS typically occurs in patients who have experienced a major trauma or insult to the body. Some common precipitating factors include shock, trauma, infection, aspiration of gastric contents, pancreatitis, and fat emboli.

The patient who has ARDS is in acute hypoxemic respiratory failure. Hypercapnia does not develop. ARDS is characterized by hypoxemia, severe dyspnea, and the development of diffuse bilateral pulmonary infiltrations.

Pathophysiology

ARDS is triggered by a major physical insult to the body. The insult activates the complement cascade, releasing cellular and chemical mediators that damage the alveolar-capillary membrane. This leads to an increase in alveolar-capillary permeability. The increase in capillary permeability allows for fluid, red blood cells, white blood cells, protein, and other cellular debris to shift out of the capillaries and into the interstitial spaces and alveoli. Lung compliance is decreased ("stiff" lungs develop).

The presence of the fluid and cells in the alveoli interferes with the exchange of oxygen and carbon dioxide, causing a ventilation/perfusion mismatch. Hypoxemia develops. To compensate for the hypoxemia, alveolar hyperventilation develops and eventually respiratory alkalosis develops as well.

In addition to fluid entering the alveoli, there is damage to the type II alveolar cells that produce surfactant. Surfactant production is decreased, and atelectasis develops. As normal functional lung tissue is destroyed, lung compliance continues to decrease, and eventually there is scarring of the lung tissue.

Clinical Manifestations

There is usually a brief delay between the time of the injury and the onset of signs and symptoms. The delay can be as long as twelve to forty-eight hours. Signs and symptoms include the following:

- There is sudden onset of respiratory distress, beginning with tachypnea and developing into acute dyspnea with use of accessory muscles.
- Cyanosis is present.
- The patient develops a dry cough and fever.
- Auscultation of the lungs will reveal fine crackles throughout the lung fields.
- The patient may display confusion and agitation.
- Coma may develop.

Diagnostic Tests

ARDS is diagnosed by chest X rays that show bilateral, diffuse infiltrations. ABGs demonstrate hypoxemia with a PaO_2 of less than 50 mm Hg and hypocapnia. The patient will be in respiratory alkalosis. The hypoxemia is refractory (does not respond) to the administration of supplemental oxygen. As the patient enters the end stage of the disorder, hypercapnia and respiratory acidosis develop.

Medical Management

The underlying cause of ARDS must be diagnosed and treated. To provide adequate oxygenation, the patient will most likely require intubation and mechanical ventilation due to the lack of response to supplemental oxygen. Additional goals of medical management include maintaining adequate circulatory support and tissue perfusion, providing adequate nutritional support, and maintaining fluid balance.

The success of the treatment will be evaluated by closely monitoring the patient's ABGs, pulse oximetry readings, and pulmonary function testing. Positive-end expiratory pressure (PEEP) will be set on the ventilator to prevent alveolar collapse and improve the ventilation/perfusion ratio.

Nursing Management

The assessments, nursing diagnoses, nursing care, and evaluation of the patient with ARDS is similar to the nursing care described for the patient with ARF. The patient is critically ill and requires continual monitoring. The patient will be very frightened because of the increasing dyspnea and will require much emotional support from the nurse. The nurse should deliver care in a calming and reassuring manner. Family members will also require much support during this time of crisis.

Chapter 7 Study Questions

1.   Describe the clinical manifestations of asthma.

2.   A patient who is in status asthmaticus is being assessed by the nurse. The nurse notes the patient's wheezing has stopped. What is the significance of this clinical finding?

3.   What ABG findings would the nurse expect to find during an asthma attack?

4.   The patient is using a corticosteroid inhaler and an adrenergic agonist inhaler for treatment of his asthma. The nurse should instruct the patient to use the inhalers in what order?

5.   Describe pertinent assessments to be made by the nurse when caring for a patient who has asthma.

6.   Describe how a patient should be instructed to use a metered-dose inhaler.

7.   Describe the pathophysiological changes that occur in the lungs of a patient with emphysema.

8.   Describe the typical clinical manifestations of a patient with emphysema.

9.   Oxygen is prescribed for the patient with emphysema. What should the nurse remember when administering oxygen to a patient with emphysema?

10.   Identify three priority nursing diagnoses for the patient with COPD.

11.   What breathing techniques should the nurse teach the patient with emphysema in order to improve his breathing patterns?

12.   Who should be encouraged to receive a pneumococcal vaccine?

13.   Describe the signs and symptoms elderly patients with pneumonia may display.

14.   Describe a nursing plan of care for a patient with pneumonia.

15.   Define a closed, traumatic, open, and tension pneumothorax.

16.   Describe the signs and symptoms of a tension pneumothorax. What is the significance of a tension pneumothorax?

17.   What care should the nurse anticipate when caring for a patient with an open pneumothorax?

18. What pharmacological intervention will be used when treating a patient who has developed a pulmonary embolus?

19. Describe the laboratory tests that should be monitored by the nurse when the patient is receiving heparin and warfarin.

20. What signs and symptoms should the nurse assess the patient for when assessing a patient for the development of a deep vein thrombosis?

21.   What specific nursing actions are appropriate for promoting gas exchange and tissue perfusion in a patient with a pulmonary embolus?

22.   Describe the physiological criteria used to define acute respiratory failure.

23.   What is the basic pathophysiological finding in a patient with acute respiratory failure?

24.   Briefly describe the primary nursing interventions related to the care of a patient with acute respiratory failure.

25.   What are the characteristics of ARDS?

Answers to Chapter 7 Study Questions

1. The most common clinical manifestations of asthma are a cough, wheezing, and dyspnea. These symptoms may occur suddenly or may develop over a matter of days. The cough can be nonproductive or productive of mucus. Wheezing is heard upon expiration as air is pushed through the narrowed airways. Wheezing may be present upon inspiration as well. The patient will complain of a feeling of chest tightness and dyspnea. The patient must work hard to move air out of the lungs, and, as a result, expiration becomes prolonged. As the attack continues, hypoxemia can develop.

2. This is an ominous sign and a dire indication that the patient has stopped moving air in and out of the lungs. Respiratory failure and death are imminent if prompt medical intervention is not implemented.

3. Because of the patient's rapid breathing, hypocapnia may develop, leading to respiratory alkalosis. If the patient has a severe asthma attack, severe hypoxemia and respiratory acidosis may develop. Between asthma attacks, pulmonary function and other diagnostic tests are likely to be normal.

4. When using these drugs together, it is recommended that the patient use the inhaled bronchodilators first, and then the corticosteroid inhaler. By dilating the airways first with the bronchodilators, the corticosteroid will be more effective.

5. Subjective assessment data that is gathered by the nurse includes information about the patient's history of asthma and any known precipitating factors. The nurse should also gather information about the patient's self-care activities and compliance with the prescribed medication regimen. Objective assessment data that is gathered includes assessment of vital signs, including the presence of tachypnea, tachycardia, and pulsus paradoxus, which is best detected by confirming a drop in systolic blood pressure (6 to 8 mm Hg) during inspiration. The patient will likely be anxious or apprehensive. The nurse should assess for any changes in the patient's sensorium. Inspection of the patient may reveal dyspnea, use of accessory muscles, prolonged expiration, use of the orthopneic position, and cyanosis. Percussion reveals hyperresonance and decreased excursion of the diaphragm. Inspiratory and expiratory wheezing and rhonchi can be heard upon auscultation. However, the nurse should note that as the patient becomes fatigued or develops status asthmaticus, there will be only faint or absent breath sounds. This is a critical finding that indicates the patient is approaching respiratory failure and is a medical emergency. The nurse will evaluate ABG findings that will typically reveal mild hypoxemia and respiratory alkalosis in a mild to moderate asthma attack, and severe hypoxemia and respiratory acidosis in a severe attack.

6.   1) Hold the inhaler upright and shake. 2) Sit upright and breathe out slowly. 3) Hold inhaler one to two inches from mouth or use a spacer device. If using a spacer, put lips around the mouthpiece. 4) Inhale slowly while pushing down on the inhaler cartridge to deliver medication. Inhalation should be slow and deep, lasting around five seconds. 5) Hold breath for about ten seconds after completing inhalation. 6) If taking more than one puff of medication, allow one to two minutes to elapse between puffs. 7) If using a corticosteroid inhaler, rinse mouth with water following each use to prevent the development of oral thrush.

7.   The pathophysiological changes that occur in the lungs due to emphysema include increased lung compliance due to loss of elastic recoil, causing the lungs to become overdistended. In addition, there is an increased airway resistance due to collapse of small airways, especially during expiration. The collapse of airways leads to air trapping, causing further lung overdistension. The overdistension of the lungs applies pressure to the diaphragm, decreasing diaphragmatic excursion. As the diaphragm becomes fixed in position, its ventilatory effectiveness is decreased. Destruction of the alveolar and bronchiole walls affects the alveolar-capillary membrane surface and eventually results in decreased diffusion of oxygen and carbon dioxide.

8.   In emphysema, the first noticeable symptom is usually dyspnea upon exertion. As the disease progresses, the dyspnea becomes more constant. The patient can also develop orthopnea, in which the patient cannot assume a recumbent position without developing dyspnea. Patients may report requiring two or more pillows to elevate the head when sleeping to decrease dyspnea; many may report sleeping upright in a recliner. When awake, the patient may assume an orthopneic position, in which the patient sits forward with the forearms propped up on an over-bed table to ease breathing. The patient is usually thin in appearance with a barrel chest. Unlike chronic bronchitis, there is little to no sputum production with emphysema. Patients are likely to develop pursed-lip breathing, which helps decrease airway collapse and prolong expiration. Accessory muscle breathing can also be present.

9.   When administering oxygen to patients with COPD, it is important that the oxygen flow rate be kept at a low rate, usually 1 to 2 L of oxygen per nasal cannula. Many patients with COPD develop a chronic excess of carbon dioxide; as a result, their stimulus to breathe becomes their low PaO_2 levels. Administering a high flow rate of oxygen can raise the low PaO_2 level and remove the patient's stimulus to breathe, causing respiratory failure to develop.

10.   Three priority nursing diagnoses are as follows: impaired gas exchange related to altered ventilation/perfusion ratio; ineffective airway clearance related to excess sputum production, decreased energy, and ineffective cough; and ineffective breathing pattern due to airway obstruction and fatigue.

11.   There are several breathing techniques and positions that can help the patient breathe more comfortably. Pursed-lip breathing is a technique that helps the patient slow down the respiratory rate and prolong the expiratory phase of the respiratory cycle. It also helps prevent the airways from collapsing and decreases air trapping. The nurse should also encourage the patient to assume a forward-leaning position when exhaling. This position helps the patient remove more air from the lungs during the exhalation period. Teaching the patient to do abdominal breathing will allow the diaphragm to elevate more and improve breathing efficiency.

12.   Those who are sixty-five years of age or older, have a chronic illness, live in an environment that promotes risk of disease (crowded living conditions, poor sanitation, etc.), or are immunocompromised should receive a pneumococcal vaccine.

13.   Elderly patients who develop pneumonia may have subtle signs and symptoms, such as generalized weakness and deterioration, anorexia, tachycardia, tachypnea, and confusion. It is possible for the elderly patient to develop pneumonia without demonstrating a fever, cough, sputum production, or chest pain. It is important for the nurse to be vigilant in monitoring elderly patients, especially those with an underlying chronic illness, as the signs and symptoms of pneumonia can be easily obscured in the elderly.

14.   Maintaining a patent airway and ensuring adequate gas exchange are priority nursing interventions in the patient with pneumonia. The nurse should encourage the patient to cough and deep breathe at frequent intervals to help move secretions out of the lungs. If the patient is experiencing pleuritic chest pain, the nurse should help the patient splint the chest wall by placing his or her hands, or a folded blanket, on the rib cage to provide support during the coughing and deep breathing process. Warm, humidified air can be used to help loosen secretions and aid expectoration of sputum. The nurse should also ensure that the patient has a fluid intake of 2 to 3 L/day to thin secretions. Chest percussion and postural drainage may also be used to loosen and mobilize pulmonary secretions. If the patient is not able to cough up secretions, the nurse may need to use nasotracheal suctioning to assist in the removal of secretions. The nurse may also administer oxygen to maintain adequate oxygenation levels. Pulse oximetry and ABG levels will be used to determine the effectiveness of oxygen therapy. It is important for the nurse to encourage the patient to conserve energy and rest during the acute phase of the illness. The patient is usually on bed rest during this time and will require assistance with completing the activities of daily living. Frequent position changes will help mobilize secretions and help prevent skin breakdown in the patient who is confined to bed. The patient should be placed in a comfortable position to promote ease of breathing. A semi-Fowler's position is usually most comfortable for the patient. As the patient's condition improves, activity will be gradually resumed, with the nurse closely monitoring the patient for signs of respiratory distress and fatigue. The patient may experience anorexia and

difficulty eating due to shortness of breath and fatigue. The nurse should ensure an adequate intake of fluids and observe the patient closely for any indication of fluid and electrolyte imbalances. Intravenous fluids with electrolytes are frequently administered to maintain the patient's fluid and electrolyte balance. The patient may best tolerate a liquid diet during the acute phase of the illness, with the diet progressing as the patient's condition improves. A diet high in carbohydrates, vitamins, and protein is appropriate for the patient with pneumonia.

15.   A closed (simple or spontaneous) pneumothorax develops when air enters the pleural space through an opening in the parietal or visceral pleura. A traumatic pneumothorax is caused by a laceration or puncture of the lung itself allowing air to leave the lung and enter the pleural space. A traumatic pneumothorax can also be an open pneumothorax. If the chest wound is large enough, air will move freely in and out of the wound with each respiration. This condition is also commonly called a "sucking chest wound." A tension pneumothorax can develop when air is drawn into the pleural space through a small puncture in the chest wall or a lacerated lung.

16.   The air that enters into the pleural space becomes trapped and cannot escape through the opening. Each time the patient takes a breath, more air is drawn into the lungs, increasing the intrathoracic pressure. The lung collapses and the heart, great vessels, and the trachea shift towards the unaffected side. This is called mediastinal shift. Respirations and circulation are greatly compromised. A tension pneumothorax is a medical emergency and requires immediate intervention. In the case of a tension pneumothorax, respiratory distress is acute. Signs and symptoms include air hunger, restlessness and agitation, cyanosis, hypotension, and tachycardia. The patient will be profusely diaphoretic. The trachea will be deviated from the midline towards the unaffected side. Jugular venous distention can occur. Diminished heart sounds, shock, and subcutaneous emphysema (air leakage into surrounding tissue—produces a "crackling" sound when the skin is lightly compressed) can develop, along with ineffective ventilation.

17.   If caring for a patient with an open pneumothorax, the nurse should be prepared to cover the wound with an airtight, nonporous dressing and secure it with several strips of wide tape. After the opening has been covered, it is essential to monitor the patient closely for the development of a tension pneumothorax, which is even more serious than an open pneumothorax. If a tension pneumothorax develops, the dressing must be immediately removed.

18.   Anticoagulant therapy is the major component of medical management in approximately 95 percent of the cases of PE. Intravenous heparin infusions are administered. Usually the patient receives a bolus (around 5000 u) of heparin followed by continuous IV infusions. Heparin serves to prevent the further expansion of the already existing emboli and helps prevent the development of

additional emboli. Anticoagulant therapy does not "dissolve" the existing clot. Following initial treatment with heparin infusions, the patient may require long-term anticoagulant therapy. Warfarin (Coumadin) will be used to provide this long-term therapy. Typically, the patient will be started on warfarin therapy while still receiving heparin. The heparin will be gradually tapered off, while the warfarin dosage is gradually increased to therapeutic levels. It takes two to three days of warfarin administration before therapeutic levels are reached in the bloodstream.

19.   During heparin administration, the patient's partial thromboplastin time is closely monitored with a goal of achieving and maintaining a therapeutic range of 1.5 to 2 times the control. When warfarin therapy is introduced, the prothrombin time will be monitored with a goal of achieving an international normalized ratio of 2:3. Patients are likely to be maintained on warfarin treatment for three to six months following the incident of PE.

20.   The majority of pulmonary emboli occur as a result of deep vein thrombosis. The nurse should be particularly vigilant in assessing for signs and symptoms of DVT in those patients who are at high risk for developing DVT. Immobility, surgery, obesity, trauma, and use of estrogen therapy are common causes of DVT. Of those patients who develop DVT, approximately 50 percent will develop PE. Clinical manifestations of DVT include local pain or tenderness, edema in the affected leg, warmth and redness, low-grade temperature, palpable firm vein, and positive Homans' sign.

21.   The following are specific nursing actions are appropriate for promoting gas exchange and tissue perfusion in a patient with a pulmonary embolus: placing the patient in a semi-Fowler's position (head elevated 30–40°); administering oxygen; monitoring SaO_2 with pulse oximetry; administering opioid analgesics to decrease chest pain, promote rest; encouraging deep breathing and incentive spirometry; maintaining a calm environment; and encouraging activity within prescribed limitations.

22.   The physiological criteria that are used to define ARF include a sudden onset of a PaO_2 of 50 mm Hg or less (on room air), $PaCO_2$ of 50 mm Hg or more, and pH of 7.35 or less.

23.   In respiratory failure, there is either an alteration in the gas exchange process in the lungs in which oxygen is not able to be diffused into the blood and carbon dioxide eliminated, or there is an alteration in the ventilation function of the lungs that leads to a decreased ability to move oxygen into the lungs and carbon dioxide out of the lungs. In either case, the outcome is the same: arterial oxygen levels fall, with tissues becoming hypoxic, and carbon dioxide levels rise, leading to a drop in pH and the development of respiratory acidosis.

24.   Nursing interventions are focused primarily on promoting effective gas exchange and airway clearance. If the patient is placed on mechanical ventilation, it is the

nurse's responsibility to effectively maintain the ventilation and evaluate the patient's response to the therapy. In addition, the nurse will implement nursing care that will help prevent the hazards of immobility, including promoting circulation, maintaining skin integrity, maintaining fluid and electrolyte balance, and providing adequate nutritional intake. Promoting the patient's comfort and decreasing anxiety are other important nursing interventions. Additional nursing interventions are dependent upon the underlying cause of the ARF.

25.   The patient who has ARDS is in acute hypoxemic respiratory failure. Hypercapnia does not develop. ARDS is characterized by hypoxemia, severe dyspnea, and the development of diffuse bilateral pulmonary infiltrations. The hypoxemia is refractory to the administration of supplemental oxygen. As the patient enters the end stage of the disorder, hypercapnia and respiratory acidosis develop.

UNIT III: DISORDERS OF THE CARDIOVASCULAR SYSTEM

Chapter 8: Clinical Manifestations of Cardiovascular Disorders

Key Terms

Capillary refill
Cardiac output
Clubbing
Edema
    Peripheral
    Pitting
Jugular neck vein distention
Pulse deficit
Pulse pressure
S_1 and S_2
S_3 and S_4

Introduction

This chapter discusses the clinical manifestations of cardiovascular problems. The nurse needs to carefully assess the patient to detect the frequently subtle respiratory or circulatory changes that can indicate the patient is developing a cardiovascular problem. Prompt detection of changes in the patient's condition is important to avoid potential life-threatening complications.

Altered Vital Signs

An important aspect of detecting cardiovascular problems is the nurse's assessment in the patient's vital signs. The nurse should note the quality of the patient's respirations, observing rate, rhythm, and depth. When cardiovascular problems cause hypoxemia and hypoxia, the patient may develop an increased respiratory rate (tachypnea) and shortness of breath.

Initial blood pressure assessment should be conducted with the patient in a lying, sitting, and standing position. The blood pressure should be taken in both arms. The nurse should make note of the **pulse pressure**, which is the difference between the systolic (higher) reading and the diastolic (lower) blood pressure reading. The pulse pressure is a measure of the **cardiac output**. Typically, the pulse pressure is 30–40 mm Hg. A pulse pressure of less than 30 mm Hg indicates a decrease in the cardiac output.

The patient's pulse should be taken, noting the rate and rhythm. The quality of the pulse is also evaluated, indicating whether the pulse is normal, weak and thready, or full and bounding. Pulse quality is indicative of cardiac output. A thready pulse can be indicative of a decrease in cardiac output. A full and bounding pulse can indicate an increased cardiac output as a result of fluid volume overload.

The nurse should also auscultate the apical heart rate and compare it to the radial rate to determine if a **pulse deficit** is present. A pulse deficit exists when the apical heart rate is faster than the radial pulse rate. The significance of a pulse deficit is that some of the heart's contractions are ineffective in producing cardiac output that reaches the peripheral extremities. Auscultating the apical pulse is also appropriate for assessing the presence of cardiac arrhythmias.

The patient's temperature should also be assessed. Frequently in cardiovascular disorders that are caused by inflammation and infection, the patient has either a low-grade or high-grade temperature.

Altered Heart Sounds

The nurse should also carefully auscultate the patient's heart sounds. There are normally two heart sounds heard during auscultation: S_1 and S_2.

- The **first heart sound**, S_1, is also referred to as the "lub" sound, and is associated with the closure of the mitral and tricuspid heart valves and the beginning of systole.
- The **second heart sound**, S_2, is also referred to as the "dub" sound, and is associated with the closure of the aortic and pulmonic valves and the beginning of diastole.

Some cardiovascular disorders can lead to the development of "extra" heart sounds, which can be auscultated. These heart sounds are abnormal.

- The S_3, or **ventricular gallop**, is an extra heart sound that occurs immediately after the S_2. This heart sound commonly occurs in congestive heart failure or mitral regurgitation.
- The S_4 heart sound, also known as an **atrial gallop**, occurs immediately before the S_1 heart sound and is common in patients who have left ventricular hypertrophy and coronary artery disease.

Altered Skin Color and Temperature

The patient's skin color can be altered by cardiovascular disorders. Skin color indicates the adequacy of tissue oxygenation, cardiac output, and circulation.

- **Cyanosis** indicates a decreased oxygenation of tissues.

- **Pallor** (deficiency of color, especially in the face) is present in patients who have anemia. Pallor can also develop in extremities that have impaired arterial flow and in edematous tissue.
- **Erythema** can develop in the extremities when venous congestion and edema develop.

Skin temperature should also be assessed. When cardiac output is decreased, the patient's skin may feel cool to the touch. The temperature of the extremities may also be cool when extremities are affected by conditions that impair circulation, such as peripheral vascular disease.

In addition to assessing skin color and temperature, **peripheral pulses** should also be palpated and rated.

Some pulse rating scales range from 0 to 4+, with the ratings defined as follows:

- A rating of "**0**" indicates the pulse is absent.
- A rating of "**1+**" indicates that the pulse is weak.
- A rating of "**2+**" or "**3+**" is considered normal.
- A rating of "**4+**" indicates the pulse is very full and bounding.

Other pulse rating scales range from 0 to 3+, with the ratings defined as follows:

- "**0**" indicates absent pulse.
- "**1+**" indicates the pulse is weak and thready.
- "**2+**" indicates the pulse is normal.
- "**3+**" means the pulse is full and bounding.

The nurse should be familiar with the rating scale used in the institution in which he or she practices. For clarity, it is best to chart pulse scales as 1+/3 or 1+/4 to clearly indicate the rating scale being used.

Altered Physical Appearance

The nurse should assess the patient for alterations in physical appearance.

When assessing the cardiovascular system, the nurse should inspect the patient for **jugular neck vein distention (JVD)**. Distended neck veins suggest the development of right-sided heart failure or circulatory volume overload.

The nails should be inspected for **clubbing**. Clubbing, which is a rounding and enlargement of the distal portion of the finger, is present in chronic conditions of hypoxia, such as chronic obstructive pulmonary disease (COPD). **Capillary refill**, or blanching, should also be checked. When the fingernail is compressed and released, the color should return to the nail bed within three seconds. Capillary refill is delayed when there is a decrease in peripheral circulation.

The nurse should also assess the patient for **peripheral edema**, which is the accumulation of fluid in the tissues. A common cause of peripheral edema is congestive heart failure. Edema is likely to develop when the extremities are in a dependent position; when the legs are elevated, the edema subsides. Poor venous return can also lead to the development of peripheral edema when extremities are in a dependent position.

The development of **pitting edema**, where the tissue can be depressed and an imprint remains, indicates that the patient is experiencing fluid volume overload. This circulatory overload can be due to congestive heart failure. Pitting edema can be rated on a scale from 1+ to 4+. Pitting edema that is considered a "trace" is rated 1+, whereas 4+ pitting edema can reach a depth of one-inch depression and stay depressed for up to five minutes after the release of pressure. Pitting edema typically develops in the feet, ankles, and legs. It can also develop in the sacrum if the patient is in a supine (lying) position. Pitting edema does not disappear upon elevation, but instead requires pharmacological intervention with diuretics.

Alterations in Comfort

When caring for a patient with cardiac problems, the nurse should carefully assess the patient for pain or discomfort related to breathing. Chest pain can have many causes. Careful assessment by the nurse can help determine the origin of the pain. For example, sharp chest pain that increases upon inspiration could be pleuritic pain. Midsternal chest pain that is described as "crushing" and radiating into the neck is likely to be cardiac in origin.

Intermittent claudication is another example of pain that can occur in a cardiovascular disorder as a result of lack of tissue oxygenation in the lower extremities. Intermittent claudication is pain that occurs in the calf muscles when walking, but the pain disappears upon rest.

Other alterations in comfort that the patient with a cardiac problem may experience include difficulty breathing, fatigue, and difficulty sleeping due to dyspnea.

Altered Sensory Perception

Altered sensory perception can also develop due to hypoxia and impaired circulation. For example, the patient may experience numbness and tingling in extremities with impaired circulation. A common cause of peripheral vascular problems and impaired circulation is diabetes mellitus. The nurse should teach the patient to carefully inspect the lower extremities for breaks in skin integrity, as the patient may not be able to feel or sense the development of any pressure areas or injuries. The patient may not be able to feel any extremes in temperature as well, and he or she should be told to protect the extremities from cold weather, heating pads, and hot water. In addition, the nurse should closely assess the patient for dizziness, syncope, or blurred vision. All of these symptoms can be indications of hypoxia.

Chapter 8 Study Questions

1. Define pulse pressure. What is the significance of the pulse pressure?

2. A nurse assesses that a patient has distended jugular neck veins. What conditions are associated with this clinical finding?

3. What patient education would be appropriate for a patient who has an alteration in sensory perception due to impaired circulation to the lower extremities?

4. What is the meaning of the S_3 and S_4 heart sounds?

5. The nurse assesses the peripheral pulses of a patient who has peripheral vascular disease and notes that the pulses are weak and difficult to palpate. On a scale of 0 to 4+, how should the nurse chart this finding?

6.   A patient tells the nurse that whenever he walks, he develops pain in his calf
      muscles. When he rests, the pain stops. How should the nurse interpret this
      symptom?

Answers to Chapter 8 Study Questions

1.   The nurse should make note of the pulse pressure, which is the difference between the systolic reading and the diastolic reading. The pulse pressure is a measure of the cardiac output.

2.   Distended neck veins suggest the development of right-sided heart failure or circulatory volume overload.

3.   The nurse should teach the patient to carefully inspect the lower extremities for breaks in skin integrity, as the patient may not be able to feel or sense the development of any pressure areas or injuries. The patient may not be able to feel any extremes in temperature as well, and he or she should be told to protect the extremities from cold weather, heating pads, and hot water.

4.   Some cardiovascular disorders can lead to the development of "extra" heart sounds that can be auscultated. These heart sounds are abnormal. S_3, or ventricular gallop, is an extra heart sound that occurs immediately after the S_2. This heart sound commonly occurs in congestive heart failure or mitral regurgitation. The S_4 heart sound, also known as an atrial gallop, occurs immediately before the S_1 heart sound and is common in patients who have left ventricular hypertrophy and coronary artery disease.

5.   A rating of "1+" indicates that the pulse is diminished. The nurse should chart the pulse rating as "1+/4."

6.   The nurse should interpret these symptoms as being indicative of decreased circulation and a lack of tissue oxygenation in the lower extremities. The patient's symptoms are suggestive of intermittent claudication.

Chapter 9: Laboratory and Diagnostic Tests for Cardiovascular Disorders

Key Terms

BUN (blood urea nitrogen)
Cardiac catheterization
Cardiac enzymes
Cardiac stress testing
Computed tomography (CT)
Creatinine
Echocardiography
Electrocardiography (ECG)
    Holter monitoring
    12-Lead ECG
    Continual ECG monitoring
International normalized ratio (INR)
Partial thromboplastin time (PTT)
Prothrombin time (PT)
Radionuclide imaging
Serum electrolytes
Serum glucose
Serum lipids

Introduction

This chapter discusses the laboratory and diagnostic tests that are used to diagnose and monitor cardiovascular problems. Included are patient instructions and nursing interventions related to the tests.

Laboratory Tests for Cardiovascular Disorders

Laboratory tests are used primarily in cardiovascular disorders to diagnose myocardial muscle damage, evaluate the patient's blood chemistry levels, and assess the therapeutic levels of medications used to treat cardiovascular disorders. In addition, since cardiovascular problems can cause oxygen transportation problems that affect the respiratory system, other laboratory tests that are used to diagnose the status of the patient's respiratory system, such as pulse oximetry, ABGs, hemoglobin, and hematocrit, may also be ordered. Common laboratory tests for cardiovascular disorders are discussed below.

Cardiac Enzymes

Cardiac enzymes (CK, CK-MB, LDH, troponin, myoglobin) are used in combination with other diagnostic tests to diagnose a myocardial infarction (heart attack). The enzymes are released from injured myocardial cells. The enzymes are elevated at different times relative to the infarction.

- The **CK** and **CK-MB** are elevated within four to six hours of the event and return to normal within three to four days.
- The **LDH** begins to rise approximately six to eight hours after the infarction and remains elevated for five to seven days.
- **Troponin** and **myoglobin** begin to elevate within three to four hours and remain elevated for anywhere from one to three weeks. Troponin is more specific for cardiac ischemia than myoglobin.

Blood Chemistry

The patient's **blood chemistry** levels can reflect the development of health problems that will eventually lead to a cardiovascular problem, or they can reflect an alteration in normal body functioning as a result of a cardiovascular problem. Common blood chemistries that can be abnormal in cardiovascular disorders include serum lipids, electrolytes, creatinine, blood urea nitrogen (BUN), and glucose. See Table 9.1 for normal blood chemistry values commonly monitored in cardiovascular disorders.

- **Serum lipids** include **lipids, cholesterol,** and **triglycerides**. Increased values of serum lipids predispose the patient to cardiovascular disease. The patient should be fasting for twelve hours prior to lipid and triglyceride tests.
- **Serum electrolytes** specific to cardiac functioning include sodium, potassium, and calcium. The levels of these electrolytes are crucial to myocardial cell depolarization and repolarization. Cardiac arrhythmias (irregular heart rhythms) may develop if the electrolyte levels are either too high or too low. Patients who are on diuretic therapy need to have their potassium levels routinely monitored, as diuretics can either promote the excretion or retention of potassium. Hypokalemia, which is a decreased serum potassium level, can predispose a patient who is taking digitalis medication to digitalis toxicity—the blood levels of digitalis exceed the therapeutic level. Altered sodium levels may be indicative of fluid imbalance.
- Elevated **creatinine** and **blood urea nitrogen (BUN)** are reflective of the state of the patient's renal functioning. Renal functioning can be adversely affected by cardiovascular disease if blood flow to the kidneys is decreased. Decreased renal perfusion leads to decreased renal functioning and increased creatinine and BUN levels.
- Elevation of the **serum glucose level** may indicate the presence of diabetes mellitus, which occurs commonly in individuals who develop cardiovascular disease.

| Table 9.1 Blood Chemistry Values ||
Blood chemistry	Normal values
Lipid proteins	HDL: 35–65 mg/dL, male; 35–85 mg/dL, female
	LDL: Less than 130 mg/dL
Cholesterol	Less than 200 mg/dL
Triglycerides	40–150 mg/dL
Serum potassium	3.5–5.5 mEq/L
Serum sodium	135–145 mEq/L
Serum calcium	8.5–10.5 mg/dL
Blood urea nitrogen (BUN)	10–20 mg/dL
Serum creatinine	0.7–1.5 mg/dL
Serum glucose	70–110 mg/dL

Coagulation Studies

Many patients with cardiovascular disease are placed on anticoagulation therapy to prevent the development of emboli (blood clots). Anticoagulation therapy requires careful patient monitoring to maintain therapeutic levels of anticoagulation therapy and prevent the development of bleeding. **Coagulation studies** include partial thromboplastin time, prothrombin time, and international normalized ratio.

- **Partial thromboplastin time (PTT)** is used to monitor patients receiving heparin therapy. Normal reference value for PTT is twenty-five to thirty-eight seconds; therapeutic values are 1.5 to 2.5 times reference value.
- **Prothrombin time (PT)** is used to monitor patients receiving warfarin (Coumadin). Normal reference value for PT is less than thirteen seconds; therapeutic value is 1.5 to 2.5 times reference value.
- **International normalized ratio (INR)** is the standardized method of reporting PT to eliminate laboratory variations. INR is maintained between 2.0 and 3.0 for patients receiving warfarin (Coumadin).

Drug Levels

Various **drug levels** may be drawn to determine therapeutic levels of drugs prescribed to treat cardiovascular disease. For example, a patient receiving digoxin (Lanoxin) will have routine digoxin levels drawn. The therapeutic drug levels of digoxin are 1 to 2 mg/ml. A toxic level for digoxin is over 3 mg/ml.

Diagnostic Tests for Cardiovascular Disorders

A variety of noninvasive and invasive diagnostic tests are used to visualize cardiac structures, evaluate cardiac functioning, detect cardiac dysrhythmias, and evaluate the patient's response to treatment.

Electrocardiography

Electrocardiography (ECG) produces tracings that measure the electrical forces of the heart. Common ECG procedures include the following:

- **12-Lead ECG** is used for diagnosing dysrhythmias, myocardial infarction, and ischemia; it records cardiac electrical activity.
- **Holter monitoring** is continuous ambulatory monitoring for approximately twenty-four to forty-eight hours during normal patient activity. The patient maintains a log of activity and any symptoms experienced during the monitored time period. This is usually an outpatient procedure.
- **Continual ECG monitoring** is implemented for patients who are at high risk for developing a dysrhythmia. Continual monitoring may occur in critical care settings or on units equipped with telemetry.

Cardiac Stress Testing

Cardiac stress testing is a noninvasive test used to evaluate how the cardiovascular system responds to stress. Typically, the patient is connected to an ECG monitor and asked to walk on a treadmill for a prescribed period of time at increasing rates of speed until the patient reaches the target heart rate. The patient is closely monitored for symptoms such as chest pain, dyspnea, and leg cramps. The blood pressure is taken periodically and the ECG is monitored for signs of ischemia or dysrhythmias. Patients are instructed to wear comfortable walking shoes and may be told to not take their regular medications prior to the test.

Patients who are physically unable to perform the standard walking stress test may receive **pharmacologic stress testing** that stimulates the heart and mimics the effects of exercise. This type of test would require the insertion of an intravenous line to administer the drug.

Chest X ray

A **chest X ray** is used to determine the size and position of the heart within the chest cavity. Usually, the technician takes an anterior/posterior and left lateral X ray.

Echocardiography

Echocardiography is painless, noninvasive ultrasound testing of the heart. This produces pictures of cardiac motion. It is useful for examining cardiac function, ventricular motion, and valvular abnormalities.

Radionuclide Imaging

In **radionuclide imaging**, radioisotopes, such as thallium, are used to evaluate cardiac perfusion and detect areas of myocardial ischemia. This noninvasive test requires intravenous injection of the radioisotope. Scans are repeated periodically over a period of minutes to hours as the isotope is circulated throughout the heart's circulatory system. This test is also frequently combined with stress testing.

Cardiac Catheterization

Cardiac catheterization is an invasive procedure used to visualize the coronary arteries. A catheter is usually threaded from a femoral puncture site to the heart. Dye is injected to visualize the blood vessels and detect any areas of obstruction.

Preoperative nursing care for a cardiac catheterization includes the following:

- Having the patient fast for eight to twelve hours prior to the procedure
- Giving patient instruction about procedure and post-op care
- Inserting an intravenous line
- Administrating prescribed sedatives

Postoperative nursing care following a cardiac catheterization includes the following:

- Careful assessment of the circulation of the affected extremity.
- Peripheral pulses, temperature, and color of extremity are assessed every fifteen minutes for the first hour following the procedure and every one to two hours thereafter.
- The catheter insertion site is observed frequently for bleeding or swelling.
- Patients are encouraged to drink fluids to flush the dye out of their system.
- The patient should be closely monitored for the development of dysrhythmias and chest pain.
- If a femoral site was used, the patient will be placed on bed rest for approximately three to four hours, with the affected leg extended and the head of the bed elevated no more than thirty degrees.
- If a brachial site was used, the arm will be kept straight by an arm board, but the patient will not be required to be on bed rest as long as the vital signs are stable.

Chapter 9 Study Questions

1. Why is it important for the nurse to monitor the serum potassium level of a patient with a cardiovascular disorder?

2. Describe three coagulation laboratory studies and explain why they are used in cardiovascular disorders.

3. Describe echocardiography and its purpose.

4. A patient who has been experiencing episodes of chest pain is scheduled for a cardiac catheterization. Describe the preoperative nursing care for this patient.

5.   Describe the postoperative nursing care of a patient who has had a cardiac catheterization.

Answers to Chapter 9 Study Questions

1. Cardiac arrhythmias may develop if the serum potassium level is either too high or too low. Patients who are on diuretic therapy need to have their potassium levels routinely monitored, as diuretics can either promote the excretion or retention of potassium. Hypokalemia, which is a decreased serum potassium level, can predispose a patient who is taking digitalis medication to digitalis toxicity.

2. Partial thromboplastin time is used to monitor patients receiving heparin therapy; prothrombin time is used to monitor patients receiving warfarin (Coumadin); and international normalized ratio is the standardized method of reporting PT to eliminate laboratory variations. Anticoagulation therapy requires careful patient monitoring to maintain therapeutic levels of anticoagulation therapy and prevent the development of bleeding.

3. Electrocardiography is a painless cardiac ultrasound test that is noninvasive. It produces pictures of cardiac motion and is useful for examining ventricular motion and valvular abnormalities.

4. Preoperative nursing care for a cardiac catheterization includes having the patient fast for eight to twelve hours prior to the procedure; giving patient instruction about procedure and post-op care; inserting an intravenous line; and administrating prescribed sedatives.

5. Postoperative nursing care for a cardiac catheterization includes careful assessment of the circulation of the affected extremity. Peripheral pulses and the temperature and color of the extremity are assessed every fifteen minutes for the first hour following the procedure and every one to two hours after that. The catheter insertion site is observed frequently for bleeding or swelling. Fluids are encouraged to flush dye out of system. The patient should be closely monitored for the development of dysrhythmias and chest pain. If a femoral site was used, the patient will be placed on bed rest for approximately three to four hours, with the affected leg extended and the head of the bed elevated no more than thirty degrees. If a brachial site was used, the arm will be kept straight by an arm board, but the patient will not be required to be on bed rest as long as the vital signs are stable.

Chapter 10: Therapeutic Interventions for Cardiovascular Disorders

Key Terms

Antiembolic stockings
Cardiac monitor
Cardiac pacemaker
Central venous pressure monitor
Doppler
Intermittent compression devices
Medications
    Angiotensin converting enzyme (ACE) inhibitors
    Anticoagulants
    Antihyperlipidemics
    Antihypertensives
    Antiarrhythmics
    Beta-adrenergic blocking agents
    Calcium channel blockers
    Cardiac glycosides
    Diuretics
    Iron supplements
    Nitrites
    Thrombolytics
    Vasodilators
Pulse oximeter

Introduction

This chapter discusses the therapeutic interventions commonly used to treat the patient with cardiovascular disorders. Pharmacological treatment will be covered as well as dietary modifications and therapeutic devices.

Medications Commonly Used to Treat Cardiovascular Disorders

Pharmacological therapy is the cornerstone of treatment for most cardiovascular disorders. The nurse's role in pharmacological therapy is to administer the drugs safely, evaluate the patient's response to the drug, monitor for side effects, and provide patient education. Medications discussed in this study guide include angiotensin converting enzyme (ACE) inhibitors, anticoagulants, antihypertensives, antiarrhythmics, antihyperlipidemics, beta-blocking agents, calcium channel blockers, cardiac glycosides, diuretics, iron preparations, nitrites, thrombolytics, and vasodilators.

Angiotensin Converting Enzyme (ACE) Inhibitors

Angiotensin converting enzyme (ACE) inhibitors are used as antihypertensives to treat high blood pressure. ACE inhibitors prohibit angiotensin I from converting into angiotensin II, thus decreasing vasoconstriction and inhibiting aldosterone release, which results in less reabsorption of sodium and water. The combination of decreased vascular tone (decreasing vasoconstriction) and decreased reabsorption of sodium and water leads to a decreased blood pressure.

Some commonly used ACE inhibitors are **captopril (Capoten)** and **lisinopril (Prinivil; Zestril)**.

Probably the most common side effect of ACE inhibitors is a chronic cough. Other common side effects include rash, orthostatic hypotension, tachycardia, chest pain, and gastrointestinal distress. Nursing interventions include monitoring the patient's blood pressure and fluid balance. Neutropenia and agranulocytosis can develop in some patients. Therefore, the nurse should monitor the patient's laboratory tests to check the white cell count.

Hyperkalemia may develop, so it is important to monitor the patient's electrolytes. The patient should be instructed to avoid potassium supplements or salt substitutes that contain potassium to avoid the risk of hyperkalemia. Other important information to teach the patient about is to take the first dose of the medication at bedtime to avoid first-dose hypotension. The patient should be instructed to report sore throat, fever, chest pain, irregular pulse, and swelling of hands, feet, face, lips, eyes, and tongue.

Anticoagulants

Anticoagulants are used in cardiovascular disorders in the treatment of a thrombus (blood clot), or prophylactically to prevent the formation of a thrombus and potential embolus. For example, anticoagulant therapy may be prescribed for patients who have coronary artery disease, myocardial infarction, or thrombophlebitis. Anticoagulants do not break down existing blood clots; instead, they keep additional clots from forming.

The most commonly used anticoagulants are **heparin** and **coumarin** derivatives (e.g., **Coumadin**). Heparin is administered parenterally, either subcutaneously or intravenously. Coumadin is an oral anticoagulant.

Heparin

Heparin interferes with the conversion of fibrinogen to fibrin and prolongs clotting time, thus making it difficult for blood clots to develop. Heparin does not dissolve blood clots that have already formed. Patients who are receiving heparin must have the laboratory values of their **activated partial thromboplastin time (APTT)** closely monitored to maintain an effective, therapeutic level of the drug in the patient's bloodstream. Too much heparin can lead to bleeding. The antagonist for heparin therapy is **protamine sulfate**. Protamine sulfate is administered if the patient has received too much heparin or demonstrates evidence of bleeding.

Heparin Administration
The nursing care of the patient receiving heparin includes safely administering the medication and observing the patient for signs of bleeding. If the heparin is administered intravenously, the medication will be infused through an infusion pump to regulate the flow.

If the heparin is administered subcutaneously, it is important that the nurse minimize tissue trauma upon injection in order to minimize bleeding at the site. Usually, a small gauge (25g or finer) needle is selected to administer the heparin, and the nurse does not aspirate prior to injecting the medication. The abdomen is typically the site of choice for heparin administration, although other sites may be selected. The site should not be rubbed or massaged following the injection, as this can encourage bruising.

Prior to the administration of heparin, the nurse should check the patient's APTT levels. The nurse should instruct the patient to report any blood in the urine or stool, or evidence of bleeding from the gums, nose, or other tissues.

Coumadin

Coumadin prevents clot formation by blocking the action of Vitamin K and selected coagulation factors. Coumadin is administered orally. Coumadin therapy is frequently started when patients are still receiving heparin. As the heparin dose is tapered off, the Coumadin dose will be increased. This allows for a continuation of anticoagulant effects in the body as the medications are adjusted. Coumadin may be used for long-term anticoagulant therapy.

It is the nurse's responsibility to educate the patient about the potential side effects of Coumadin therapy. Like heparin, Coumadin can lead to bleeding. The patient must be taught to report any bleeding tendencies. The laboratory values of the patient's prothrombin time (PT) or international normalized ratio (INR) are monitored to ensure that therapeutic levels are maintained. In addition, since Vitamin K is the antidote for Coumadin, patients should be instructed to not increase their intake of Vitamin K, as this can counteract the desired anticoagulant effect. Vitamin K is found in green vegetables.

Antihypertensives

Antihypertensives are used to decrease blood pressure. The most commonly prescribed drugs classified as antihypertensives include the following:

Centrally Acting Adrenergic Inhibitors

Centrally acting adrenergic inhibitors, such as **clonidine hydrochloride (Catapres)** and **methyldopa (Aldomet)**, decrease blood pressure by decreasing sympathetic nervous system output from the brain, causing decreased heart rate, blood pressure, and vasodilation. They may increase sodium and fluid retention, so they are most effective at reducing blood pressure when combined with a diuretic. Nursing interventions include weighing the patient daily and monitoring intake and output. Side effects include fluid retention. If clonidine is discontinued, the medication must be tapered off gradually to avoid rebound hypertension. Clonidine may also interact with beta-blockers to cause severe rebound hypertension if the clonidine is abruptly stopped.

Peripheral Acting Adrenergic Inhibitors

Peripheral acting adrenergic inhibitors, such as **guanethidine sulfate (Ismelin)**, decrease blood pressure by decreasing vascular tone and decreasing venous return. Nursing interventions include weighing the patient daily and monitoring intake and output. Side effects include fluid retention and orthostatic hypotension.

Alpha-Adrenergic Blocking Agents

Alpha-adrenergic blocking agents, such as **prazosin hydrochloride (Minipress)**, block alpha receptors, causing a decrease in peripheral vascular resistance. Patients may experience a hypotensive reaction with first dose; clients should be instructed to lie down if dizziness occurs. Nursing interventions include weighing the patient daily and monitoring intake and output. Side effects include fluid retention and orthostatic hypotension. Patients should be told to avoid driving or operating machinery after the first dose of medication due to the drowsiness that can occur with the first dose. Instruct the patient that changing position slowly can also decrease the likelihood of orthostatic hypotension.

Antiarrhythmic Agents

Antiarrhythmic agents are used to treat and prevent cardiac dysrhythmias. All antiarrhythmic agents suppress the automaticity of the myocardial cells. Some also decrease conduction velocity and increase the refractory period. Examples of commonly prescribed antiarrhythmic agents are the following:

- **Procainamide (Pronestyl)**
- **Quinidine**
- **Propranolol (Inderal)**
- **Lidocaine**

Common side effects of antiarrhythmic agents include hypotension, dizziness, and gastrointestinal distress. Nursing interventions include monitoring blood pressure and pulse and instructing the patient how to take their own pulse.

Quinidine interacts significantly with many other medications, especially antiarrhythmic, cardiac, CNS, and anticoagulant drugs. It is important that the nurse review with the patient other drugs that he or she might be taking so that drug interactions with quinidine can be avoided. It is especially important to monitor the patient's potassium levels, as too much potassium can enhance the action of quinidine, and too little can reduce the effectiveness.

Lidocaine is used in emergency situations to treat ventricular arrhythmias. Lidocaine is only administered intravenously.

Antihyperlipidemic Agents

Antihyperlipidemic agents are used to reduce lower serum lipid levels and decrease the risk of developing atherosclerosis. Commonly prescribed antihyperlipidemics include the following:

- **Cholestyramine (Questran)**
- **Simvastatin (Zocor)**
- **Atorvastatin (Lipitor)**

Antihyperlipidemic agents have few serious side effects and are usually well tolerated. However, cholestyramine (Questran) can cause severe constipation. Simvastatin (Zocor) and atorvastatin (Lipitor) can both affect liver functioning. As a result, regular liver function tests should be obtained. Serum cholesterol and triglyceride levels will also be monitored to evaluate effectiveness of the drug therapy.

Beta-Adrenergic Blocking Agents

Beta-adrenergic blocking agents or antagonists affect the cardiovascular system by decreasing heart rate, contractility, conduction velocity, and cardiac output. Beta-blockers are classified according to their specific action with the beta-1 and beta-2 receptors.

- **Beta-1 receptor stimulation** will cause tachycardia, increased myocardial contractility, and increased lipolysis.
- **Beta-2 receptor stimulation** will cause vasodilation, decreased peripheral resistance, and bronchodilation.

Nonselective beta-adrenergics act on both beta-1 and beta-2 receptors. Beta-blockers are used to treat angina, hypertension, and dysrhythmias. Commonly used beta-blockers include the following:

- **Atenolol (Tenormin)—beta-1**
- **Metoprolol (Lopressor)—beta-1**
- **Propranolol (Inderal)—nonselective**

Common side effects include bradycardia, impotence, fatigue, gastrointestinal upset, and dizziness.

Nursing interventions include the following:

- Take the apical pulse prior to administering the drug; if fewer than sixty beats per minute or irregular, withhold the drug and notify the patient's physician.
- Monitor for possible fluid retention.
- Patient education includes teaching the patient to take pulse.
- It is important to stress that the patient not abruptly discontinue taking the medication; this could precipitate rebound symptoms.

Beta-adrenergic blocking agents are contraindicated in patients who have sinus bradycardia, peripheral vascular disease, second- and third-degree heart block, heart failure, and asthma. They should also be used with caution in patients who have diabetes mellitus, chronic obstructive lung disease, hepatic disease, and allergic disorders.

Beta-adrenergic blockers also have numerous interactions with other medications. Some of the drugs that beta-blockers interact with include epinephrine, verapamil, aminophylline, lidocaine, insulin, cimetidine, and alcohol. It is important for the nurse to carefully evaluate all of the medications the patient is on, to avoid potentially serious interactions. The patient should also be cautioned against taking over-the-counter drugs without seeking medical advice.

Calcium Channel Blockers

Calcium channel blockers block the influx of calcium across the cell membrane of cardiac and smooth muscle cells. This action causes a decrease in myocardial contraction, automaticity in the SA node, and AV node conduction. Calcium channel blockers also decrease smooth muscle contraction, thus causing coronary artery dilation. Examples of calcium channel blockers include the following:

- **Diltiazem (Cardizem)**
- **Nifedipine (Procardia)**
- **Verapamil (Calan)**

Common side effects include hypotension, fatigue, dizziness, nausea, and fluid volume excess. Constipation is a particularly common side effect. A potentially life-threatening side effect is the development of ventricular arrhythmias.

Nursing interventions include the following:

- Monitor blood pressure and pulse. If the patient's pulse is below fifty beats per minute, the drug should be withheld and the physician notified. If an irregular pulse occurs, the physician should be notified.
- Patients should be instructed to increase fluid intake and fiber intake to help decrease the incidence of constipation.
- Patients should also be taught to take their blood pressure and pulse, and to report an irregular heartbeat.
- The drug should not be abruptly discontinued.
- If verapamil is administered intravenously, the patient's ECG and blood pressure should be continually monitored. The solution must be protected from light during administration.

Cardiac Glycosides

Digoxin (Lanoxin) is the most commonly prescribed cardiac glycoside. **Cardiac glycosides** affect heart function by increasing myocardial contraction strength and decreasing rate. They are used to treat congestive heart failure.

Nursing interventions include closely monitoring the patient for digitalis toxicity. Hypokalemia, which is a decreased serum potassium level, can predispose the patient to digitalis toxicity. Digoxin drug levels will be drawn periodically to be sure that the patient's drug levels are within therapeutic ranges. The nurse should monitor the patient's digoxin levels as well as the serum potassium levels. Signs and symptoms of toxicity include visual disturbances (yellow vision, seeing halos, double vision), headache, dizziness, anorexia, nausea and vomiting, or diarrhea.

The apical pulse should be taken for one minute prior to administration of the dose. The dose should be withheld if the pulse rate is below 60 or above 110, and the physician notified.

Diuretics

Diuretics are used to treat congestive heart failure and hypertension. Diuretics cause elimination of body water through urination. Diuretics affect the nephron's tubular function: decreasing sodium reabsorption and increasing its excretion in water. In addition to the increased excretion of sodium and water, diuretics may also affect the reabsorption and excretion of potassium, leading to electrolyte imbalances if not regularly monitored.

There are several categories of diuretics. The categories most commonly used to treat cardiovascular disorders are **thiazide**, **loop**, and **potassium-sparing** diuretics.

Thiazide Diuretics

Hydrochlorothiazide (HydroDIURIL) is the prototype thiazide diuretic. **Thiazide diuretics** act on the distal tubule of the nephron to promote excretion of sodium and water, and they are used to decrease the volume of circulating fluid in congestive heart failure and essential hypertension, as well as cirrhosis and chronic renal disease.

Side effects of thiazide diuretics include electrolyte imbalances such as hyponatremia, hypochloremia, hypercalcemia, and hypokalemia. Hyperuricemia and hyperglycemia may also develop. The most common side effects include hypotension, dizziness, lightheadedness, anorexia, nausea, and vomiting.

Nursing interventions include monitoring the patient's fluid and electrolyte status, especially potassium and sodium levels. Monitoring daily weights, intake and output, pulse, and blood pressure are important aspects of nursing care. Patients should be instructed in foods that are high in potassium. Patients with diabetes may need to adjust diet and insulin to avoid hyperglycemia.

Loop Diuretics

Furosemide (Lasix) is the prototype loop diuretic. **Loop diuretics** act upon the loop of Henle to prevent reabsorption of sodium and water. Loop diuretics are potent diuretics that promote the excretion of large amounts of fluid and electrolytes.

Side effects of loop diuretics include fluid and electrolyte loss, especially potassium, as well as gastrointestinal distress. Ototoxicity can also develop with high-dose intravenous administration of furosemide. The hearing loss is usually reversible, but permanent damage can result.

Nursing interventions include monitoring the patient's fluid and electrolyte status, particularly serum potassium levels. Many patients who are taking loop diuretics are also placed on potassium supplements to maintain normal potassium levels. The nurse should also monitor the patient's weight, intake and output, pulse, and blood pressure.

Furosemide increases the action of several drugs, including anticoagulants, beta-blockers, digitalis, and lithium. Patients should be monitored carefully for toxicity and adverse effects related to these drugs.

Potassium-Sparing Diuretics

Spironolactone (Aldactone) and **triamterene (Dyrenium)** are common potassium-sparing diuretics. **Potassium-sparing diuretics** act upon the distal tubule to promote the excretion of sodium and water. With these diuretics, potassium is not excreted; instead, potassium is reabsorbed. This can lead to hyperkalemia, or elevated serum potassium levels, if potassium levels are not closely monitored. This is especially true in the elderly and diabetics. These drugs are considered to be weak diuretics and are typically given in combination with thiazide or loop diuretics to decrease potassium loss.

Side effects of potassium-sparing diuretics include gastrointestinal distress and fluid and electrolyte imbalances.

Nursing care is similar to other diuretics, except patients should be cautioned not to eat foods that are high in potassium, such as bananas, oranges, apricots, and cabbage.

Iron Supplements

Iron supplements are used to treat iron-deficiency anemias. Iron supplements can either be given orally or parenterally. Iron is best absorbed in an acidic environment. For this reason, the nurse should instruct the patient to take the iron one hour before meals. Taking the iron with orange juice is also recommended. If the patient is taking a liquid iron supplement, it should be diluted and taken through a straw to avoid staining the teeth.

If the iron needs to be taken with meals to avoid gastrointestinal distress, the patient should be instructed to avoid taking the iron with milk products, eggs, chocolate, or liquids with caffeine. These foods can prevent the absorption of iron. Iron should also be taken one to two hours apart from antacids or tetracycline. Iron reduces the absorption of tetracycline.

The most common side effect of oral iron supplements is gastrointestinal distress. Constipation is common, and some patients experience heartburn. Oral iron preparations turn the patient's stools black.

If the nurse is required to give iron preparations intramuscularly, there are certain precautions that must be taken. First of all, because the iron solution is irritating to the skin, the nurse should change needles after drawing up the medication and use a new needle for the injection. Iron is given by deep, intramuscular injection. The **Z-track** injection technique is used to prevent the iron from tracking back through the skin after the injection. To minimize tissue trauma, the injection site is not massaged following the injection.

Nitrites

Nitrites are used to treat angina. **Nitroglycerin** is the most commonly used nitrite. It is used to treat acute angina and is also used prophylactically to prevent an angina attack. Nitroglycerin is administered through several different routes: sublingually, transdermally, topically, or intravenously. The most common side effect of nitroglycerin is a headache, which can be severe. Other side effects can include tachycardia, palpitations, and hypotension.

Nitroglycerin needs to be shielded from light to avoid losing its potency. For this reason, it is important to instruct the patient to keep the medication in its original container. The nurse should also teach the patient how to correctly take the nitroglycerin during an angina attack. The patient should sit or lie down to avoid an episode of hypotension. One sublingual tablet is placed under the tongue. If after five minutes the pain is unrelieved, another nitroglycerin tablet may be taken. If the pain is still unrelieved, a third tablet may be taken after another five minutes have passed. If after three tablets the angina is unrelieved, the patient should seek emergency medical assistance.

Nurses who administer nitroglycerin ointment should wear gloves to avoid absorbing the medication. Absorption of the drug can cause the nurse to develop a severe headache. It is also important to instruct the patient to always use the ointment applicator provided for accurate dose measurement. The ointment should never be applied to broken skin, and old ointment should be removed from the skin before a new application is applied.

Vasodilators

Vasodilators are used to treat hypertension. They decrease blood pressure by relaxing arterioles and decreasing peripheral resistance. Common vasodilators are **diazoxide (Hyperstat)** and **minoxidil (Loniten)**. The prototype vasodilator is **hydralazine (Apresoline)**. Hydralazine is not used singly for treatment of hypertension; instead, in order to minimize side effects, it is given in conjunction with other drugs to control blood pressure.

The most common side effects associated with hydralazine and other vasodilators are headache, dizziness, flushing, anorexia, nausea, tachycardia, palpitations, and angina.

Nursing interventions include taking the blood pressure prior to administering the drug, as hypotension can develop.

Dietary Modifications for Cardiovascular Disorders

Diet is an integral component of the prevention and treatment of cardiovascular disorders. A healthy diet can decrease an individual's chance of developing a cardiovascular disorder such as coronary artery disease or hypertension. Healthy dietary modifications can also delay the progression of cardiovascular disorders.

It is important for the nurse to assist the patient in understanding the dietary modifications necessary to have a "heart healthy" diet. Essentially, the diet should be low in saturated fat and cholesterol. Intake of fruits, vegetables, and grains should increase, while meat intake should be limited. Limiting calories is also important if the patient needs to lose weight. In combination with a healthy diet, the patient is encouraged to engage in physical activity. The nurse can encourage the patient to seek the expertise of a dietician to learn how to prepare meals that are well balanced and low in fat and cholesterol.

Patients who have been diagnosed with hypertension, congestive heart failure, or a myocardial infarction (heart attack) may also need to modify their sodium and fluid intake. Sodium and fluid restrictions are implemented when it is necessary for the patient to avoid fluid overload and reduce cardiac workload.

Typically, the patient is placed on a sodium-restricted diet to help decrease fluid retention and reduce cardiac workload. The degree of sodium restriction will vary (usually between 1000 mg and 4000 mg/day of sodium) depending upon the extent of fluid retention. If the patient has developed edema, fluid restrictions may also be implemented to help decrease the edema.

If the patient is on diuretic therapy, the nurse will need to monitor the patient's serum electrolytes, especially sodium and potassium levels. Depending upon the diuretic, the patient may become hyponatremic (low serum sodium) or hypokalemic (low serum potassium). In these cases, the patient would not be restricted in sodium intake and would be encouraged to eat foods high in potassium (e.g., bananas, oranges, and other fruits and vegetables). Some diuretics are potassium-sparing and may lead to the development of hyperkalemia (high serum potassium). Patients who are taking potassium-sparing diuretics should be encouraged to limit their potassium intake in their diet. It is important that the nurse be aware of the patient's medications and potential drug actions that might impact the patient's dietary intake.

Therapeutic Devices for Cardiovascular Disorders

There are a variety of therapeutic devices that the nurse uses to support the nursing care provided to patients with cardiovascular disorders. This section will cover Doppler ultrasound devices, antiembolic stockings, intermittent compression devices, pulse oximeter, cardiac pacemakers, cardiac monitors, and central venous pressure (CVP) monitors, as well as nursing interventions associated with these devices.

Doppler Ultrasound Device

The **Doppler ultrasound** is a noninvasive device that enables the nurse and other practitioners to determine the quality of blood flow through a vessel. It is used in the care of patients with carotid artery disease, peripheral vascular disease, and deep vein thrombosis. The nurse may use the Doppler to determine the presence of carotid or peripheral pulses (femoral, popliteal, posterior tibial, dorsalis pedis) that are difficult to palpate manually.

Antiembolic Stockings

Antiembolic stockings are used to support venous blood return from the periphery to the heart. They are a preventive device to discourage the development of thrombi and pulmonary emboli. Care should be used to apply the stockings so that wrinkles or rolls do not develop in the stockings and constrict blood flow. Stockings are removed each shift to inspect the skin and provide skin care. A second pair of stockings may be used to allow for alternating wear and washing of the stockings.

Intermittent Compression Devices

Intermittent compression devices are pneumatic devices that are applied to the patient's calves to facilitate the return of venous blood flow and prevent blood pooling. The compression devices need to be applied within twenty-four hours of when the patient is initially bedridden and remain in place until the patient is allowed to ambulate. The nurse should inspect the compression devices and assess the neurovascular status of the extremities to ensure that the patient's circulation is not impaired by the operation of the devices.

Pulse Oximeter

The **pulse oximeter** is a noninvasive device used to measure the patient's oxygenation levels. The device is typically attached to the patient's ear or fingertip. The pulse oximeter can be attached to the patient for continual monitoring or used intermittently to measure oxygen saturation levels.

Cardiac Monitors

Cardiac monitors are used to assess the patient's cardiac rhythm and to quickly detect abnormal rhythms that require treatment. The ECG leads are attached to the patient. The ECG is continually displayed on a monitor oscilloscope for the nurse to observe. When desired, a rhythm strip can be printed out to record and document the patient's cardiac rhythm. It is important that the nurse ensure that the leads and electrodes are firmly attached to the patient in order to avoid artifact. An **artifact** is interference with the ECG waveforms that leads to a distortion of its appearance and makes it difficult to accurately assess the rhythm being displayed.

Telemetry is another form of cardiac monitoring. Telemetry does not require attaching the patient to wiring that restricts the patient's activities. A radio wave signal is transmitted through antennae to display cardiac rhythms on a centrally located oscilloscope. This allows the patient to walk around while being monitored.

Cardiac monitors have alarms that are set off when abnormal rhythms are detected. It is important that the nurse frequently assess the patient who is being monitored. Monitors can malfunction. Patients can also develop important symptoms, such as chest pain, that do not necessarily lead to changes in cardiac rhythms. The cardiac monitor does not replace a nurse's responsibility for close monitoring of the patient.

Central Venous Pressure Monitor

Central venous pressure monitoring is used when the patient has a change in fluid volume, either fluid overload or fluid deficit. CVP monitoring is a form of **hemodynamic** monitoring. A central venous catheter is threaded through the subclavian and inserted into the superior vena cava. Central venous pressure is measured in the right atrium and is used to assess the functioning of the right ventricle.

- A normal CVP reading using a pressure monitoring system ranges from 0 to 8 mm Hg.
- An increased CVP reading indicates the patient is in a state of hypervolemia or increased preload. An increased reading can also be caused by decreased myocardial contractility.
- A decreased CVP reading indicates hypovolemia or decreased preload.

The nurse is responsible for obtaining CVP readings and caring for the insertion site. When obtaining a CVP reading, it is important that the nurse properly align the manometer's zero mark or the pressure monitor's transducer with the phlebostatic axis. The phlebostatic axis is determined by locating the 4th intercostal space where it connects to the sternum and drawing a line beneath the axilla. This line should intersect with a line that is midway between the anterior and posterior aspects of the chest. The zero mark or transducer should be aligned with this axis to obtain an accurate measurement. The insertion site is covered with a sterile dressing. Potential complications associated with a CVP line include air embolism and infection.

Cardiac Pacemakers

Cardiac pacemakers are electronic devices that assume the role of the heart's pacemaker (SA node). Pacemaker electrodes are placed on the heart's right ventricle or atrium. A battery provides the electrical stimulus for the heart to beat. A pacemaker may be **permanent** or **temporary**.

- A **permanent** pacemaker is implanted in the chest or abdomen. This is done when the patient has a cardiac conduction disorder that will require permanent "pacing" for the heart to maintain a normal rate.

- A **temporary** pacemaker is used in emergency situations and is not implanted into the patient.

A pacemaker is inserted with the patient sedated and the use of a local anesthetic. Following insertion of the pacemaker, the nurse will monitor the patient for complications such as perforation, pneumothorax, hemothorax, and cardiac tamponade. The patient will be on bed rest for approximately twelve hours. The nurse should monitor the insertion site for bleeding and monitor the patient's ECG to detect lead dislodgement. Hiccuping, as a result of diaphragmatic stimulation, can be an indication of lead dislodgement. Aspirin and anticoagulants should not be administered for forty-eight hours following surgery. Infection of the site is another potential complication.

Types of **pacemaker malfunction** include loss of sensing, loss of pacing, and loss of capture.

- In **loss of sensing**, the pacemaker can either oversense or undersense the heart's impulse. These malfunctions can be caused by electrical interference, too high or too low of a sensitivity sensing, or battery depletion.
  1. In **oversensing**, the pacemaker picks up extraneous signals and misinterprets them as heart impulses, thus not pacing.
  2. In **undersensing**, the pacemaker does not detect heart impulses and therefore tries to pace the heart when it is not necessary.
- In **loss of pacing**, electrical impulses are not generated. This can be due to a dislodged lead, battery or generator malfunction, or loose wires.
- In **loss of capture**, the pacemaker is firing, but not enough to depolarize the ventricle. This is likely due to not enough energy being delivered, misplaced wires, battery or generator depletion, or a break in electronic insulation.

The nurse should teach the patient how to take a radial pulse. The patient should be instructed to report a heart rate that falls outside the parameters of the programmed pulse rate. In addition, it is important that the patient understand the need to have the pacemaker's battery function periodically checked. This can be done in the office or over the telephone lines. If the patient's previous cardiac symptoms return, this could indicate malfunctioning of the pacemaker. The patient should be told to report the return of any symptoms.

Chapter 10 Study Questions

1.   Describe how ACE inhibitors act to decrease blood pressure. Identify two
        common ACE inhibitor medications.

2.   What are common side effects associated with ACE inhibitors and nursing
        interventions related to the administration of these drugs?

3.   Why would an anticoagulant be prescribed for a patient who has a cardiovascular
        disorder?

4. Describe the technique the nurse should use to correctly administer heparin subcutaneously.

5. The nurse is caring for a patient who is on Coumadin. What dietary instructions should the nurse give the patient?

6. Identify three classifications of antihypertensives along with the common side effects and nursing interventions associated with the administration of them.

7.   A patient has been placed on the antiarrhythmic agent procainamide (Pronestyl). The nurse should evaluate the patient for the development of what side effects?

8.   The nurse is preparing to administer propranolol (Inderal). Upon taking the patient's pulse, the nurse notes a pulse rate of 52. What is the appropriate nursing action for the nurse to take?

9.   What electrolyte imbalance can predispose a patient to digitalis toxicity?

10.   Describe the side effects of loop diuretics, such as furosemide (Lasix).

11.   Describe the precautions the nurse should take when administering iron intramuscularly.

12.   A patient is experiencing an angina attack. The nurse administers nitroglycerin (NTG) tablets to treat the angina pain. Describe the technique the nurse should use to correctly administer the NTG.

13.   A patient has been diagnosed with congestive heart failure. What types of dietary modifications can the nurse expect to teach the patient to incorporate into his diet?

14.   The nurse is caring for a patient who has an intermittent compression device applied to her calves. Describe the purpose of this device and the appropriate nursing assessments associated with its use.

15.   The nurse is caring for a patient who had a pacemaker inserted earlier in the day. The patient begins to complain of hiccuping that will not stop. How should the nurse interpret this finding?

Answers to Chapter 10 Study Questions

1.   ACE inhibitors prohibit angiotensin I from converting into angiotensin II, thus decreasing vasoconstriction and inhibiting aldosterone release, which results in less reabsorption of sodium and water. The combination of decreased vascular tone (decreasing vasoconstriction) and decreased reabsorption of sodium and water leads to a decreased blood pressure. Some commonly used ACE inhibitors are Captopril (Capoten) and Lisinopril (Prinivil; Zestril).

2.   Probably the most common side effect of ACE inhibitors is a chronic cough. Other common side effects include rash, orthostatic hypotension, tachycardia, chest pain, and gastrointestinal distress. Nursing interventions include monitoring the patient's blood pressure and fluid balance. Neutropenia and agranulocytosis can develop in some patients. Therefore, the nurse should monitor the patient's laboratory tests to check the white cell count. Hyperkalemia may develop, so it is important to monitor the patient's electrolytes. The patient should be instructed to avoid potassium supplements or salt substitutes that contain potassium to avoid the risk of hyperkalemia. Other important information to teach the patient about is to take the first dose of the medication at bedtime to avoid first-dose hypotension. The patient should be instructed to report sore throat, fever, chest pain, irregular pulse, and swelling of hands, feet, face, lips, eyes, and tongue.

3.   Anticoagulants are used in cardiovascular disorders in the treatment of a thrombus (blood clot), or prophylactically to prevent the formation of a thrombus and potential embolus. For example, anticoagulant therapy may be prescribed for patients who have coronary artery disease, myocardial infarction, or thrombophlebitis. Anticoagulants do not break down existing blood clots; instead, they keep additional clots from forming.

4.   If the heparin is administered subcutaneously, it is important that the nurse minimize tissue trauma upon injection, in order to minimize bleeding at the site. Usually a small gauge (25g or finer) needle is selected to administer the heparin, and the nurse does not aspirate prior to injecting the medication. The abdomen is typically the site of choice for heparin administration, although other sites may be selected. The site should not be rubbed or massaged following the injection, as this can encourage bruising. Prior to the administration of heparin, the nurse should check the patient's APTT levels. The nurse should instruct the patient to report any blood in the urine or stool, or evidence of bleeding from the gums, nose, or other tissues.

5.   Since Vitamin K is the antidote for Coumadin, patients should be instructed to not increase their dietary intake of Vitamin K, as this can counteract the desired anticoagulant effect. Vitamin K is found in green vegetables.

6.   1) Centrally acting adrenergic inhibitors—clonidine hydrochloride (Catapres) and methyldopa (Aldomet): decrease blood pressure by decreasing sympathetic

nervous system output from the brain, causing decreased heart rate, blood pressure, and vasodilation. They may increase sodium and fluid retention, so they are most effective at reducing blood pressure when combined with a diuretic. Nursing interventions include weighing the patient daily and monitoring intake and output. Side effects include fluid retention. If clonidine is discontinued, the medication must be tapered off gradually to avoid rebound hypertension. Clonidine may also interact with beta-blockers to cause severe rebound hypertension if the clonidine is abruptly stopped. 2) Peripheral acting adrenergic inhibitors—guanethidine sulfate (Ismelin): decrease blood pressure by decreasing vascular tone and decreasing venous return. Nursing interventions include weighing the patient daily and monitoring intake and output. Side effects include fluid retention and orthostatic hypotension. 3) Alpha-adrenergic blocking agents—prazosin hydrochloride (Minipress): block alpha receptors, causing a decrease in peripheral vascular resistance. Patients may experience a hypotensive reaction with first dose; clients should be instructed to lie down if dizziness occurs. Nursing interventions include weighing the patient daily and monitoring intake and output. Side effects include fluid retention and orthostatic hypotension. Patients should be told to avoid driving or operating machinery after the first dose of medication due to the drowsiness that can occur with the first dose. Instruct the patient that changing position slowly can also decrease the likelihood of orthostatic hypotension.

7.   Common side effects of antiarrhythmic agents include hypotension, dizziness, and gastrointestinal distress. Nursing interventions include monitoring blood pressure and pulse and instructing the patient how to take their own pulse.

8.   Nursing interventions include taking the apical pulse prior to administering the drug; if fewer than sixty beats per minute or irregular, withhold the drug and notify the patient's physician.

9.   Hypokalemia, which is a decreased serum potassium level, can predispose the patient to digitalis toxicity.

10.   Side effects of loop diuretics include fluid and electrolyte loss, especially potassium, as well as gastrointestinal distress. Ototoxicity can also develop with high-dose intravenous administration of furosemide. The hearing loss is usually reversible, but permanent damage can result.

11.   If the nurse is required to give iron preparations intramuscularly, there are certain precautions that must be taken. First of all, because the iron solution is irritating to the skin, the nurse should change needles after drawing up the medication and use a new needle for the injection. Iron is given by deep, intramuscular injection. The Z-track injection technique is used to prevent the iron from tracking back through the skin after the injection. To minimize tissue trauma, the injection site is not massaged following the injection.

12. The nurse should teach the patient how to correctly take the nitroglycerin during an angina attack. The patient should sit or lie down to avoid an episode of hypotension. One sublingual tablet is placed under the tongue. If, after five minutes, the pain is unrelieved, another nitroglycerin tablet may be taken. If the pain is still unrelieved, a third tablet may be taken after another five minutes have passed. If after three tablets the angina is unrelieved, the patient should seek emergency medical assistance.

13. It is important for the nurse to assist the patient in understanding the diet modifications necessary to have a "heart healthy" diet. Essentially the diet should be low in saturated fat and cholesterol. Intake of fruits, vegetables, and grains should increase, while meat intake should be limited. Limiting calories is also important if the patient needs to lose weight. In combination with a healthy diet, the patient is encouraged to engage in physical activity. The nurse can encourage the patient to seek the expertise of a dietician to learn how to prepare meals that are well balanced and low in fat and cholesterol. Patients who have been diagnosed with hypertension, congestive heart failure, or a myocardial infarction may also need to modify their sodium and fluid intake. Sodium and fluid restrictions are implemented when it is necessary for the patient to avoid fluid overload and reduce cardiac workload.

14. Intermittent compression devices are pneumatic devices that are applied to the patient's calves to facilitate the return of venous blood flow and prevent blood pooling. The compression devices need to be applied within twenty-four hours of when the patient is initially bedridden and remain in place until the patient is allowed to ambulate. The nurse should inspect the compression devices and assess the neurovascular status of the extremities to ensure that the patient's circulation is not impaired by the operation of the devices.

15. Hiccuping, as a result of diaphragmatic stimulation, can be an indication of lead dislodgement. Aspirin and anticoagulants should not be administered for forty-eight hours following surgery. Infection of the site is another potential complication.

Chapter 11: Nursing Care for Cardiac Dysrhythmias

Key Terms

Atrial fibrillation
Atrial flutter
Bigeminy
Cardioversion
Catheter ablation
Defibrillation
Normal sinus rhythm
Paroxysmal supraventricular tachycardia
Premature atrial contraction (PAC)
Premature ventricular contraction (PVC)
Pulse deficit
Pulse pressure
Sinus bradycardia
Sinus tachycardia
Trigeminy
Ventricular fibrillation
Ventricular tachycardia

Introduction

Cardiac dysrhythmias are caused by alterations in the heart's electrical impulse generation or conduction. These disturbances lead to changes in the heart's rate and rhythm. Some dysrhythmias have more serious consequences than others. The purpose of this chapter is to review common sinus node, atrial, and ventricular dysrhythmias and the nursing care associated with them.

Normal Cardiac Electrical Conduction

Normally, cardiac electrical impulses originate in the **sinoatrial (SA) node** that is located in the right atrium of the heart. This electrical impulse, which usually occurs between 60 and 100 times per minute, is then transmitted throughout the atria to the **atrioventricular (AV) node**, causing the atria to contract. From the AV node, the impulse then moves through the **bundle of His** and out through the bundle branches to the **Purkinje fibers**, causing the ventricles to contract. This electrical conduction cycle is continuously repeated to produce a normal cardiac rhythm, or **normal sinus rhythm**.

Characteristics of a Normal ECG

The **ECG** or **EKG** (**electrocardiogram**) represents the electrical activity produced by the heart. It is a graphic tracing of the atria and ventricles as they depolarize and repolarize. The ECG paper is a grid divided into one-millimeter squares. Each square represents 0.04 seconds of time elapsed. Each thick line, which occurs every fifth square, is 0.20 seconds.

The horizontal lines measure time duration, and the vertical lines measure amplitude. The letters P, Q, R, S, T, and U designate the heart wave on an ECG.

Table 11.1 Normal Sinus Rhythm	
Rate	60–100 beats/minute
Rhythm	Regular
P wave	Normal, unchanging contour; 0.06–0.12 seconds
ST segment	0.12 seconds
QT interval	0.34–0.43 seconds
PR interval	0.12–0.20 seconds
QRS	0.04–0.12 seconds
T wave	0.16 seconds

Figure 11.1 Normal Sinus Rhythm

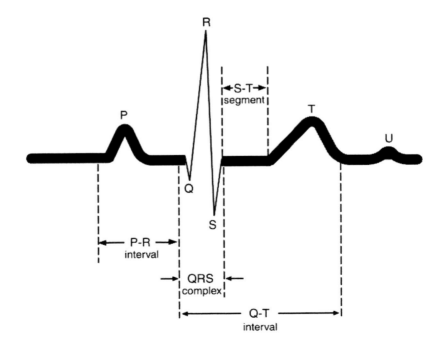

An explanation of the specific heart waves represented by each interval follows:

1. **P wave**: Represents atrial depolarization (two to three millimeters in amplitude; 0.11 seconds or less in duration).
2. **PR interval**: A measurement of the amount of time for an electrical impulse to go from the SA node to the ventricular muscles (0.12 to 0.20 seconds).
3. **QRS complex**: Represents ventricular depolarization (0.05 to 0.10 seconds).
4. **ST segment**: Represents the completion of ventricular polarization and beginning of ventricular repolarization.
5. **T wave**: Represents ventricular repolarization (height not to exceed five millimeters in a limb lead or ten millimeters in a precordial lead).
6. **QT interval**: Represents the entire duration of ventricular depolarization and repolarization.
7. **U wave**: Represents late repolarization of papillary muscles (muscular columns that are located on the inner surface of the ventricles); not always visible.

Cardiac Dysrhythmias

Pathophysiology

When the normal electrical impulse cycle is interrupted, cardiac dysrhythmias develop. Many etiologies are associated with the development of dysrhythmias. Some dysrhythmias are common in the general population and lead to no problems with cardiac output. Other dysrhythmias are commonly associated with cardiac disease, hypoxia, electrolyte and acid-base imbalances, altered thyroid functioning, and vagal or sympathetic stimulation. These dysrhythmias may seriously disrupt cardiac output and lead to death.

Essentially three pathophysiological processes can underlie these causes and lead to the development of a dysrhythmia:

1. The first process is **altered automaticity** (or the ability to depolarize). This can either increase or decrease the heart rate, depending upon the etiology of the alteration.
2. The second process is **altered electrical conduction**. Conduction is slowed down, leading to a delay of the conduction of the electrical impulse throughout the heart, or even a complete block.
3. The third process is **reentry**, during which an impulse is blocked from the normal pathway and reenters surrounding tissues to establish a circuitous pathway.

This study guide addresses some of the most common dysrhythmias associated with the sinus node, atria, and ventricles.

Types of Sinus Node Dysrhythmias

Two common sinus node dysrhythmias include **sinus bradycardia** and **sinus tachycardia**.

Sinus Bradycardia

Sinus bradycardia develops when the SA node creates electrical impulses more slowly than normal. This type of heart rhythm may develop gradually or occur suddenly. It results from excessive vagal or decreased sympathetic tone.

Table 11.2 Sinus Bradycardia	
Rate	Less than 60 beats/minute
Rhythm	Regular
P wave	Precedes QRS
PR interval	Varies (0.18–0.20 seconds)
QRS	0.09 seconds
Associated with	Occurs commonly during sleep, vomiting, vagal stimulation, eye surgery, intracranial tumors, and myocardial infarctions
Treatment	Usually not needed; if patient is symptomatic, a permanent pacemaker may be required. Atropine, administered intravenously, may also be used to treat bradycardia.

Figure 11.2 Sinus Bradycardia

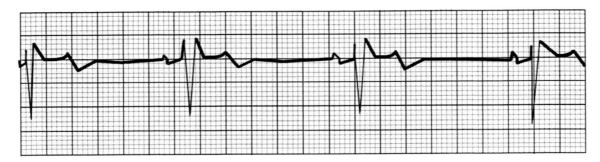

Sinus Tachycardia

Sinus tachycardia is caused by the SA node creating an electrical impulse more quickly than normal. The onset of sinus tachycardia is usually gradual. It is a normal physiological response to fever, exertion, fear, excitement, or ingestion of caffeine, alcohol, or tobacco.

Table 11.3 Sinus Tachycardia	
Rate	100–180 beats/minute (or more)
Rhythm	Regular
P wave	Normal; can be hidden by preceding T wave
PR interval	Varies (0.12–0.24 seconds)
QRS	0.09 seconds
Associated with	Congestive heart failure, shock, hemorrhage, anemia, increased metabolic demands, decreased oxygen delivery
Treatment	Treat the underlying cause; occasional sedatives; calcium channel blockers and beta-blockers may be administered.

Figure 11.3 Sinus Tachycardia

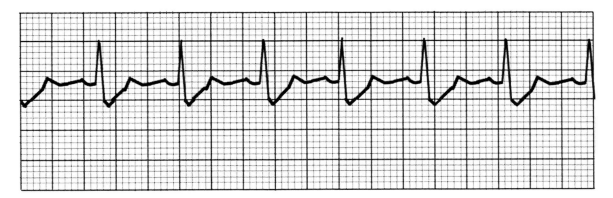

Types of Atrial Dysrhythmias

Four types of common atrial dysrhythmias that will be discussed are **premature atrial contractions (PACs)**, **paroxysmal supraventricular tachycardia**, **atrial flutter**, and **atrial fibrillation**.

Premature Atrial Contraction (PAC)

Premature atrial contraction (PAC) is a fairly common dysrhythmia, even in individuals with normal hearts. PAC is a premature contraction originating in the atria.

Table 11.4 Premature Atrial Contraction (PAC)	
Rate	Varies with frequency of the PAC and underlying sinus rhythm
Rhythm	Irregular
P wave	Early, different in appearance; can be hidden in preceding T wave
PR interval	Varies (0.12–0.24 seconds)
QRS	Usually normal; 0.09 seconds
Associated with	Caffeine, anxiety, nicotine, and alcohol, as well as pathophysiological etiologies, such as hypokalemia and myocardial infarcts and hypermetabolic states
Treatment	PACs are only treated if they occur frequently, more than six per minute. The patient may have a pulse deficit, which is a difference between the apical and radial beats.

Figure 11.4 Premature Atrial Contraction (PAC)

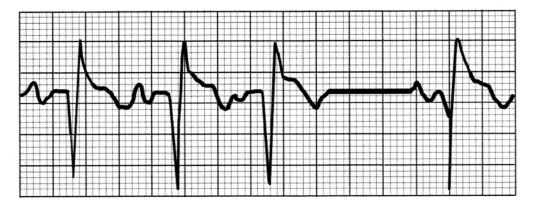

Paroxysmal Supraventricular Tachycardia

Paroxysmal supraventricular tachycardia (PSVT) occurs with an abrupt onset and is caused by an ectopic focus located somewhere above the bundle of His. Essentially, an impulse reenters over and over again, resulting in a fast, regular heart rate. The tachycardia may also cease abruptly. Clinical symptoms may vary, but indicate a decreased cardiac output when they do occur. PSVT leads to myocardial ischemia if underlying pathology exists.

Table 11.5 Paroxysmal Supraventricular Tachycardia	
Rate	150–250 beats/minute (atrial); 75–250 beats/minute (ventricular)
Rhythm	Regular
P wave	Present; may have an abnormal shape; frequently hidden in receding T waves
PR interval	0.14 seconds; may be prolonged or shortened (PR interval progressively lengthens until P wave is not followed by a QRS complex.)
QRS	0.07–0.09 seconds
Associated with	Coronary artery disease, digitalis toxicity, stress and anxiety, caffeine, and nicotine
Treatment	Correct the underlying cause. Treatment includes vagal stimulation, such as the Valsalva maneuver or carotid massage. Drug therapy includes the use of IV adenosine (Atenolol), which converts the dysrhythmia to a normal sinus rhythm. Other drugs that can be used are verapamil (Calan) or diltiazem (Cardizem). Cardioversion may also be used if drugs are not successful in treating the condition.

Figure 11.5 Paroxysmal Supraventricular Tachycardia

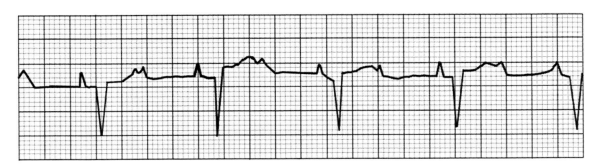

Atrial Flutter

Atrial flutter produces an atrial rate of approximately 250–350 beats/minute with a regular rhythm. However, some of these impulses are blocked and not conducted through the AV node. Therefore, the ventricular rate does not increase to the level of the atria, but instead remains around 75–150 beats/minute. The patient's signs and symptoms are related to a decreased cardiac output that can be significant.

Table 11.6 Atrial Flutter	
Rate	250–350 beats/minute (atrial); 75–150 beats/minute (ventricular)
Rhythm	Regular
P wave	Present, sawtooth shape (F waves)
PR interval	Immeasurable
QRS	0.07–0.09 seconds
Associated with	Usually indicates an underlying disease process such as a cardiac or respiratory disorder
Treatment	The goal is to control the ventricular heart rate and increase cardiac output—usually accomplished through drugs such as beta-blockers, digoxin, verapamil (Calan), and diltiazem (Cardizem), to name a few. Cardioversion may also be used in acute situations or if drug therapy is not successful.

Figure 11.6 Atrial Flutter

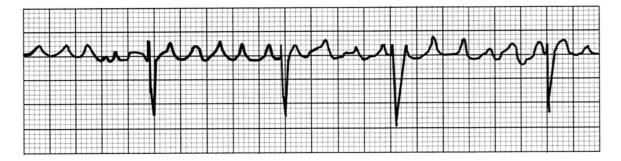

Atrial Fibrillation

Atrial fibrillation represents rapid, disorganized atrial electrical activity that results in a completely ineffective atrial contraction. The etiology of atrial fibrillation is similar to that of atrial flutter, usually resulting from underlying cardiac disease. Cardiac output is decreased. The potential increases for an atrial thrombus to develop and an embolus to occur, resulting in a cerebrovascular accident (CVA).

Table 11.7 Atrial Fibrillation	
Rate	350–600 beats/minute (atrial), chaotic; 120–200 beats/minute (ventricular)
Rhythm	Irregular
P wave	Not definable
PR interval	Not measurable
QRS	0.08 seconds
Associated with	Pericarditis, cardiomyopathy, hypertensive heart disease, rheumatic mitral valve disease, coronary artery disease, congestive heart failure, large amounts of alcohol intake, and advanced age
Treatment	Depends on the circumstances. Treatment is similar to atrial flutter. Anticoagulation therapy may be prescribed in some cases to prevent the development of a thrombus. Usually, correction of the underlying condition will convert the rhythm back to normal sinus rhythm. Prevention of complications such as the formation of thrombi causing embolisms is optimal.

Figure 11.7 Atrial Fibrillation

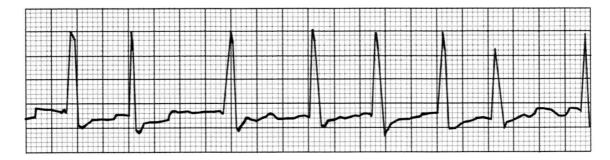

Types of Ventricular Dysrhythmias

Premature Ventricular Contraction (PVC)

Premature ventricular contraction (PVC) is a premature contraction originating in the ventricles. PVCs can occur in normal hearts as a result of stimulation from caffeine, alcohol, or nicotine, or be the result of a pathophysiological disturbance such as myocardial ischemia, electrolyte imbalances, and hypoxia. Some drugs may stimulate the development of PVCs, especially digoxin.

Table 11.8 Premature Ventricular Contraction (PVC)	
Rate	Depends on underlying rhythm
Rhythm	Irregular
P wave	No P wave associated with beat
PR interval	Not measurable
QRS	Wide; usually greater than 0.12 seconds
Associated with	Stress, electrolyte imbalance, myocardial infarction, digoxin toxicity, hypoxemia, hypercapnia, congestive heart failure
Treatment	An occasional PVC does not require treatment. However, if PVCs occur more than six times per minute or in groups of twos or threes (bigeminy or trigeminy), they will be treated immediately by medication, as they can be potentially lethal. In **bigeminy**, every other beat is a PVC; in **trigeminy**, every third beat is a PVC. The most commonly prescribed medication for the treatment of PVCs is lidocaine. Treatment is instituted to prevent the development of ventricular tachycardia or fibrillation.

Figure 11.8 Premature Ventricular Contraction (PVC)

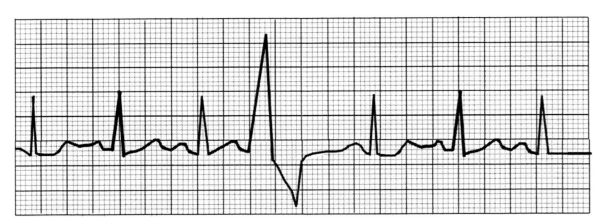

Ventricular Tachycardia

Ventricular tachycardia is diagnosed when three or more PVCs in a row are detected on an ECG. Ventricular tachycardia may lead to ventricular fibrillation. Ventricular tachycardia is considered to be a life-threatening dysrhythmia because of the severe decrease in cardiac output that can occur.

Table 11.9 Ventricular Tachycardia	
Rate	110–250 beats/minute (ventricular); atrial rate varies
Rhythm	Regular or slightly irregular
P wave	May be present; not associated with the QRS complex
PR interval	Cannot be determined
QRS	Wide, > 0.11 seconds
Associated with	Causes of ventricular tachycardia are the same as those for PVCs, especially the presence of cardiac disease. Other causes include hypoxemia, electrolyte imbalance, bradycardia, and drug toxicity.
Treatment	The drug of choice to treat ventricular tachycardia is a bolus of IV lidocaine. If lidocaine does not work, procainamide (Pronestyl) may be administered by an IV. If the patient is not stable, cardioversion will be tried. If patient is unconscious and without a pulse, defibrillation will be used.

Figure 11.9 Ventricular Tachycardia

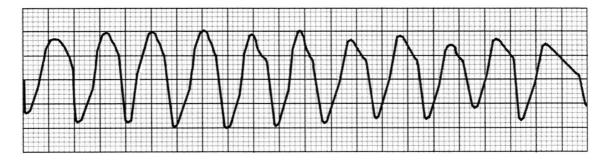

Ventricular Fibrillation

Ventricular fibrillation is the disorganized, irregular contractions of the ventricles resulting in no effective contractions and no cardiac output. Ventricular fibrillation occurs primarily as a result of cardiac disease, but can also occur in hyperkalemia or as a result of accidental electrical shock. A patient who is in ventricular fibrillation has no pulse, is unconscious, and stops breathing. Without prompt treatment and reversal of the ventricular fibrillation, the patient will die. Immediate CPR, defibrillation, and advanced cardiac life support is necessary to save the patient's life.

Table 11.10 Ventricular Fibrillation	
Rate	Cannot be determined
Rhythm	Grossly irregular
P wave	Cannot be seen
PR interval	Cannot be determined
QRS	No recognizable complex; cannot be measured
Associated with	Coronary heart disease, acute myocardial infarction, advanced forms of heart block, electrocution, fresh water drowning, and drug toxicity
Treatment	Immediate defibrillation, epinephrine, sodium bicarbonate, bretylium, and CPR

Figure 11.10 Ventricular Fibrillation

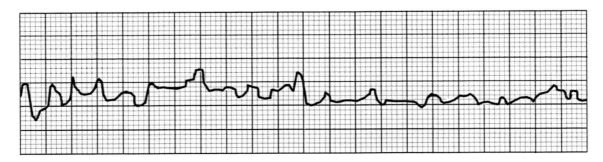

Table 11.11 Features of the ECG for Common Dysrhythmias

ECG	Rate (beats/min.)	Rhythm	P wave	PR interval	QRS
Normal sinus rhythm	60–100	Regular	Normal, unchanging contour	0.14 sec.	0.08 sec.
Sinus bradycardia	< 60	Regular	Precedes QRS	Varies (0.18–0.20 sec.)	0.09 sec.
Sinus tachycardia	100–180	Regular	Normal; can be hidden by T wave	Varies (0.12–0.24 sec.)	0.09 sec.
Premature atrial contraction	Varies	Irregular	Early; may be hidden by T wave	Varies (0.12–0.24 sec.)	0.09 sec.
Paroxysmal supraventricular-tachycardia	150–250 (atrial)	Regular	Present; may be hidden in T waves	0.14 sec.	0.07–0.09 sec.
Atrial flutter	250–350 (atrial)	Regular	Present; sawtooth (F wave)	Not measurable	0.07–0.09 sec.
Atrial fibrillation	350–600	Irregular	Not definable	Not measurable	0.08 sec.
Premature ventricular contraction	Depends on underlying rhythm	Irregular	No P wave associated with beat	Not measurable	Wide; usually greater than 0.12 sec.
Ventricular tachycardia	110–250 (ventricular)	Regular or slightly irregular	May be present; not associated with QRS complex	0.12 sec.	Wide, >0.11 sec.
Ventricular fibrillation	Cannot be determined	Grossly irregular	Cannot be seen	Cannot be determined	Not recognizable or measurable

Clinical Manifestations

Clinical manifestations related to dysrhythmias will vary depending upon the nature and severity of the dysrhythmia. Some dysrhythmias do not cause any symptoms. When symptoms do occur, it is because of a decreased cardiac output. Some of the most common clinical manifestations include the following:

- Palpitations (alterations in heart rate and/or rhythm)
- Sense of fatigue, anxiety
- Dizziness, light-headedness (may faint)
- Cool, clammy skin; pallor
- Decreased blood pressure
- Shortness of breath
- Chest discomfort

Diagnostic Tests

Dysrhythmias are usually diagnosed through the analysis of a 12-lead ECG. Ambulatory Holter monitoring over an extended time period may also be conducted to capture the occurrence of the dysrhythmia during the course of the patient's normal activities. Electrophysiology studies may also be conducted.

Medical Management

Medical management of the dysrhythmia depends upon the etiology, whether it is acute or chronic in nature, and the extent of the symptoms. Antiarrhythmic medications are usually used first to treat the dysrhythmia. Many antiarrhythmic drugs are available, and the drug of choice will depend upon the specific type of dysrhythmia.

If medications are not successful in treating the dysrhythmia or the condition is acute, other treatment modalities can be used. **Cardioversion** or **defibrillation** can be used to intervene in the case of a tachydysrhythmia. While the two procedures are used for different circumstances, they both deliver an electrical current to the myocardial cells in an attempt to allow the heart's sinus node to reestablish normal sinus rhythm.

- Cardioversion is usually a scheduled procedure, used when a patient has failed to respond to drug therapy. In **cardioversion**, the electrical current is synchronized to be delivered during ventricular depolarization or during the QRS complex. This synchronization with the QRS complex is done to prevent ventricular tachycardia or fibrillation.
- **Defibrillation** is used during an emergency when the patient is in ventricular fibrillation. The electrical current delivered during defibrillation is usually greater than the amount used for cardioversion.

A pacemaker may also be used to treat dysrhythmias that result in a conduction problem or when the heart generates electrical impulses slower than normal. A pacemaker may be placed as a temporary measure, or it may be permanent. It delivers an electrical impulse that stimulates the myocardial cells.

Electrophysiology studies can also be performed to treat some forms of dysrhythmias that are not responsive to medications. Examples of such dysrhythmias include atrial fibrillation and atrioventricular (AV) nodal reentry tachycardia. A cardiac catheterization is performed and electrodes are threaded into the heart. The area of the heart that causes the dysrhythmia is identified by electrically stimulating the heart to reproduce the arrhythmia. Once the area is identified, a **catheter ablation** procedure can be performed to destroy the cells causing the dysrhythmia. The cells can be destroyed through cryoablation (use of cold to freeze the cells), electrical ablation (use of electrical shocks to burn the tissue), or radiofrequency ablation (use of high-frequency sound waves). Postoperative care is the same as for any patient who undergoes a cardiac catheterization.

Nursing Process: Assessment

When caring for the patient with a dysrhythmia, the nurse's assessment should be focused on the cardiovascular system, the potential causes of the dysrhythmia, and the dysrhythmia's effect on cardiac output. If a decreased cardiac output is present, the nurse should gather data to evaluate how the lack of tissue oxygenation is affecting vital organ functioning.

The health history should be targeted to uncover potential causes of the dysrhythmia. The patient should be assessed for any of the clinical manifestations commonly associated with decreased cardiac output.

The physical examination will include assessment of the heart rate and rhythm. Apical and radial pulses should be assessed to detect any possible pulse deficit. Auscultation of the heart may reveal extra heart sounds, such as S_3 or S_4. Blood pressure should be monitored and the pulse pressure assessed. A decreasing **pulse pressure** (difference between systolic and diastolic blood pressure) is indicative of decreasing cardiac output. Lungs should be assessed for signs of fluid accumulation, such as crackles and wheezes. Neck vein distention should be noted. Skin color and temperature are also noted.

Nursing Process: Nursing Diagnosis and Planning

Based upon an analysis of the gathered data, the following **nursing diagnoses** may be appropriate for a patient with a dysrhythmia:

- Potential complication of decreased cardiac output related to a dysrhythmia
- Anxiety related to the diagnosis of a potentially life-threatening dysrhythmia
- Activity intolerance related to compromised tissue oxygenation secondary to a dysrhythmia
- Ineffective management of the therapeutic regimen related to lack of knowledge of the disease process and treatment

Primary goals for the patient with a dysrhythmia include the following:

- Management or elimination of the dysrhythmia
- Maintenance of a normal cardiac output
- Maintenance of a normal activity level
- Knowledge of the dysrhythmia and the treatment regimen
- Decreased anxiety

Nursing Process: Implementation

The nurse's primary responsibility is to monitor the patient closely for the development of a dysrhythmia and intervene promptly, as appropriate, should one occur. Careful and regular assessment of the patient's vital signs is important. Accurate administration of the prescribed drug therapy and patient education related to any prescribed antiarrhythmia drugs are also essential. Another important nursing measure is to reduce any anxiety the patient may be experiencing by keeping the patient informed and maintaining a calm attitude.

Nursing Process: Evaluation

The effectiveness of nursing interventions can be measured by the achievement of the following **expected outcomes** by the patient:

- Maintenance of normal cardiac output
- Expressed understanding of disease process and its treatment
- Adherence to prescribed therapeutic regimen
- Decreased anxiety

Chapter 11 Study Questions

1.   Describe the three pathophysiological processes that can lead to the development of a dysrhythmia.

2.   Describe four common atrial dysrhythmias.

3.   Describe three common ventricular dysrhythmias.

4.   What is the drug of choice for treatment of premature ventricular contractions or ventricular tachycardia?

5.   What care would the nurse anticipate giving to a patient who develops ventricular fibrillation?

6.   Describe the clinical manifestations related to dysrhythmias.

7.   Describe cardioversion and defibrillation.

8.   What is the implication of a decreasing pulse pressure?

9.   Identify four possible nursing diagnoses for a patient with a dysrhythmia.

10.   Identify four expected outcomes that would be appropriate for a patient with a dysrhythmia.

Answers to Chapter 11 Study Questions

1. Many etiologies are associated with the development of dysrhythmias. Some of the most common causes include coronary artery disease and other cardiac diseases, hypoxia, sympathetic stimulation, and vagal stimulation. Essentially, three pathophysiological processes can underlie these causes and lead to the development of a dysrhythmia. The first process is altered automaticity. This can either increase or decrease the heart rate, depending upon the etiology of the alteration. The second process is altered electrical conduction. Conduction is slowed down, leading to a delay of conduction or even a complete block. The third process is reentry, during which an impulse is blocked and reenters surrounding tissues to establish a circuitous pathway.

2. PAC is a premature contraction originating in the atria. Paroxysmal supraventricular tachycardia occurs with an abrupt onset and is caused by an ectopic focus located somewhere above the bundle of His. Essentially, an impulse reenters over and over again, resulting in a fast heart rate (150–250 beats/minute) that is regular in rhythm. The tachycardia may also cease abruptly. Atrial flutter produces an atrial rate of approximately 250–350 beats/minute with a regular rhythm. However, some of these impulses are blocked and not conducted through the AV node. Therefore, the ventricular rate does not increase to the level of the atria, but instead remains around 150 beats/minute. Atrial fibrillation represents rapid, disorganized atrial electrical activity that results in a completely ineffective atrial contraction.

3. Premature ventricular contraction (PVC) is a premature contraction originating in the ventricles. Ventricular tachycardia is diagnosed when three or more PVCs in a row are detected on an ECG. The ventricular rate is over 100 beats/minute and the rhythm is usually regular. Ventricular tachycardia may lead to ventricular fibrillation. Ventricular fibrillation is the disorganized, irregular contractions of the ventricles resulting in no effective contractions and no cardiac output.

4. The most commonly prescribed medication for the treatment of PVCs is lidocaine.

5. A patient who is in ventricular fibrillation has no pulse, is unconscious, and stops breathing. Without prompt treatment and reversal of the ventricular fibrillation, the patient will die. Immediate CPR, defibrillation, and advanced cardiac life support is necessary to save the patient's life.

6. Clinical manifestations related to dysrhythmias will vary depending upon the nature and severity of the dysrhythmia. Some dysrhythmias do not cause any symptoms. When symptoms do occur, it is because of a decreased cardiac output. Some of the most common clinical manifestations include palpitations (alterations in heart rate and/or rhythm); a sense of fatigue; anxiety; dizziness; light-

headedness (may faint); cool, clammy skin; pallor; decreased blood pressure; shortness of breath; and chest discomfort.

7. Cardioversion or defibrillation can be used to intervene in the case of a tachydysrhythmia. While the two procedures are used for different circumstances, they both deliver an electrical current to the myocardial cells in an attempt to allow the heart's sinus node to reestablish normal sinus rhythm. Cardioversion is usually a scheduled procedure, used when a patient has failed to respond to drug therapy. In cardioversion the electrical current is synchronized to be delivered during ventricular depolarization. This synchronization with the QRS complex is done to prevent ventricular tachycardia or fibrillation. Defibrillation is used during an emergency when the patient is in ventricular fibrillation. The electrical current delivered during defibrillation is usually greater than the amount used for cardioversion.

8. A decreasing pulse pressure (difference between systolic and diastolic blood pressure) is indicative of decreasing cardiac output.

9. Four nursing diagnoses are as follows: potential complications include decreased cardiac output related to a dysrhythmia; anxiety related to the diagnosis of a potentially life-threatening dysrhythmia; activity intolerance related to compromised tissue oxygenation, secondary to a dysrhythmia; and ineffective management of the therapeutic regimen related to lack of knowledge of the disease process and treatment.

10. A patient would maintain normal cardiac output, express an understanding of the disease process and its treatment, adhere to the prescribed therapeutic regimen, and have decreased anxiety.

Chapter 12: Nursing Care for Coronary Vascular Disorders

Key Terms

Angina pectoris
Atherosclerosis
Cardiac enzymes: total CK, CK-MB, LDH, myoglobin, and troponin
Cardiogenic shock
Congestive heart failure (CHF)
Coronary artery bypass graft (CABG)
Coronary artery disease (CAD)
Ischemia
Left-sided heart failure
Myocardial infarction (MI)
Percutaneous transluminal coronary angioplasty (PTCA)
Right-sided heart failure
Streptokinase
Thrombolytic drugs
Tissue-type plasminogen activator (t-PA)

Introduction

This chapter will discuss the nursing care of patients who have coronary vascular disorders, most specifically coronary artery disease and angina. Myocardial infarction and congestive heart failure are also discussed, as both can be complications of coronary artery disease.

Coronary Artery Disease

Coronary artery disease (CAD) is the most common form of cardiovascular disease in the United States. It is the number one health problem in the United States, resulting in approximately 400,000 deaths annually. It also leads to the development of other cardiac disorders, such as myocardial infarction and congestive heart failure.

Several risk factors are associated with CAD. Uncontrollable risk factors include age, race, gender, and family history. However, numerous risk factors are controllable or modifiable. Modifiable risk factors include dietary intake of fats and cholesterol, obesity, tobacco use, activity levels, stress levels, hypertension, and diabetes.

Pathophysiology

CAD is caused by the development of atherosclerosis in the coronary arteries. **Atherosclerosis** is the accumulation of lipid deposits in the intima of the arterial wall. These lipid deposits create plaque that eventually narrows the lumen of the coronary arteries, leading to an obstruction of the blood flow to the myocardial tissue. Approximately 75 percent of the artery lumen must be obstructed before blood flow will be significantly decreased.

Obstruction of the blood flow causes **ischemia**, which is inadequate oxygenation of the tissues. Because of the obstruction, the heart is not able to supply enough oxygenated blood to meet the myocardial demand, and ischemia develops, causing chest pain. This chest pain is known as **angina pectoris** and is caused by a temporary lack of oxygen to the tissues. If the obstruction is significant and results in severe ischemia, a **myocardial infarction (MI)** may occur. An MI causes actual heart tissue damage, which is caused by lack of blood flow to myocardial tissue.

Clinical Manifestations

The most common clinical manifestation of CAD is angina pectoris. However, it is possible that the patient's first indication of CAD will be an MI or sudden cardiac death.

Anginal pain can be associated with the following factors:

- Physical exertion (any activity that increases oxygen demand)
- Smoking
- Stressful situations
- Activities that promote vasoconstriction, such as exposure to cold
- Eating a large meal (diverts blood flow from myocardial tissue)

Characteristics of anginal pain can be variable. Some of the most common indicators of anginal pain include the following:

- Deep retrosternal chest pain (can be described as viselike or heavy)
- Pain radiating down the left arm, both arms, or into the neck or jaw
- Weakness or numbness in the arms
- Dizziness, light-headedness
- Pallor, diaphoresis, cool skin
- Nausea, vomiting
- Feeling of anxiety
- Shortness of breath

These signs and symptoms may not occur in everyone who experiences angina. Some people complain of indigestion or heartburn. Women may experience different, more vague symptoms consisting of fatigue, feeling of heartburn, shortness of breath, and "heaviness" in the chest. Patients who have diabetes mellitus or who are elderly may not experience any sensation of pain with angina due to decreased sensation.

Other clinical manifestations of angina may include changes in the patient's vital signs, such as increased or decreased blood pressure, tachycardia, or bradycardia. Angina typically will subside promptly when the patient rests or takes nitroglycerin.

Unstable angina may develop as CAD continues to progress. In unstable angina, chest pain occurs more frequently, is more severe, and may not respond easily to treatment with sublingual nitroglycerin. The pain may even develop when the patient is at rest. Unstable angina is usually precipitated by atherosclerotic plaque that ruptures, thus further obstructing the artery's lumen.

Diagnostic Tests

CAD and angina are typically diagnosed by the following tests:

- The **ECG** demonstrates changes in the ST segment (ST depression), indicating ischemia.
- An **exercise stress test** indicates underperfused myocardial tissue.
- **Cardiac catheterization** allows direct visualization of coronary arteries and will identify areas of blockage.

Medical Management

The goal of medical management for CAD is to increase the oxygen flow to the myocardial tissues and to control the risk factors associated with CAD. CAD can be treated with pharmacological therapy or through surgical intervention. Pharmacological therapy will be used first, unless the patient's condition is unstable.

Pharmacological Therapy

The following pharmacological agents have a role in the treatment and management of CAD:

- **Antiplatelet drugs**: The major antiplatelet drug used in the treatment of CAD is **acetylsalicylic acid**, or **ASA** (aspirin). Antiplatelet drugs prevent platelets from adhering to the plaque in the coronary arteries and decrease the likelihood of thrombus formation.
- **Nitrate drugs**: **Nitroglycerin** is a nitrate drug used to treat angina. Nitrates cause vasodilation, which can increase perfusion of the coronary arteries. The vasodilation also decreases the preload by causing blood to pool in the periphery and reducing the workload of the heart. Nitrates also decrease afterload by decreasing resistance in the systemic vascular system. These effects decrease the oxygen consumption of the heart.
- **Beta-blockers**: Beta-blockers are prescribed to treat angina. Beta-blockers decrease heart rate and blood pressure, thus reducing the oxygen demand of the

heart. **Atenolol (Tenormin); metoprolol (Lopressor); and propranolol (Inderal)** are examples of beta-blockers.

- **Calcium channel blockers:** Calcium channel blockers decrease the heart rate and relax blood vessels. This can increase the perfusion of the coronary arteries and increase oxygen supply. Common calcium channel blockers are **verapamil (Calan), diltiazem (Cardizem), and nifedipine (Procardia).**
- **Angiotensin-converting enzyme (ACE) inhibitors:** ACE inhibitors are used to decrease preload and afterload, ultimately decreasing the workload of the heart. By decreasing the workload of the heart, hypertrophy of the left ventricle may be prevented. **Captopril (Capoten)** and **lisinopril (Prinivil, Zestril)** are examples of commonly used ACE inhibitors.
- **Cholesterol-lowering drugs:** Cholesterol-lowering drugs, or **antihyperlipidemics**, may be prescribed for patients with CAD to help lower total cholesterol levels and low-density lipoprotein (LDL). Cholesterol-lowering drugs that are commonly prescribed to treat high cholesterol include **lovastatin (Mevacor)** and **simvastatin (Zocor)**, which lowers triglycerides as well as cholesterol levels.
- **Oxygen:** Oxygen is routinely used when a patient experiences angina or an acute myocardial infarction to increase the myocardial oxygen supply.

Surgical Intervention

If pharmacological therapy is not successful in treating CAD and angina, surgical intervention may be planned. Two surgical procedures are most commonly used in treatment of CAD: percutaneous transluminal coronary angioplasty (PTCA) and coronary artery bypass graft (CABG).

Percutaneous Transluminal Coronary Angioplasty

Percutaneous transluminal coronary angioplasty (PTCA) is an invasive procedure that is performed in the cardiac catheterization laboratory. The femoral artery is most commonly used for insertion of a sheath, through which a catheter is threaded to the aorta. Through the use of angiography, the obstructed areas are identified. A balloon catheter is then inserted through the sheath and inflated over the area of plaque, thus reopening the obstructed artery. A stainless steel mesh **stent** may be left in place to hold the coronary artery open. Patients who have a PTCA are typically admitted to the hospital the day of the procedure and discharged the following day.

Postoperative nursing care after a PTCA is the same as with a cardiac catheterization and includes the following:

- Observing the insertion site (usually groin) for bleeding or swelling
- Monitoring the neurovascular status of the involved leg every fifteen minutes; every thirty minutes; then hourly
- Keeping the patient on bed rest for four to six hours, with the involved leg kept straight until the sheath is removed
- Keeping HOB elevated less than 30°

- Monitoring vital signs; assessing for the presence of dysrhythmias and chest pain
- Encouraging fluid intake to eliminate dye from system

Complications of PTCA may include bleeding, perforation or vasospasm of the artery, MI, dysrhythmias, or cardiac arrest. Another disadvantage of PTCA is the potential for the vessel to re-occlude, usually within six months.

Coronary Artery Bypass Graft

In a **coronary artery bypass graft (CABG)**, a blood vessel, usually the greater saphenous vein, and/or the internal mammary artery is grafted onto the coronary artery around the area of obstruction so that blood can flow around the obstruction. A large mediastinal incision is made. Patients are placed on a cardiopulmonary bypass machine during the surgery.

Preoperative care of the patient who is going to have a CABG includes providing emotional support to the patient and family members as they face this health-care crisis. Allowing the patient and family to verbalize fears and concerns is an essential component of the preoperative care. A fear of dying is very common, and the patient should be encouraged to discuss such fears. The nurse should answer all questions and seek out other support services, such as clergy and social workers, as appropriate. A tour of the critical care facility and an explanation of the monitors and other medical equipment that will be used postoperatively can also help reduce the patient's and family member's apprehension. Some patients do not desire detailed information, so the nurse should assess and respect the patient's need for detailed preoperative preparation.

Various tests and laboratory procedures will be performed in preparation of surgery, including a chest X ray, ECG, and complete laboratory blood tests, including CBC, electrolytes, PT/PTT, cardiac enzymes, BUN, and creatinine. ABGs may be obtained if the patient has a history of pulmonary disease. Urinalysis will also be obtained. Typing and cross-matching of blood and possible autologous blood donation will be performed. If the patient has any chronic health problems, the status of these conditions will be verified by the appropriate tests to determine if the patient's health status is stable enough to tolerate the surgery.

Prophylactic intravenous antibiotics are initiated prior to surgery. Other preoperative preparations may include showers or scrubs with an antiseptic solution and the insertion of a urinary catheter.

Following a CABG, the **primary goals** of postoperative nursing care include maintaining or achieving the following:

- Adequate cardiac output and tissue perfusion
- Adequate renal perfusion
- Adequate fluid and electrolyte balance
- Effective gas exchange

- Normal body temperature
- Reduction of sensory overload
- Relief from pain
- Performance of self-care activities
- Avoidance of complications (hemorrhage; cardiac complications such as MI, dysrhythmias, congestive heart failure, cardiac arrest; pulmonary complications such as pneumothorax, pneumonia, pulmonary emboli, respiratory failure; neurological complications such as cerebrovascular accident (stroke); renal failure; electrolyte imbalances; infection)

The goals of postoperative nursing care for patients who have had a CABG are met through the following nursing interventions:

- Monitoring the patient closely for cardiac arrhythmias.
- Assessing vital signs frequently; monitoring pulmonary artery and arterial pressures to determine cardiac output status.
- Maintaining mechanical ventilation for approximately twenty-four hours or less; encouraging turning, coughing, and deep breathing following extubation.
- Monitoring mediastinal and pleural chest tube drainage system for patency and excessive bleeding. Chest tube drainage should not exceed more than 100 cc/hour during the first hours following surgery and should not exceed 500 cc within the first twenty-four hours. *A sudden decrease in drainage may indicate an obstructed chest tube, which can lead to cardiac tamponade, a medical emergency.*
- Monitoring neurovascular status closely to detect any decrease in cerebral perfusion. Note pupil reactions to light, patient's orientation and alertness.
- Monitoring fluid and electrolyte balance. Assessment of hourly urine output is essential. The nurse should report any urinary output below 30 cc/hour; serum electrolytes are monitored closely.
- Alleviating pain through administration of prescribed analgesia.
- Promoting leg and arm exercises while in bed, and assisting patient with ambulation as activity progresses.
- Observing patient closely for signs of sensory overload, sleep deprivation, and other subtle behavior changes that can develop as a result of heart surgery and ICU experiences.
- Teaching patient's self-care in preparation for discharge approximately two to three days after surgery.

Myocardial Infarction

When pharmacological therapy or surgical intervention does not successfully treat coronary artery disease, a myocardial infarction (MI) may be the result. In the United States, approximately one million individuals a year experience an MI; of these individuals, 25 percent will die.

Pathophysiology

A **myocardial infarction** is most commonly caused by an obstruction of a coronary artery. A thrombus or an embolus may cause the obstruction. The obstruction impedes blood flow throughout the myocardium, resulting in ischemia (a lack of oxygen to the tissues). The lack of oxygenation eventually leads to an infarction, which is the death of the tissue cells. The size and location of the infarction determines the clinical outcome of the patient.

Clinical Manifestations

The classical presenting symptom of an MI is sudden chest pain that is unrelieved by rest or nitroglycerin. Frequently, skin is cool, moist, and pale. Patients may also appear to be restless and anxious. Respirations and pulse rate may be increased. Shortness of breath may be present. The patient may experience nausea and vomiting. Dysrhythmias can also occur.

Diagnostic Tests

An MI is diagnosed through the use of a 12-lead ECG and laboratory tests. During an MI, ECG changes include ST segment elevation and T-wave changes. The serum laboratory tests include **cardiac enzymes**: total CK, CK-MB, LDH, myoglobin, and troponin. The cardiac enzymes are elevated when myocardial tissue is damaged.

Medical Management

The primary goal of medical management for an MI is to minimize damage to the heart muscle. Other goals include preserving heart function and preventing the development of complications. To achieve these goals, it is important that the area of infarction be reperfused as soon as possible. This can be achieved through the emergency use of PTCA, in which the obstructed area is reopened.

Thrombolytic drugs, which dissolve the thrombus, may also be used. The thrombolytic drugs may be administered directly into the coronary artery during the PTCA or may be infused intravenously. The most commonly used thrombolytic drugs are **streptokinase** and **tissue-type plasminogen activator (t-PA)**.

Other drugs that may be administered during an MI include **ACE inhibitors**. ACE inhibitors are used to decrease the oxygen demand of the heart.

Analgesics are also used to treat the chest pain. The drug of choice is intravenous morphine sulfate. Morphine is used to relieve pain and to decrease the heart's workload and oxygen consumption.

Oxygen therapy will be implemented immediately in patients who are experiencing an MI. The patient will also initially be placed on bed rest to conserve myocardial tissue oxygen consumption.

Nursing Process: Assessment

When caring for a patient with an MI, the nurse's assessments are focused on the symptoms that the patient is presenting. A careful, thorough assessment is essential to detect early changes in the patient's condition and prevent complications. An assessment also establishes a baseline against which the patient's condition can be further evaluated. It is important that the nurse assesses each of the patient's symptoms and determines the factors precipitating the symptoms, as well as the duration of occurrence and response to treatment.

Nursing Process: Nursing Diagnosis and Planning

Based upon an analysis of the gathered data, the following **nursing diagnoses** may be appropriate for the patient with an MI:

- Decreased cardiac tissue perfusion related to decreased coronary blood flow from coronary artery obstruction and myocardial damage
- Chest pain related to myocardial ischemia
- Potential for decreased peripheral tissue perfusion related to decreased cardiac output
- Anxiety related to pain and fear of dying
- Activity intolerance related to decreased cardiac output and impaired tissue perfusion
- Ineffective management of therapeutic regimen related to lack of knowledge of disease process and cardiac rehabilitation

Primary goals for the patient with an MI include the following:

- Relief of chest pain
- Prevention of further myocardial tissue damage
- Restoration of normal cardiac tissue perfusion
- Maintenance of normal respiratory function
- Reduction of anxiety
- Participation in self-care and the rehabilitation process
- Prevention of complications

Nursing Process: Implementation

A primary goal of nursing interventions is to relieve chest pain and promote tissue perfusion. Nursing interventions appropriate for relieving pain and promoting tissue perfusion include the following:

- Administering oxygen (two to four liters per nasal cannula to increase oxygenation of myocardial tissue)
- Administering morphine sulfate intravenously to control pain
- Administering nitroglycerin intravenously to relieve chest pain

- Administering aspirin and anticoagulant therapy to prevent clot formation, and thrombolytic therapy to lyse clots that have formed
- Maintaining bed rest with the head of the bed elevated to semi-Fowler's position

Promoting rest and reducing anxiety are other goals of nursing care. Nursing interventions appropriate for promoting rest and reducing anxiety include the following:

- Maintaining the patient on bed rest or limiting his/her activity to a chair
- Providing a quiet, calm environment
- Providing rest after periods of activity
- Encouraging the patient to gradually return to normal levels of activity
- Giving the patient opportunities to ask questions and share concerns
- Encouraging the use of relaxation techniques

Monitoring for and preventing complications is another essential goal of nursing care. The nurse will closely monitor the patient for any change in the following:

- Vital signs
- Cardiac functioning (chest pain, rate, rhythm, heart sounds)
- Respiratory status (respiratory rate, rhythm, and lung sounds)
- Level of consciousness
- Color and temperature of skin
- Renal functioning (urinary output, BUN, and creatinine)
- Fluid and electrolyte status (serum electrolyte values, weight, edema, lung sounds)

Nursing Process: Evaluation

The effectiveness of nursing interventions can be measured by the achievement of the following **expected outcomes** by the patient:

- Verbalizes relief of chest pain
- Normal vital signs
- Maintains normal respiratory status
- Expresses relief of anxiety
- Demonstrates adequate tissue perfusion
- Expresses an understanding of the disease process and treatment
- Participates in cardiac rehabilitation program
- Avoids complications

Complications of a Myocardial Infarction

Complications of a myocardial infarction are related to the myocardial damage that occurs. The most common complications are dysrhythmias. Ventricular dysrhythmias, such as premature ventricular contractions, ventricular tachycardia, and ventricular fibrillation, are life-threatening dysrhythmias and must be treated promptly with intravenous lidocaine when they occur.

Other potential complications include cardiogenic shock and congestive heart failure.

- **Cardiogenic shock** develops when there is extensive left ventricular failure and the heart is not capable of delivering oxygen to vital organ tissues. Cardiogenic shock is a medical emergency with a high mortality rate. (Cardiogenic shock is discussed in further depth in chapter 15.)
- **Congestive heart failure** develops following an MI when the pumping ability of the heart has been decreased due to myocardial damage.

Congestive Heart Failure

Congestive heart failure (CHF) develops when the heart is not able to pump effectively enough to move blood through the body and adequately supply the body's tissues with oxygen and other nutrients. Some of the more common causes of congestive heart failure include hypertension, coronary artery disease, myocarditis, and myocardial infarction. CHF is the most common cause of hospitalization in patients over sixty-five years of age. CHF may be acute or chronic in onset.

Pathophysiology

CHF develops as a result of decreased contractility of the heart muscle. Any disorder that leads to decreased contractility of the heart muscle can lead to the development of CHF. CAD is a common cause of decreased contractility due to decreased oxygen supply to the myocardium. The contractility of the left ventricle of the heart is usually affected first.

When the left ventricle cannot contract effectively enough to eject its blood volume, ejection fractions decrease and blood is left in the left ventricle at the end of systole. The left atrium must then increase its pressure in an attempt to move its volume of blood into the left ventricle. When the left atrium cannot move its blood volume forward, blood begins to back up into the pulmonary circulation. Pulmonary capillary pressure increases, leading to a leakage of fluid into the alveoli and interstitial tissues. This causes pulmonary edema. Because of the high pulmonary pressure, the right ventricle must work harder to overcome this resistance and push blood through the pulmonary system. When the right ventricle cannot move its volume of blood forward into the pulmonary system, the right atrium becomes congested with blood, ultimately affecting the flow of the peripheral venous circulation. Because of these pathophysiological changes, it can be seen how left-sided ventricular heart failure can lead to right-sided ventricular heart failure.

As CHF develops, the heart tries to compensate for its declining performance. The heart muscle hypertrophies and the ventricle chambers dilate. In addition, the sympathetic nervous system is stimulated, resulting in an increase in heart rate and contractility. The sympathetic nervous system response also stimulates renin release, which causes vasoconstriction and fluid retention. All of these compensatory mechanisms only serve to further increase the heart's workload and can eventually lead to decompensation.

Clinical Manifestations

The clinical manifestations of CHF can be classified according to left-sided heart failure and right-sided heart failure.

In **left-sided heart failure**, it is common for the patient to experience respiratory problems related to pulmonary congestion and edema. When the left ventricle cannot pump blood forward, the pressure within the ventricle chamber increases, causing the pressure in the left atrium to rise as well, as blood flow out of the left atrium into the left ventricle is decreased. As the pressure within the left atrium increases, the blood flow from the pulmonary system into the left atrium is decreased, forcing fluids into the pulmonary tissues and impairing gas exchange. The resulting signs and symptoms of left-sided heart failure include the following:

- Cough
- Dyspnea (upon exertion or at rest)
- Paroxysmal nocturnal dyspnea (PND)
- Crackles
- Orthopnea
- Pink, frothy sputum (indicative of pulmonary edema)
- Restlessness, anxiety
- Tachycardia
- Fatigue, activity intolerance

In **right-sided failure**, the heart cannot pump the blood that is returning from the peripheral circulation. Thus the venous system becomes congested, as do the organs. The signs and symptoms of right-sided failure are the result of this organ and venous congestion and include the following:

- Dependent edema (may be pitting)
- Weight gain
- Nocturia
- Anorexia, nausea
- Hepatomegaly
- Ascites
- Distended neck veins
- Fatigue

Diagnostic Tests

A variety of diagnostic tests may be used to diagnose CHF and its underlying etiology. Some of the most common diagnostic and laboratory tests include the following:

- Chest X ray
- Echocardiogram
- ECG
- Serum electrolyte (sodium, potassium, chloride) and blood chemistry studies (creatinine, BUN); CBC
- Arterial blood gases

Medical Management

The goal of medical management for congestive heart failure is to reduce the workload of the heart, increase cardiac output, decrease fluid volume excess, improve oxygenation, and treat the underlying cause of the CHF. Depending upon the severity of the CHF, these goals are achieved through the use of patient education regarding lifestyle modifications and pharmacological therapy.

Patients with CHF will be encouraged to quit smoking, limit alcohol intake, and decrease sodium intake. A regular exercise program, within the limits of the patient's tolerance, will also be encouraged. Some patients may require supplemental oxygen during activity. Patients also need instructions for monitoring their weight daily and taking their prescribed medications daily.

Pharmacological therapy for CHF is an integral part of treatment and will vary depending upon the severity of the patient's condition. However, the most commonly prescribed drugs for treatment of CHF include the following:

- **Diuretics** are prescribed to eliminate excess fluid. Commonly prescribed diuretics include loop diuretics (furosemide), thiazides (hydrochlorothiazide), and potassium-sparing diuretics (spironolactone).
- **ACE inhibitors** are used to promote vasodilation and decrease cardiac workload. ACE inhibitors also decrease sodium and water retention.
- **Digitalis** is used to increase the force of myocardial contraction. **Digoxin** is the most commonly prescribed form of digitalis. Patients should be monitored closely for signs of digitalis toxicity. Hypokalemia, which can result from the use of diuretics, is a common cause of digitalis toxicity.

Nursing Process: Assessment

The nurse will focus the assessment on gathering data about the patient's respiratory and cardiovascular status. The nurse should assess the patient for the clinical manifestations of CHF.

It is especially important for the nurse to closely monitor the patient for signs and symptoms of fluid overload. Subtle signs of fluid overload can often be detected through careful auscultation of lung sounds. The lungs should be auscultated frequently to detect the presence of crackles or wheezes. The nurse should also note the presence of a cough and the quality of respirations.

The nurse should also note the blood pressure and heart rate and rhythm. Auscultation of the heart sounds may reveal an S_3 heart sound, which indicates incomplete emptying of the ventricles. The neck veins should be examined for distention.

The lower extremities are examined for edema and adequate tissue perfusion. The patient should be weighed daily at the same time, and accurate intake and output records maintained. The nurse should carefully measure urinary output. **Oliguria** (less than 400 cc output per twenty-four hours) or **anuria** (less than 50 cc output in twenty-four hours) is indicative of low renal perfusion due to diminished cardiac output. Alterations in mental status may indicate decreased cerebral perfusion due to decreased cardiac output. Weakness, fatigue, or dizziness may also be noted.

Nursing Process: Nursing Diagnosis and Planning

Based upon an analysis of the gathered data, the following **nursing diagnoses** may be appropriate for the patient with CHF:

- Fluid volume excess related to decreased contractility
- Activity intolerance related to lack of adequate tissue oxygenation
- Fatigue related to decreased cardiac output
- Impaired gas exchange related to alveolar congestion
- Anxiety related to shortness of breath and decreased oxygenation
- Sleep pattern disturbance related to paroxysmal nocturnal dyspnea
- Potential for impaired skin integrity related to edema
- Ineffective management of treatment regimen related to lack of knowledge about CHF and pharmacological therapy

Primary goals for the patient with CHF include the following:

- Maintenance of normal fluid and electrolyte balance
- Increased activity tolerance
- Decreased fatigue
- Normal respiratory rate and rhythm
- Decreased anxiety
- Maintenance of skin integrity
- Knowledge of self-care program and treatment regimen

Nursing Process: Implementation

Nursing interventions will be directed toward improving cardiac functioning, restoring normal fluid volume, improving oxygenation of tissues, increasing activity tolerance, and implementing a patient education plan. The following nursing interventions would be appropriate for a patient with CHF:

- Place the patient in a supported semi-Fowler's position to improve respiratory status.
- Administer oxygen per nasal cannula, as needed, for dyspnea.
- Encourage the patient to balance activity and rest, conserving energy.
- Assist the patient with activities of daily living as needed.
- Provide skin care to prevent skin breakdown, especially in areas where edema is present.
- Encourage adequate nutrition; small, frequent feedings may be tolerated better than regular meals.
- Monitor fluid status closely; maintain careful regulation of any intravenous fluids; and auscultate lung sounds frequently to detect subtle changes due to developing fluid overload.
- Monitor weight and intake and output daily.
- Monitor bowel elimination pattern to avoid constipation and administer prescribed stool softeners.
- Maintain medication administration schedule and evaluate patient for potential side effects of therapy.
- Monitor potassium, sodium lab values; BUN, creatinine; digitalis levels.
- Maintain quiet, restful environment.
- Decrease anxiety by encouraging the patient to discuss fears/concerns and providing psychological support.
- Encourage family members' presence to help decrease patient anxiety; teach relaxation techniques.

Nursing Process: Evaluation

The effectiveness of nursing interventions can be measured by the achievement of the following **expected outcomes** by the patient:

- Tolerates increased levels of activity
- Maintains vital signs within normal limits
- Denies respiratory distress
- Maintains normal fluid and electrolyte balance
- Maintains normal sleep pattern
- Demonstrates knowledge of CHF and treatment regimen
- Demonstrates self-care and a decrease in anxiety
- Experiences minimal side effects from drug therapy
- Avoids complications

Discharge teaching will focus on promoting self-care activities. The patient needs to understand the importance of taking the prescribed pharmacological therapy, monitoring the effects of the drugs, and keeping follow-up medical appointments. The patient should be taught how to take a radial pulse and blood pressure, and what side effects to report.

Monitoring fluid balance is another important self-care activity for the patient to understand. The patient should be instructed to weigh daily and report immediately any weight gain of two to three pounds over a couple of days, and the development of edema, cough, or shortness of breath.

Dietary modifications should be followed, and sodium restrictions should be implemented as prescribed. Dietary instructions may be necessary to help the patient develop "heart healthy" eating habits that are low in cholesterol, fat, and sodium.

The patient should be encouraged to maintain a regular exercise schedule within levels of tolerance. Temperature extremes should be avoided to decrease cardiac workload.

Chapter 12 Study Questions

1.   Describe the pathophysiology of coronary artery disease (CAD).

2.   What is the most common clinical manifestation of CAD?

3.   What are the most common clinical indicators of angina?

4.   What interventions typically cause angina to subside?

5.   What diagnostic tests are used to diagnose CAD and angina?

6.   Identify the pharmacological agents that are typically used to manage CAD.

7.   Describe the postoperative care following a percutaneous transluminal coronary angioplasty (PTCA).

8.   What are the primary goals of postoperative nursing care following a coronary artery bypass graft (CABG)?

9.   What are the clinical manifestations of a myocardial infarction (MI)?

10.   What is the drug of choice to treat the pain associated with an MI?

11.   What four nursing interventions would be appropriate for promoting rest in a patient with an MI?

12.   Identify the nursing goals of care for a patient with MI.

13.   Describe the signs and symptoms of left-sided heart failure.

14.   Describe the signs and symptoms of right-sided heart failure.

15.   Describe the appropriate nursing assessment for a patient with congestive heart failure (CHF).

16.   Identify nursing interventions appropriate for a patient with CHF.

Answers to Chapter 12 Study Questions

1. CAD is caused by the development of atherosclerosis in the coronary arteries. Atherosclerosis is the accumulation of lipid deposits in the intima of the arterial wall. These lipid deposits create plaque that eventually narrows the lumen of the artery, leading to an obstruction of the blood flow to the myocardial tissue.

2. The most common clinical manifestation of CAD is angina pectoris.

3. Angina is typically indicated by deep retrosternal chest pain (can be described as viselike or heavy); pain radiating down the left arm, both arms, or into the neck or jaw; weakness or numbness in the arms; dizziness and light-headedness; pallor, diaphoresis, and cool skin; nausea and vomiting; feeling of anxiety; and/or shortness of breath.

4. Angina typically will subside when the patient rests or takes nitroglycerin.

5. ECG demonstrates changes in the ST segment (ST depression), indicating ischemia; exercise stress test indicates underperfused myocardial tissue; cardiac catheterization allows direct visualization of coronary arteries and will identify areas of blockage.

6. CAD is typically managed by administering antiplatelet drugs, nitrate drugs, beta-blockers, calcium channel blockers, angiotensin-converting enzyme (ACE) inhibitors, or cholesterol-lowering drugs.

7. Postoperative nursing care after a PTCA is the same as with a cardiac catheterization and includes observing the insertion site for bleeding or swelling; monitoring the circulatory status of the involved extremity; keeping the patient on bed rest for four to six hours, with the involved leg kept straight; monitoring vital signs; assessing for the presence of dysrhythmias and chest pain; and encouraging fluid intake.

8. The primary goals of postoperative nursing care following a CABG include maintaining adequate cardiac status and tissue perfusion, adequate renal perfusion, fluid and electrolyte balance, effective gas exchange, normal body temperature, and relief from pain.

9. The classical presenting symptom of an MI is sudden chest pain that is unrelieved by rest or nitroglycerin. Skin is frequently cool, moist, and pale. Patients may also appear to be restless and anxious. Respirations and pulse rate may be increased. Shortness of breath may be present. The patient may experience nausea and vomiting. Dysrhythmias can also occur.

10. The drug of choice is intravenous morphine sulfate. Morphine is used to relieve pain and to decrease the heart's workload and oxygen consumption.

11.   Maintain the patient on bed rest or limiting activity to a chair; provide a quiet environment; provide rest after periods of activity; and encourage the patient to gradually return to normal levels of activity.

12.   Primary goals for the patient with an MI include relief of chest pain; prevention of further myocardial tissue damage; restoration of normal cardiac tissue perfusion; maintenance of normal respiratory status; reduction of anxiety; participation in self-care and the rehabilitation process; and prevention of complications.

13.   In left-sided heart failure, it is common for the patient to experience respiratory problems related to pulmonary congestion and edema. When the left ventricle cannot pump blood forward, the pressure within the ventricle chamber increases, causing the pressure in the left atrium to rise as well, as blood flow out of the left atrium into the left ventricle is decreased. As the pressure within the left atrium increases, the blood flow from the pulmonary system into the left atrium is decreased, forcing fluids into the pulmonary tissues and impairing gas exchange. The resulting signs and symptoms of left-sided heart failure include cough, dyspnea (upon exertion or at rest), paroxysmal nocturnal dyspnea, crackles, orthopnea, pink and frothy sputum, fatigue, activity intolerance, restlessness, anxiety, or tachycardia.

14.   In right-sided failure, the heart cannot pump the blood that is returning from the peripheral circulation. Thus the venous system becomes congested, as do the organs. The signs and symptoms of right-sided failure are the result of this organ and venous congestion and include dependent edema (may be pitting), weight gain, nocturia, anorexia, nausea, hepatomegaly, ascites, distended neck veins, and fatigue.

15.   It is especially important for the nurse to closely monitor the patient for signs and symptoms of fluid overload. Subtle signs of fluid overload can often be detected through careful auscultation of lung sounds. The lungs should be auscultated frequently to detect the presence of crackles or wheezes. The nurse should also note the presence of a cough and the quality of respirations. The nurse should also note the blood pressure and heart rate and rhythm. Auscultation of the heart sounds may reveal an S_3 heart sound, which indicates incomplete emptying of the ventricles. The neck veins should be examined for distention. The lower extremities are examined for edema and adequate tissue perfusion. The patient should be weighed at the same time daily, and accurate intake and output records maintained.

16.   Place the patient in a semi-Fowler's position to improve respiratory status; administer oxygen per nasal cannula, as needed. For dyspnea, encourage the patient to balance activity and rest, conserving energy. Assist the patient with activities of daily living, as needed. Provide skin care to prevent skin breakdown, especially in areas where edema is present. Encourage adequate nutrition; small, frequent feedings may be tolerated better than regular meals. Monitor fluid status

closely; maintain careful regulation of any intravenous fluids, daily weights, intake and output. Maintain medication administration schedule and evaluate the patient for potential side effects of therapy. Monitor potassium and sodium lab values and BUN, creatinine, and digitalis levels. Maintain a quiet, restful environment. Encourage patient to discuss their fears and concerns.

Chapter 13: Nursing Care for Hypertension and Vascular Disorders

Key Terms

Abdominal aortic aneurysm
Endarterectomy
Femoral-popliteal bypass
Hypertension
    Primary (essential)
    Secondary
Intermittent claudication
Orthostatic hypotension
Peripheral vascular disease
    Arterial insufficiency
    Venous insufficiency
Ulcers
    Arterial
    Venous
Varicose veins
Venous ligation

Introduction

This chapter discusses the nursing care of patients who have hypertension and vascular disorders. Hypertension affects approximately 20 to 25 percent of the adults who live in the United States. As a chronic disease, hypertension is a significant risk factor for the development of peripheral vascular disease, as well as coronary, cerebral, and renal vascular disease. Peripheral vascular disease, which may be either arterial or venous in nature, is the result of decreased blood flow through peripheral blood vessels. Varicose veins are the result of incompetent venous valves. Aortic aneurysms are the result of atherosclerotic changes in the aorta.

Hypertension

Hypertension is defined as a persistent elevation of the systolic blood pressure over 140 mm Hg and/or a persistent elevation of the diastolic blood pressure over 90 mm Hg. There are two types of hypertension: primary and secondary.

- **Primary**, or **essential**, **hypertension** is defined as hypertension that has no known cause.
- **Secondary hypertension** is defined as hypertension that has an identified cause, such as renal artery stenosis.

Primary hypertension is more common than secondary hypertension, with approximately 90 percent of the individuals affected having primary hypertension. Major risk factors for hypertension include the following:

- Family history
- Age and gender (increase with age and in males)
- Obesity
- Sedentary lifestyle
- Smoking and alcohol intake
- Atherosclerosis

Pathophysiology

Blood pressure is regulated primarily by blood flow and peripheral vascular resistance. When blood vessels are constricted, causing increased peripheral resistance to blood flow, the blood pressure will be elevated. The sympathetic nervous system and the renin-angiotensin system control the constriction and dilation of the peripheral blood vessels. When the sympathetic nervous system is stimulated or the renin-angiotensin system is activated, vasoconstriction occurs, resulting in an increased blood pressure. Eventually, continued hypertension leads to systemic blood vessel damage, especially in the heart, brain, and kidneys.

Clinical Manifestations

Frequently the patient with hypertension will have no symptoms. When symptoms do occur, it is usually as the result of vascular damage to specific target organs, such as the heart, kidneys, brain, or eyes. Some of the signs and symptoms that may occur in the advanced stages of hypertension include blurred vision, headache, nocturia, or spontaneous nosebleeds. Retinal changes may be found on funduscopic examination.

Diagnostic Tests

Hypertension is diagnosed when at least two elevated blood pressure readings are obtained on two separate occasions after the initial screening. Other diagnostic tests will be conducted to determine the extent of damage to target organs. These tests may include the following:

- CBC and serum electrolytes
- Blood urea nitrogen (BUN), creatinine
- Lipid and cholesterol levels
- Urinalysis
- ECG

Medical Management

The goal of medical management for hypertension is to keep the blood pressure below 140/90 mm Hg and to prevent damage to target organs. This is usually achieved through the use of medication. Initial drug treatment for uncomplicated hypertension consists of diuretics and/or beta-blockers. Other drugs that can be prescribed include ACE inhibitors, angiotensin II receptor blockers, alpha-blockers, and calcium antagonists. It is important that the nurse emphasize to the patient the necessity of regularly taking the prescribed medications. Because of the lack of symptoms associated with hypertension, patients may assume that they do not need to adhere to the plan of care. Patient education about the important role of drug therapy in the treatment of hypertension is essential.

In addition to drug therapy, the patient is also encouraged to make positive lifestyle adjustments. These adjustments include the following:

- Stopping smoking and reducing alcohol intake
- Reducing and managing stress
- Modifying diet to decrease fat intake and lose weight
- Incorporating aerobic exercise into daily schedule

Nursing Process: Assessment

Subjective assessment data gathered by the nurse should include the following:

- Family history
- Risk factors
- Diet
- Activity levels; occupation
- Stress levels and coping techniques
- Factors influencing health behaviors, e.g., social, economical, cultural, environmental, health beliefs
- Symptoms of target organ involvement, e.g., nocturia, dyspnea upon exertion, chest pain, dizziness, nosebleeds, blurred vision, headaches (The nurse should assess the history of these symptoms, as well as the current status, as symptoms may fluctuate.)

Objective assessment data should include the following:

- Blood pressure readings (two or more)
- Assessment of target organ involvement
- Eyes: retinopathy changes
- Cardiovascular: rate, rhythm, apical pulses, peripheral pulses, and warmth, color, edema in extremities
- Cerebrovascular: neurological assessment, mental status, carotid bruits

Nursing Process: Nursing Diagnosis and Planning

Based upon an analysis of the gathered data, the following **nursing diagnoses** may be appropriate for the patient with hypertension:

- Ineffective management of therapeutic regimen related to a lack of knowledge regarding drug therapy, the side effects of drug therapy, or the financial cost of drug therapy
- Knowledge deficit regarding the disease process and treatment regimen, including needed lifestyle changes

Primary goals for the patient with hypertension include the following:

- Knowledge of hypertension and how it is treated
- Self-care and management of the treatment regimen
- Maintenance of normal blood pressure
- Avoidance of complications: left ventricular hypertrophy and heart failure; cerebrovascular disease; peripheral vascular disease; retinopathy; renal damage

Nursing Process: Implementation

A primary nursing intervention for the patient with hypertension is to provide patient education and increase the patient's knowledge about hypertension and its treatment. The nurse needs to emphasize the importance of lifestyle changes that will help control hypertension. The nurse can work with the patient to identify a plan for incorporating dietary, exercise, and stress management strategies into the patient's daily living activities. The nurse should advise the patient to eat a "heart healthy" diet, decreasing the amounts of fat, cholesterol, and sodium in the diet. A dietary consultation can help the patient modify eating habits and lose weight, if needed. Alcohol intake should be limited and smoking eliminated. A regular exercise program should be integrated into the patient's schedule. Stress management programs can help patients cope with stress more effectively.

The nurse should also instruct the patient about prescribed drug therapy, including side effects and the importance of compliance. Two common side effects of antihypertensive drug therapy are orthostatic hypotension and decreased serum potassium levels.

- **Orthostatic hypotension** is a side effect of many antihypertensive drugs and may lead to fainting. The nurse should instruct the patient on how to avoid orthostatic hypotension by changing position slowly and avoiding activities that promote vasodilation.
- **Potassium depletion (hypokalemia)** is a side effect of thiazide and loop diuretics. Potassium-rich foods should be encouraged, as well as regular monitoring of serum potassium levels.

In addition, the nurse should emphasize the importance of regularly monitoring the blood pressure and keeping follow-up medical appointments. Maintaining a blood pressure journal is a helpful aid to managing treatment.

Nursing Process: Evaluation

The effectiveness of nursing interventions can be measured by the achievement of the following **expected outcomes** by the patient:

- Maintenance of normal blood pressure
- Adherence to prescribed therapeutic regimen
- Expressed understanding of disease process and treatment
- Incorporation of lifestyle changes into daily pattern of health habits
- Minimal side effects resulting from drug therapy
- Absence of complications

Peripheral Vascular Disease

Peripheral vascular disease (PVD) is caused by pathological changes in the **arterial** or **venous** vascular systems that result in decreased perfusion of tissues, usually in the lower extremities. It can also be caused by obstruction of the lymphatic system, although this is less common. The signs and symptoms of PVD vary, depending on if the PVD is arterial or venous in origin.

Pathophysiology

The most common causes of PVD that lead to insufficient arterial blood flow are arteriosclerosis and atherosclerosis. In **arteriosclerosis**, the lining of arterial vessel walls becomes thickened ("hardened"), leading to a narrowing of the vessel lumen. In **atherosclerosis**, the accumulation of atherosclerotic plaque causes a narrowing of the arterial lumen by thickening the intima and media of the artery. The narrowing of the arterial lumen leads to obstruction of the blood flow throughout the extremities. Other causes of arterial obstruction can include a thrombus or embolus, infectious or inflammatory process, trauma, or vasospasm.

Regardless of the cause of obstruction, the obstruction of blood flow leads to a lack of tissue oxygenation, causing ischemia. If the ischemia is severe enough, tissue damage, including ulcers and gangrene, can develop. Amputation of the lower extremity can be the outcome. Arterial insufficiency due to arterial obstruction can be either acute or chronic in nature.

- If the occlusion is sudden and **acute** in nature, the ischemia can be profound, resulting in irreversible tissue death.
- If the occlusion is **chronic** and gradual in onset, collateral circulation has a chance to develop, thus decreasing the chance for sudden tissue death.

PVD can also be caused by **insufficient venous blood flow**. Insufficient venous blood flow is usually the result of incompetent venous valves, obstruction of the venous system by a thrombus, or a decrease in the pumping action of the muscles that surround the peripheral venous system. When venous blood flow becomes obstructed and starts to pool in the periphery, there is an increase in venous pressure and hydrostatic capillary pressure, causing the development of edema. These edematous tissues are poorly oxygenated and receive inadequate nutrition, thus leading to tissue breakdown.

Clinical Manifestations

Clinical manifestations vary depending on whether the PVD is related to arterial insufficiency or venous insufficiency.

Arterial Insufficiency

The classic clinical manifestation of PVD related to **arterial insufficiency** is **intermittent claudication**, which is ischemic pain that develops with activity and is relieved by rest. As the occlusion becomes more severe, pain will occur at rest and, frequently, at night. The pain can become sharp and unrelenting. The temperature of the extremity may be cool, with pale skin color when the legs are elevated. When the legs are in a dependent position, a reddish discoloration (**rubor**) can develop. Numbness and tingling in the extremities may also occur. Additional clinical manifestations include dry skin, diminished hair growth over the toes and dorsum of the foot, and decreased or absent peripheral pulses. Nails will be thick and brittle. Arterial ulcers can develop, usually on or between the toes and on the heel.

Venous Insufficiency

The clinical manifestations of PVD related to **venous insufficiency** include an aching or cramping sensation of pain. The skin may become pigmented in the area of the medial and lateral malleolus, usually in a tawny or reddish-blue color. The skin is thickened and feels tough. Peripheral pulses are present, but the peripheral edema that is also typical of venous insufficiency can make the pulses difficult to palpate. Stasis dermatitis may also occur. Venous ulcers can develop, usually on the medial malleolus.

Diagnostic Tests

Noninvasive tests that are used to diagnose PVD are the **Doppler ultrasound flow study** and the **Duplex ultrasound**. Exercise testing can also be conducted to determine the extent of arterial obstruction. Invasive testing includes angiography, which is used to determine the location and extent of the disease. Venography can be done to diagnose the extent of venous insufficiency.

The **ankle-brachial index (ABI)** is the ratio of ankle systolic blood pressure to the systolic blood pressure of the arm. Using a Doppler device and blood pressure cuff, the systolic blood pressure of the posterior tibialis and dorsalis pedis is obtained. Normally, the systolic pressure in the ankle should be equal to or slightly higher than the brachial blood pressure. In that case, the ratio is 1.0. Patients with claudication have a ratio less than 1.0.

Medical Management

Medical management of PVD related to arterial disorders includes modification of risk factors, drug therapy, and surgical intervention. Patients are encouraged to eliminate smoking and adopt a low-fat, low-cholesterol diet. An exercise program that will increase circulation, such as walking, will also be encouraged.

Drug therapy includes medications that will improve blood flow and prevent the development of clot formation. Vasodilators and antiplatelet medications may be prescribed. These medications may also be used after arterial bypass surgery to prevent occlusion of the graft.

Surgical intervention usually consists of arterial bypass surgery to supply an adequate blood flow around the area of obstruction. **Femoral-popliteal bypass** is a common surgical procedure used to treat PVD. An **endarterectomy**, which is the removal of the atherosclerotic plaque from the vessel, may also be performed.

Nursing Process: Assessment

The nursing assessment of the patient with PVD includes identifying risk factors the patient may have, such as smoking and diet, as well as any history of predisposing chronic illnesses such as hypertension, coronary artery disease, and diabetes. The nurse should assess the patient's activity levels and whether any leg pain develops with exercise or activity. The nurse should also question the patient about any numbness or tingling in the extremities.

Assessment of the lower extremities includes palpation of peripheral pulses and assessment of the appearance of the skin, hair, and nails. Any discoloration of the skin should be noted, as well as the presence of edema. The patient's legs should be inspected in positions of dependence and elevation to note any temperature and color changes. The skin should be inspected for evidence of breakdown or ulcerations.

Nursing Process: Nursing Diagnosis and Planning

Based upon an analysis of the gathered data, the following **nursing diagnoses** may be appropriate for the patient with PVD related to arterial or venous insufficiency:

- Altered tissue perfusion related to obstructed arterial (venous) blood flow
- Risk for impaired skin integrity related to tissue ischemia
- Pain in lower extremities related to inadequate tissue oxygenation
- Knowledge deficit regarding the disease process and treatment regimen

Primary goals for the patient with PVD include the following:

- Promotion of adequate tissue perfusion
- Relief of ischemic pain

- Maintenance of lower extremity tissue integrity
- Adherence to prescribed therapeutic regimen

Nursing Process: Implementation

Nursing interventions for PVD are similar for patients with arterial and venous insufficiency. Nursing interventions should be designed to promote peripheral circulation and tissue perfusion, relieve pain, and maintain tissue integrity.

The nurse should provide patient education that encourages the patient to promote tissue perfusion and relieve pain:

- Maintain the warmth of the extremities through the use of socks and blankets.
- Avoid constrictive clothing.
- Position the legs in a position of slight dependence for arterial insufficiency, and elevation for venous insufficiency and edema.
- Avoid pressure on the arteries and veins in the legs.
- Eliminate smoking.
- Participate in a walking program.
- Avoid prolonged standing or sitting.
- Perform active postural exercise to encourage arterial blood flow. **Buerger-Allen exercises** are an example of active postural exercise in which the patient lies with legs elevated for two to three minutes, then sits with legs dependent for three minutes will exercising the feet, and then lies flat with legs level for about five minutes. This routine is repeated about six times, usually four times a day.

Tissue integrity can be maintained by doing the following:

- Wearing well-fitting shoes
- Avoiding the use of heating pads
- Avoiding extremes of temperature
- Inspecting the extremities daily for redness, irritation, skin breakdown, and/or injuries
- Cleansing the feet gently and drying thoroughly

When patients undergo surgical intervention to improve circulation, the nurse is primarily concerned with maintaining circulation postoperatively. The nurse should assess the extremity's pulses, temperature, color, capillary refill, and sensory and motor functions hourly for twenty-four hours postoperatively. Leg crossing is discouraged to avoid compromising circulation.

Nursing Process: Evaluation

The effectiveness of nursing interventions can be measured by the achievement of the following **expected outcomes** by the patient:

- Maintenance of tissue integrity
- Relief of pain
- Improved peripheral circulation
- Adequate knowledge of therapeutic regimen and self-care activities

Varicose Veins

Varicosities, or **varicose veins**, are veins that become dilated and tortuous as a result of incompetent valves. Due to the valvular incompetence, blood pools in the veins resulting in venous stasis and enlargement of the affected vessels. The condition can develop in superficial or deep veins, and it most commonly occurs in the lower extremities, although varicosities occur in any veins. One risk factor for the development of varicosities is prolonged standing.

Patients with varicose veins usually complain of **dull pain** in the extremity. They may also experience **muscle cramps** and a **sense of heaviness** in the affected extremity. Signs of chronic venous insufficiency may also develop. Varicose veins are diagnosed with the use of the **duplex scan** that demonstrates backflow and pooling of the venous blood flow.

Prevention of varicose veins includes avoiding any activities that promote the constriction of venous blood flow. Standing in a stationary position, crossing legs, wearing tight socks or hosiery are examples of such activities. Walking and swimming are beneficial activities that help promote circulation. If the patient is overweight, they should be encouraged to lose weight.

Varicose veins that are problematic can be treated either by **vein ligation** or **sclerotherapy**. In vein ligation, a small incision is made in the groin and another incision is made near the ankle. The saphenous vein is then cut (ligated) and "stripped" out through the incision. Smaller varicosities can be treated with sclerotherapy, which involves injecting a chemical into the vein to irritate the vessel and cause sclerosing, or closure of the vein's lumen.

Most patients who have vein ligation surgery are treated as outpatients or discharged the following day. The patient is kept on bed rest for approximately twenty-four hours and then encouraged to walk for about ten minutes every two hours to promote circulation. Elastic stockings will be used to promote circulation and maintain compression. Dressings are inspected for bleeding and the incision lines are kept clean and dry. The nurse instructs the patient to elevate the legs when lying down and to avoid standing and sitting for long periods. Analgesics are administered for pain control. Long-term care includes the use of elastic stockings and leg exercises to promote circulation.

Aortic Aneurysm

Aortic aneurysms are dilations of the aorta at weakened areas in the vessel. The weakening and dilation of the vessel wall is usually due to atherosclerosis. Aneurysms can continue to enlarge until they rupture. If an aneurysm ruptures, it is a medical emergency due to hemorrhage that can quickly lead to death. Aneurysms are most common in middle-aged and elderly males. A common site for an aneurysm to develop is in the **abdominal aorta** below the renal arteries.

An individual with an abdominal aortic aneurysm may or may not have symptoms. Symptoms include a throbbing in the abdominal area or a sensation of feeling the heart beating in the abdomen.

The aneurysm can be palpated as a pulsing mass. A bruit can be auscultated over the area. **CT scans** are used to definitively identify location and size of the aneurysm. The aneurysm is monitored closely over a period of time to determine how quickly it is enlarging and when surgery will be most desirable. The goal is to perform surgery prior to rupture. Surgery is usually performed when the aneurysm reaches two inches in diameter, or if it begins to enlarge rapidly.

Surgery involves resecting the aneurysm and inserting a bypass graft. While a major surgery, elective aneurysm surgery has a high rate of success. Surgery performed after rupture of the aneurysm carries a high mortality rate of 50 to 75 percent.

Preoperative nursing care of a patient with an aneurysm includes closely monitoring the patient for a rupture. When a patient with an aneurysm complains of severe back or abdominal pain, this can be a sign of impending rupture. If the aneurysm ruptures, the patient will experience a rapid drop in blood pressure as they hemorrhage. Immediate surgery is required. Postoperative nursing care of patients who are recovering from aortic aneurysm surgery includes monitoring the cardiovascular, renal, pulmonary, and cerebral status of the patient. Patients will be cared for in an intensive care unit immediately following surgery. Complications of surgery include infection, hemorrhage, and renal impairment or ischemic colon due to interrupted blood flow.

Chapter 13 Study Questions

1.   Identify the risk factors for hypertension.

2.   Describe the lifestyle adjustments recommended for a patient with hypertension.

3.   What are the potential complications of hypertension?

4.   What is a common side effect of thiazide and loop diuretics?

5.   Describe the clinical manifestations of peripheral vascular disease (PVD) that result from obstructed arterial blood flow.

6.   Describe the clinical manifestations of peripheral vascular disease (PVD) that result from obstructed venous blood flow.

7.   Identify three nursing diagnoses appropriate for a patient with PVD.

8.   What nursing interventions are appropriate for maintaining tissue integrity in a patient with PVD?

9.   What nursing assessments are priorities for a patient who has had a femoral-popliteal bypass graft?

Answers to Chapter 13 Study Questions

1. Risk factors for hypertension include family history, age and gender (increase with age and in males), obesity, sedentary lifestyle, smoking and alcohol intake, and atherosclerosis.

2. Stop smoking and reducing alcohol intake; reduce and managing stress; modify the diet to decrease fat, cholesterol, and sodium intake; lose weight as needed; and incorporate aerobic exercise into schedule. Taking prescribed medications and routinely monitoring blood pressure are other important adjustments for the patient to make.

3. Hypertension is potentially complicated by left ventricular hypertrophy and heart failure, cerebrovascular disease, peripheral vascular disease, retinopathy, and renal damage.

4. Potassium depletion (hypokalemia) is a side effect of thiazide and loop diuretics.

5. The classic clinical manifestation of PVD that is related to obstructed arterial blood flow is intermittent claudication, which is ischemic pain that develops with activity and is relieved by rest. As the occlusion becomes more severe, pain will occur at rest and, frequently, at night. The temperature of the extremity may be cool, with pale skin color. When the legs are in a dependent position, a reddish discoloration (rubor) can develop. Numbness and tingling in the extremities may also occur. Additional clinical manifestations include dry skin, diminished hair growth, and decreased or absent peripheral pulses. Nails will be thick and brittle.

6. The clinical manifestations of PVD related to venous insufficiency include an aching or cramping sensation of pain. The skin may become pigmented in the area of the medial and lateral malleolus, usually in a brawny or reddish-blue color. The skin is thickened and feels tough. Peripheral pulses are present, but the peripheral edema that is also typical of venous insufficiency can make the pulses difficult to palpate. Stasis dermatitis may also occur. Venous ulcers can develop, usually on the medial malleolus.

7. Three nursing diagnoses are as follows: altered tissue perfusion related to obstructed arterial (venous) blood flow; risk for impaired skin integrity related to ischemia; and pain in the lower extremities related to inadequate tissue oxygenation.

8. Wear well-fitting shoes; avoid the use of heating pads; avoid extremes of temperature; inspect the extremities daily for redness, irritation, and injuries; and cleanse the feet gently, drying thoroughly.

9. When patients undergo surgical intervention to improve circulation, the nurse is primarily concerned with maintaining circulation postoperatively. The nurse

should assess the extremity's pulses, temperature, color, capillary refill, and sensory and motor functions hourly for twenty-four hours postoperatively. Leg crossing is discouraged to avoid compromising circulation.

Chapter 14: Nursing Care for Hematologic Disorders

Key Terms

Anemia
    Acute hemorrhagic anemia
    Iron-deficiency anemia
    Pernicious anemia
    Sickle-cell anemia
Disseminated intravascular coagulation
Hemophilia
Idiopathic thrombocytopenic purpura
Polycythemia vera
Schilling test
Sickle-cell crisis

Introduction

This chapter will focus on the nursing care of the patient with hematological disorders, most specifically patients with anemia or alterations in coagulation. Specific disorders covered in this chapter of the study guide include acute hemorrhagic anemia, iron-deficiency anemia, pernicious anemia, and sickle-cell anemia. Blood coagulation disorders that are discussed include disseminated intravascular coagulation (DIC), hemophilia, polycythemia vera, and thrombocytopenia purpura. (Other hematological disorders such as leukemia and lymphoma are covered in unit 4.)

Anemias

Anemia is a term used to refer to a condition in which there are fewer than normal circulating red blood cells (RBCs), causing hemoglobin levels to be decreased. The decrease in hemoglobin levels causes a decrease in the amount of oxygen carried to tissue cells. Since anemia is the most common hematological disorder, the nurse can anticipate caring for many patients, both outpatient and hospitalized, who are suffering from anemia.

Anemia is caused by a variety of underlying disorders. There are essentially three categories of anemia:

- Loss of RBCs through bleeding (GI bleeding, trauma, and excessive menstrual flow are common causes of acute hemorrhagic anemia)
- Decreased production of RBCs (**hypoproliferative**—inadequate numbers of RBCs are produced to meet the body's need)
- Increased destruction of RBCs (**hemolytic**—RBCs are prematurely destroyed)

Examples of hypoproliferative anemias include iron-deficiency, pernicious, and folate-deficiency anemias. An example of a hemolytic anemia is sickle-cell anemia, which is a hereditary disorder.

Acute Hemorrhagic Anemia

Acute hemorrhagic anemia is caused by acute blood loss that leads to a decrease in RBCs. Common causes of acute blood loss include surgery, trauma, and coagulation disorders. Clinical manifestations of acute hemorrhagic anemia include weakness; hypotension; cool, clammy skin; tachycardia; irritability; and restlessness. These signs and symptoms are related to hypovolemia. If not corrected, hypovolemic shock can develop. Hypoxemia can also develop. Hemoglobin and hematocrit will be decreased. Care of the patient will include blood and fluid replacement therapy. The care of the patient with hypovolemic shock is covered in chapter 15.

Iron-Deficiency Anemia

Iron-deficiency anemia is the most common form of anemia in the world. It affects all age groups. Inadequate intake of iron in the diet is the most common cause of iron-deficiency anemia in children, teenagers, and women who are pregnant. Blood-sucking parasites, such as hookworms, can also cause iron-deficiency anemia. Excessive blood loss through menstruation is another common cause, as is chronic blood loss from the GI tract, which leads to the loss of iron.

Pathophysiology

A typical diet contains 12 to 15 mg/day of iron. Approximately 5 percent to 10 percent of this daily intake is absorbed. This amount of absorption can meet the needs of men and women past childbearing age, but it is insufficient to meet the nutritional needs of children, adolescents, or menstruating or pregnant women. The elderly, especially the poor elderly, are also prone to iron-deficiency anemia due to their poor nutritional intake.

Iron is normally stored in the reticuloendothelial cells of the spleen, liver, and bone marrow as **ferritin**. It is excreted in feces, urine, sweat, and bile. Women also lose iron during menstruation, which is the most common cause of iron-deficiency anemia in women. GI bleeding is a common cause for anemia in men. The use of aspirin products and nonsteroidal anti-inflammatory drugs also can lead to GI irritation, blood loss, and anemia. The GI bleeding is usually occult (can not be seen by the eye) and chronic in nature, but only a small amount of daily chronic blood loss can lead to the development of anemia. Iron absorption can also be decreased if there is an alteration in the mucosa of the small intestine. Chronic alcoholism can cause anemia due to GI irritation and blood loss.

Clinical Manifestations

The patient may be asymptomatic if the case of anemia is mild. Clinical manifestations of more serious cases of anemia can include the following:

- Pallor of skin and mucous membranes

- Sensitivity to cold
- Weakness, fatigue, malaise
- Tachycardia, palpitations, dizziness
- Orthopnea, exertion dyspnea
- Headache, numbness/tingling of extremities
- Brittle nails and hair (later stage of the disorder)
- Unusual cravings of ice, starch, or dirt (**pica**)
- Smooth, red tongue (severe cases)

Diagnostic Tests

Laboratory tests are conducted, including hemoglobin, hematocrit, and red blood cell count, all of which will be low. The mean corpuscular volume (MCV), mean corpuscular hemoglobin (MCH), and mean corpuscular hemoglobin concentration (MCHC) will be decreased. Serum iron level, total iron-binding capacity (TIBC), iron saturation, and ferritin levels are also obtained. These levels will usually be decreased, with the exception of the TIBC, which will be increased.

A bone marrow aspiration may also be performed. Other diagnostic tests will likely be ordered to help determine the underlying cause of the anemia. These tests will likely focus on the GI tract and may include obtaining a stool specimen for occult blood, upper GI and lower GI X ray studies, and performing a colonoscopy or endoscopy to rule out ulcers, gastritis, ulcerative colitis, polyps, and cancer.

Medical Management

The goal of medical management will be to treat the underlying cause of the anemia and restore iron levels to normal. **Iron supplements** will be ordered, usually in oral form. **Iron dextran (Imferon)** may be ordered IM or IV if the patient cannot absorb iron orally or requires a large amount of iron replacement. The patient will be instructed to increase iron intake in the diet.

Nursing Process: Assessment

The nursing assessment should focus on collecting subjective data about the person's usual diet, history of alcohol intake, medications, and any history of any gastrointestinal symptoms, including nausea, vomiting, or presence of tarry stools.

The cardiac status of the patient should also be assessed, especially noting the patient's tolerance for activity, presence of dyspnea during exertion, dizziness, tachycardia, and palpitations. An assessment of the integumentary system should also be completed, noting pallor; stomatitis; red, beefy tongue; brittle nails or hair; or sensitivity to cold. A woman's history of menstrual bleeding should be assessed.

Nursing Process: Nursing Diagnosis and Planning

Based upon an analysis of the gathered data, the following **nursing diagnoses** may be appropriate for the patient with anemia:

- Altered nutrition, less than body requirements related to lack of knowledge regarding adequate dietary iron intake or disease process
- Activity intolerance related to fatigue, weakness
- Altered tissue perfusion related to decreased oxygen-carrying capacity
- Ineffective management of therapeutic regimen related to a lack of knowledge regarding dietary and drug therapy

Primary goals for the patient with anemia include the following:

- Maintenance adequate nutritional intake of iron
- Regain tolerance for normal levels of activity
- Maintenance of adequate tissue perfusion
- Adherence to prescribed therapeutic regimen

Nursing Process: Implementation

Patient teaching is an important nursing intervention in preventing the development of anemia and in caring for the patient with anemia. The nurse should emphasize intake of adequate amounts of iron in the daily diet. Food sources that are high in iron include leafy green vegetables, organ meat (liver), lean meats, beans, egg yolks, carrots, apricots, and raisins. Patients who eat a vegetarian diet, menstruating women, and pregnant women are at high risk for being iron deficient and need to pay particular attention to eating foods high in iron.

If the patient is suffering from fatigue and weakness, the nurse can help the patient balance rest and exercise. Physical activity should be encouraged within the patient's level of tolerance. Activities may need to be prioritized. As the iron deficiency is corrected, the patient's energy level should return.

The nurse should teach the patient how to take the iron supplement correctly. Information about administering oral iron supplements or intramuscular iron injections can be found in chapter 10. The nurse should tell the patient that oral iron supplements could turn the stool dark green or black. The patient should be instructed to continue taking the iron supplement, even if the feelings of fatigue are gone.

If **intravenous iron dextran** is prescribed, a small test dose will be administered first to check the patient for an allergic, anaphylactic reaction.

In patients with severe anemia, supplemental oxygen may need to be provided to meet the oxygenation demands of the body. Complications of iron-deficiency anemia are rare, but do include the development of congestive heart failure.

Nursing Process: Evaluation

The effectiveness of nursing interventions can be measured by the achievement of the following **expected outcomes** by the patient:

- Maintains adequate intake of iron from diet and supplements
- Tolerates normal level of activity without fatigue, weakness
- Maintains adequate tissue perfusion
- Adheres to prescribed therapy

The patient should anticipate that it could take some time to resolve the anemia, especially if the underlying cause is not determined. Follow-up office visits will be necessary to monitor the effectiveness of the therapy and to detect any reoccurrence of the anemia.

Pernicious Anemia

Pernicious anemia is a chronic, megaloblastic anemia that usually develops in middle-aged individuals, although there is also a rare juvenile form of pernicious anemia. It is the result of an inability to absorb oral vitamin B_{12} from the gastrointestinal tract.

Pathophysiology

In pernicious anemia, the intrinsic factor that enables oral vitamin B_{12} to be absorbed is missing. The intrinsic factor is normally secreted from the gastric mucosal cells; it binds with vitamin B_{12} and carries it to the ileum, where the vitamin is subsequently absorbed. Vitamin B_{12} is one of the vitamins required for erythropoiesis (the development of RBCs). A lack of vitamin B_{12} will decrease the formation of RBCs, leading to the development of anemia.

It is not known why some individuals develop a lack of intrinsic factor. Heredity could play a role. In some cases, it is a congenital disorder. However, a common cause of pernicious anemia is gastric resection. In a gastric resection, the part of the stomach that secretes the intrinsic factor is removed, resulting in a loss of intrinsic factor and the development of pernicious anemia.

Clinical Manifestations

Clinical manifestations of pernicious anemia do not develop until the body's store of vitamin B_{12} is depleted. Onset of manifestations is gradual. The patient may complain of weakness, fatigue, and lethargy. Skin pallor is common.

In pernicious anemia, the gastrointestinal tract and the nervous system are particularly affected. The patient develops diarrhea and a smooth, red, sore tongue. Numbness and tingling of the lower legs and feet are common. The patient may experience a loss of balance and demonstrate confusion. Congestive heart failure can develop as the disorder progresses. Pernicious anemia can be fatal if untreated.

Diagnostic Tests

Pernicious anemia is diagnosed partly through blood tests that confirm a decreased hemoglobin, hematocrit, and red blood cell count. The definitive test for pernicious anemia is the **Schilling test**. In the Schilling test, a radioactive oral dose of vitamin B_{12} is administered without a parenteral dose of the intrinsic factor and then with a parenteral dose of the intrinsic factor. If the vitamin is absorbed and excreted from the urine after the administration of the intrinsic factor, then a diagnosis of pernicious anemia can be made.

Medical Management

Patients who are diagnosed with pernicious anemia need a lifetime replacement of vitamin B_{12}. Monthly intramuscular injections of the vitamin will be necessary. Response to the injections is usually rapid, with the patient demonstrating fewer symptoms within seventy-two hours. Even with treatment, severe neuropathy may remain, leading to a permanent disability.

Nursing Management

Nursing management of pernicious anemia is similar to that of iron-deficiency anemia. Cardiac status is closely monitored. A careful neurological assessment is also essential, especially noting the patient's gait and stability.

Patient teaching is another essential component of the patient's care. The patient must understand the need to maintain lifelong drug therapy for treatment of the anemia. The patient can be taught to self-administer the intramuscular injection. The importance of follow-up care must be emphasized.

Activity must be balanced with periods of rest while the patient remains symptomatic. If the patient has experienced neurological damage, assistive devices may be needed to help with ambulation. Rehabilitation may also be necessary.

Sickle-Cell Anemia

Sickle-cell anemia is a chronic, hereditary, hemolytic anemia. Individuals inherit a sickle hemoglobin gene (HbS). It is most common in those individuals of African descent and in some individuals from the Middle East and Mediterranean regions, as well as India and the Caribbean. Sickle-cell anemia is usually diagnosed in early childhood, when the child exhibits severe anemia. It is a complex disorder and a major health problem in the United States. It can be fatal.

Pathophysiology

In sickle-cell anemia, the HbS gene causes red blood cells to become crescent-shaped ("sickle") when the oxygen level in the blood decreases. When the cells sickle, they lose their round, flexible shape and become rigid and deformed. This rigid, deformed shape causes the cells to become lodged in small vessels, obstructing blood flow and leading to hypoxia. The viscosity of the blood also increases, causing blood flow to get sluggish. Ischemia, infarction, and necrosis develop in the areas where the blood flow is obstructed; areas most likely to be affected by infarction and necrosis are the kidneys, brain, bone marrow, and spleen.

The **vaso-occlusive process** described above is the most common cause of a **sickle-cell crisis**. A sickle-cell crisis results in significant pain. A sickle-cell crisis can be brought on by any factor that lowers the oxygen tension level of the RBCs. Examples of some factors are infection, stress, alcohol, smoking, overexertion, cold weather, dehydration, and high altitudes. The frequency with which a patient experiences a sickle-cell crisis varies significantly. Some patients have monthly crises, while others may only experience one or two annual episodes. Each crisis lasts from one to ten days, although this can vary. A patient in sickle-cell crisis is hospitalized.

A sickle-cell crisis may also be **megaloblastic**, **aplastic**, or **splenic sequestration**.

- A **megaloblastic** crisis occurs when folic acid levels are decreased.
- **Aplastic** sickle-cell crisis is most often caused by an infection and results in a temporary decrease in the production of RBCs.
- **Splenic sequestration** crisis develops when the spleen pools the sickled cells, which leads to hypovolemic shock.

The complications of sickle-cell anemia are numerous. Splenic infarctions are common, causing the spleen to become nonfunctional and increasing the individual's risk for infection. Pulmonary infarctions, cerebrovascular accidents, and myocardial infarctions are also common. Osteomyelitis and avascular necrosis can develop. Leg ulcers develop and are difficult to heal. Individuals may also experience retinal detachment and blindness.

Many children die as a result of infection, cerebrovascular hemorrhaging, or shock. Those who survive childhood frequently die by middle age. Death in older patients is usually caused by renal damage and failure.

Clinical Manifestations

All body organs and tissues can be affected by sickle-cell anemia. The disease is usually diagnosed in early childhood, although some individuals are not symptomatic until adulthood. The child's growth will be stunted, and the skull and facial bones may be enlarged due to hyperactivity of the bone marrow. Chronic anemia develops. Tachycardia and heart murmurs may be present. The heart may be enlarged, and heart failure can eventually develop. Jaundice, evident in the sclera, is a characteristic finding. Priapism (painful, prolonged erection) can occur, and eventually, impotence may develop.

A patient who is in sickle-cell crisis will have joint pain and swelling, back and chest pain, and low-grade temperature. Dyspnea may also be present. Since any and all organs can be involved, a careful assessment of all body systems is essential.

Diagnostic Tests

Sickle-cell anemia is diagnosed by laboratory tests. Patients will have a low hematocrit. A stained blood smear will provide evidence of sickle cells. Diagnosis of sickle-cell anemia is confirmed by hemoglobin electrophoresis. It is recommended that all newborns of high-risk populations have routine screening for sickle-cell anemia.

Medical Management

Medical management of sickle-cell anemia focuses primarily on supportive care and symptomatic management. There are currently few medications that can be used to treat sickle-cell anemia. Treatment of sickle-cell anemia is the subject of much research.

Current treatment includes the use of **hydroxyurea**, which is a chemotherapeutic agent. Hydroxyurea increases the level of fetal hemoglobin and reduces hemolysis and the formation of sickled cells. Supplemental vitamins and minerals such as iron, folic acid, and vitamin B_{12} may also be given to stimulate RBC production. Antibiotics are used to treat infections promptly, thus avoiding a potential crisis. Analgesics are used for chronic pain control and during a crisis. Narcotics are administered to treat the pain experienced during a crisis. Nonsteroidal anti-inflammatories and aspirin are commonly used for more moderate pain.

Blood transfusions may be used to prevent severe anemia or to prevent complications during times of anticipated physical stressors (e.g., surgery, anesthesia, infection, pregnancy). Bone marrow transplant (BMT) holds some promise for a cure; however, only a small percentage of individuals can benefit from BMT due to the lack of compatible donors or the preexisting organ damage that many individuals have already experienced.

During an acute crisis, the main goals of treatment are to control pain and hydrate the patient. Supplemental oxygen is administered.

Nursing Process: Assessment

Subjective data that is gathered by the nurse includes information about the patient's understanding of the disease process and knowledge of self-care activities. Feelings of powerlessness, hopelessness, and lowered self-esteem may be expressed. The nurse should assess pain characteristics and methods of pain control. The nurse should explore the impact of the disease on the patient's ability to carry out the activities of daily living.

Objective data collection focuses on vital signs; integumentary findings (swollen, painful joints; leg ulcers); respiratory findings (dyspnea, chest pain, breath sounds, cyanosis); and cardiac status (arrhythmias, murmurs, tachycardia, enlarged heart, edema). The patient's renal functioning should also be monitored through BUN and creatinine laboratory values. The patient should be assessed for signs of dehydration. Urinary output, presence of edema, skin turgor, and examination of mucous membranes can provide information about the fluid status of the patient. The patient should also be assessed for indications of cerebral hypoxia. While these assessments are pertinent at any point in the patient's care, they are especially important during an episode of sickle-cell crisis.

Nursing Process: Nursing Diagnosis and Planning

Nursing diagnoses for sickle-cell anemia are numerous and are dependent upon the patient's clinical progression. However, based upon an analysis of the gathered data, the following nursing diagnoses may be appropriate for the patient with sickle-cell anemia:

- Pain related to tissue hypoxia
- Impaired gas exchange related to ventilation/perfusion mismatch
- Activity intolerance related to pain and inadequate tissue oxygenation
- Risk for infection related to decreased immune response
- Ineffective management of therapeutic regimen related to a lack of knowledge regarding treatment
- Ineffective coping (individual) related to chronic pain, potential or actual disability

Primary goals for the patient with sickle-cell anemia include the following:

- Relief from pain
- Improved gas exchange
- Improved activity tolerance
- Maintenance of adequate tissue perfusion
- Prevention of infection
- Prevention of sickle-cell crisis episodes
- Adherence to prescribed therapeutic regimen
- Improved coping effectiveness

Nursing Process: Implementation

Nursing care will vary depending upon the patient's condition and the presence of complications. During an acute sickle-cell crisis, the nurse's main goal is to manage the patient's pain, which can be severe. Prompt administration of analgesics is necessary. Supportive measures to be used in conjunction with pain medication include relaxation techniques, distraction, and breathing exercises. Swollen, painful joints should be carefully supported and elevated.

Aggressive fluid replacement may be necessary to prevent dehydration and minimize blood viscosity and sluggish blood flow. Unless contraindicated, the patient should receive six to eight liters of fluid a day during a crisis. This fluid can be oral or intravenous.

Preventing infection is another important aspect of care. The patient should be monitored carefully for early signs of an infection, especially in the respiratory or urinary tracts.

Activity is encouraged within the patient's level of tolerance and should be balanced with periods of rest to minimize dyspnea and fatigue.

Patient and family education is an essential aspect of the nursing care. Genetic counseling and family planning should be recommended for the patient and significant others to consider. The nurse can help the patient locate appropriate community resources to help guide decision-making in these areas. The patient should also be taught appropriate self-care activities. Avoiding smoking and alcohol and effective stress management are positive lifestyle adjustments. The patient should maintain an adequate fluid intake, minimize exposure to infection, and avoid overexertion. Patients may find support groups helpful and should be encouraged to discuss their concerns.

Nursing Process: Evaluation

The effectiveness of nursing interventions can be measured by the achievement of the following **expected outcomes** by the patient:

- Verbalizes satisfactory control of pain
- Respirations are regular and relaxed
- Tolerates activities of daily living with comfort
- Demonstrates adequate tissue perfusion
- Remains free of infection
- Minimizes occurrence of sickle-cell crises
- Demonstrates appropriate self-care activities in following prescribed treatment regimen
- Verbalizes effective coping skills

Coagulation Disorders

Coagulation disorders may affect platelets or clotting factors. These disorders can result in increased blood clotting or decreased blood clotting, depending upon the nature of the disorder. Many coagulation disorders are chronic conditions that require lifelong treatment. Coagulation disorders can be life threatening. While there are many coagulation disorders, this study guide will focus on hemophilia, disseminated intravascular coagulation, polycythemia vera, and thrombocytopenia purpura as some of the more common forms.

Hemophilia

Hemophilia is a hereditary bleeding disorder that can lead to hemorrhage, even with minimal trauma. It affects males through an X-linked recessive trait, although females can be carriers. Hemophilia is usually diagnosed when the child enters the toddler years and begins to experience falls and other minor traumas. Hemophilia is not that common; the most common form of hemophilia, hemophilia A, occurs in 1 in 10,000 births. Hemophilia can range from mild to life threatening. Hemophilia can be treated, but it cannot be cured.

Pathophysiology

There are two forms of hemophilia:

- **Hemophilia A** is the most common form and is caused by a genetic deficiency of clotting factor VIII.
- **Hemophilia B** is caused by a genetic deficiency of clotting factor IX.

The decreased amount of factors VIII or IX make it difficult or even impossible for blood to coagulate following trauma to the tissues. The more severe the factor deficiency, the more severe the clotting disorder.

Clinical Manifestations

Hemophilia is manifested by prolonged bleeding that may occur anywhere in the body. The joints are one of the most common sites for internal bleeding to occur, with approximately 75 percent of all hemorrhages occurring in the joints. Bleeding into the joints is called **hemarthrosis**. Knees, ankles, hips, shoulders, elbows, and wrists are the most frequently affected joints. Bleeding can occur into muscles as well. The bleeding leads to joint pain, swelling, and limitation of movement. Repeated episodes of bleeding can lead to crippling fixation, or **ankylosis**, of the joint.

The seriousness of the bleeding episode will depend upon the extent of the factor deficiency, the seriousness of the trauma, and the location of the bleeding. The most dangerous sites for hemorrhage include the neck, chest, and oral cavity (due to potential airway obstruction), and the brain. Hemorrhage into the brain is a major cause of death. Bleeding into tissues can be subtle and difficult to detect. The nurse needs to be alert to changes in the patient's condition that indicate that bleeding is occurring, such as headache, lethargy, or changes in the level of consciousness.

Other clinical manifestations can include anemia and tarry stools from gastrointestinal bleeding, hematuria, extensive bruising, and hematomas.

Diagnostic Tests

Hemophilia is diagnosed by repeated bleeding episodes and laboratory blood assay tests that detect the presence of a factor deficiency. DNA genetic testing can be conducted for women to determine if they are carriers, and it is recommended for women whose family history indicates that there is a possibility they may be carriers.

Medical Management

The primary treatment for hemophilia is the administration of the appropriate clotting factor, either factor VIII or factor IX. These factor concentrations are administered intravenously to treat bleeding episodes or prophylactically administered prior to anticipated trauma episodes, such as surgery or dental extraction. Families and older children are taught to self-administer the factor concentrates to avoid delays in treatment and complications.

DDAVP (Desmopressin), a synthetic drug that raises factor VIII levels, is administered effectively in cases of mild hemophilia. **Aminocaproic acid (Amicar)** is used to slow down dissolution of blood clots, especially after oral surgery.

Nursing Management

Major nursing goals related to the care of the patient with hemophilia are the following:

- Prevent bleeding
- Recognize early symptoms of bleeding to achieve maximum control
- Prevent complications related to bleeding
- Support the patient and his family in acquiring appropriate self-care skills

Patient education is an essential nursing intervention to help the patient achieve a satisfactory quality of life. The nurse can help the child prevent bleeding episodes by teaching the child and family about the appropriate types of physical limitations. Contact sports should be avoided and noncontact sports encouraged. The need for protective padding during activities should be emphasized. For the toddler, restriction of activities can affect normal growth and development. Therefore, the usual approach is to "safety proof" the environment and supervise the child's play closely to minimize the chances of trauma.

Medications that affect blood clotting, such as aspirin and NSAID's, should not be taken. Using a soft-bristled toothbrush and a water-pick device can minimize oral bleeding. Invasive procedures, such as an IM, are avoided as much as possible. The child should be taught to wear a medical alert tag and disclose his medical condition in anticipation of situations that may cause bleeding, such as dental examinations.

Early recognition of bleeding helps to maximize bleeding control and minimize complications. Patients and their families should be instructed in how to recognize the signs of hemorrhage and what steps to take to control the bleeding. In addition to administering the factor concentrate, the child is instructed to rest, elevate and immobilize the affected joint, if possible, and apply pressure and ice. Active ROM should be implemented following acute bleeding episodes to help prevent the development of joint deformities.

Due to advancements in treatment, the prognosis of hemophilia is much more positive than in the past. While the risk of acquiring HIV from concentrate infusion was relatively significant prior to 1985, today's purification techniques have almost completely eliminated this risk. Children can enjoy a relatively normal life with the implementation of some preventive measures. Helping the child to assume responsibility for his care will help him achieve independence and successfully cope with this chronic disorder. One significant source of concern is financial costs. **Support groups** can be an effective source of information. The National Hemophilia Foundation is another resource that families may find useful. **Genetic counseling** for the parents and the child is beneficial for addressing future plans for childbearing.

Disseminated Intravascular Coagulation

Disseminated intravascular coagulation (DIC) is a complex disorder that occurs in response to an underlying primary disease. Common precipitating factors include, but are not limited to, sepsis, trauma, extensive burns, cancer and leukemias, obstetric complications, and shock. It is a life-threatening disorder, with death resulting from hemorrhage or multiple organ failure. The mortality rate varies, but it can be over 80 percent.

Pathophysiology

DIC is an imbalance between coagulation and anticoagulation. There is an extensive formation of tiny clots throughout the body, only to be followed by extensive bleeding.

In DIC, the underlying precipitating disease causes an activation of thrombin and fibrinogen. Fibrin is deposited throughout the body's microcirculation, resulting in a state of hypercoagulability and the development of a multitude of microthrombi. Platelet aggregation is increased. The small clots continue to develop, obstructing blood flow through vital organs and producing areas of microinfarct and tissue necrosis.

As the clotting process continues, platelets and other clotting factors are consumed, making them unavailable to control coagulation. This predisposes the patient to bleeding. This predisposition to bleeding is further compounded by the activation of the fibrinolytic mechanism, which is a normal response to the excessive clotting that is occurring. The function of the fibrinolytic mechanism is to inhibit clot formation. The combined effect of platelet and clotting factor depletion, plus the breakdown of clots by the fibrinolytic mechanism, leads to a complete loss of blood-clotting ability, and the patient begins to hemorrhage.

Clinical Manifestations

The onset of DIC is sudden. Initially, the signs and symptoms are related to the presence of thrombosis in different organs. Signs and symptoms can include chest pain, tachycardia, dyspnea, tachypnea, pulmonary emboli, confusion, decreased alertness, cyanosis, decreased peripheral pulses, gastric pain, and decreased urinary output with increased BUN and creatinine.

As DIC progresses, bleeding begins. At first the bleeding is minimal, but can eventually develop into hemorrhage. Frank bleeding can occur in all organs and tissues, and the patient will exhibit multiple sites of bleeding: oral, integumentary, gastrointestinal, genitourinary, cerebrovascular, and respiratory. Bleeding from wound sites and puncture sites, as well as from around inserted lines and catheters, will develop.

Diagnostic Tests

Diagnosis of DIC is confirmed by laboratory findings that show a prolonged prothrombin time, partial thromboplastin time, and thrombin time. Fibrinogen and platelet levels are decreased. Fibrin degradation products are elevated.

Medical Management

The first goal of treating DIC is to treat the underlying primary cause. The second goal is to control the bleeding. Fresh frozen plasma, cryoprecipitate, platelets, and whole blood may be given to replace the depleted platelets and clotting factors. Efforts will be made to increase tissue oxygenation and replace fluid loss. A controversial treatment is the administration of heparin to inhibit the clotting process and allow perfusion of vital organs. Use of heparin can cause bleeding to increase.

Nursing Management

Nurses need to identify patients who are at risk for developing DIC and closely monitor them for signs and symptoms of thrombi development and/or bleeding. The patient with DIC is critically ill, and nursing care is challenging. Nursing care will vary depending upon the extent of the disorder and presenting clinical condition.

The major goals of nursing care include maintaining the patient's hemodynamic status and fluid balance, promoting adequate tissue perfusion, and preventing complications. The patient is cared for in an intensive care setting and requires continual monitoring of all systems to detect clinical changes resulting from thrombosis or bleeding. The patient and family members will require significant emotional support during this difficult time.

Polycythemia Vera

Polycythemia vera (PV) is an increase in the volume of red blood cells, platelets, and white blood cells. The cause of PV is unknown. It usually develops in the elderly and is more common in Jewish men. PV is considered a premalignant disorder and can be fatal, with the cause of death due to thrombosis, hemorrhage, or myelogenous leukemia.

Pathophysiology

PV is a bone marrow (myeloproliferative) disorder in which the myeloid stem cells overproduce RBCs, platelets, and WBCs. It is the overproduction of RBCs that is the most prominent. The increased volume of RBCs leads to hypervolemia and increased viscosity. This increased blood thickness and volume leads to organ and tissue congestion. There is an increased risk of blood clot formation. Bleeding can also occur, as the platelets that are formed tend to be large and dysfunctional.

Clinical Manifestations

Initially, the patient will be asymptomatic. Eventually, due to the increase in blood volume, the patient will develop headache, dizziness, blurred vision, and tinnitus. The formation of thromboses and obstruction of blood flow leads to angina, dyspnea, claudication, and thrombophlebitis. Splenomegaly will develop. The patient's complexion may be ruddy. The patient could experience MI, pulmonary embolism, or a stroke. Because of the dysfunctional platelets, nosebleeds, bruising (ecchymoses), and GI bleeding may occur.

Diagnostic Tests

PV is diagnosed through laboratory studies that indicate an elevated hematocrit and increased volume in RBCs. There is an increase in platelets and WBCs. ABGs are normal.

Medical Management

The goals of medical management for PV consist of decreasing blood volume and viscosity. This is achieved through phlebotomy and removal of enough blood to lower the hematocrit to acceptable levels. Phlebotomies are repeated as often as necessary to keep the hematocrit around 45 percent. Eventually, the removal of blood leads to an iron deficiency, which decreases the rate of RBC production. Chemotherapeutic drugs may be administered to suppress bone marrow function. Radiation therapy may also be used to decrease production of RBCs.

Nursing Management

Patient teaching is an important component of the nursing care of patients with PV. PV is a chronic condition, and the patient needs to have a thorough understanding of its treatment. Patients should be instructed about the importance of maintaining an adequate fluid intake to help decrease blood viscosity. Patients should be monitored carefully for clinical signs indicating the development of a thrombosis or bleeding. The nurse should instruct the patient on how to prevent circulatory constriction, so as to not promote the development of blood clots. Using support hose, avoiding crossing the legs or sitting for prolonged periods of time, and ambulating as frequently as possible are important points of care. Patients who are undergoing phlebotomy should be warned not to eat foods high in iron, as this can counteract the effectiveness of the phlebotomy.

Idiopathic Thrombocytopenic Purpura

Idiopathic thrombocytopenic purpura (ITP) affects individuals across the life span. It is most common in children and young women. It may be acute or chronic in nature. The acute form of ITP is self-limiting and occurs most often in children.

Pathophysiology

The cause of ITP is unknown. In children, it is sometimes preceded by a viral infection. Sulfa drugs, alcohol, quinine, aspirin, and NSAIDs are examples of some drugs that have been associated with the development of ITP. Individuals who have an immune system disorder, such as systemic lupus erythematosus or rheumatoid arthritis, may be more likely to develop ITP.

In ITP, the platelets are attacked by antiplatelet autoantibodies and destroyed. In an attempt to compensate for this platelet destruction, the bone marrow increases its production of platelets.

Clinical Manifestations

Patients with ITP may be asymptomatic. Common clinical manifestations include bruising and petechiae. In women, menstrual periods may be heavy. Some individuals may have bleeding from mucosal areas, such as the GI tract, nose, oral mucosa, or the respiratory tract.

Diagnostic Tests

ITP is diagnosed by a decreased platelet count, prolonged bleeding time, and a peripheral blood smear. A bone marrow aspiration may also be performed. If the presence of megakaryocytes (platelet precursors) is noted in the aspirate, it is an indication that the platelets are being destroyed peripherally.

Medical Management

Medical management of ITP can vary. If it is determined that a medication may be causing ITP, the medication will be stopped. Corticosteroids are frequently prescribed and appear to be effective. Intravenous gamma globulin and chemotherapeutic agents may also be successful at inhibiting platelet destruction. Removal of the spleen (splenectomy) is another approach to treatment of ITP. Platelet transfusions are not effective, because the transfused platelets will be rapidly destroyed.

Nursing Management

Patient teaching is an essential component of the nursing care for a patient with ITP. The nurse should instruct the patient to avoid medications that have an anticoagulant effect and medications that can affect platelet production. The nurse should instruct the patient in measures to avoid injury. These measures include brushing with a soft toothbrush; using an electric razor; applying pressure for five to ten minutes if any bleeding occurs; avoiding constipation, rectal temperatures, rectal medications, and enemas; and avoiding contact sports.

Chapter 14 Study Questions

1.   Identify the three categories of anemia.

2.   What are some of the common causes of iron-deficiency anemia?

3.   Describe the diagnostic findings in iron-deficiency anemia.

4.   What foods are good sources of iron for individuals who need to increase their dietary intake of iron?

5.   Describe the pathophysiology of pernicious anemia.

6.   Describe the clinical manifestations of pernicious anemia.

7.   How is pernicious anemia treated?

8.   What is the pathophysiology of sickle-cell anemia?

9.   What factors can precipitate a sickle-cell crisis?

10.   What nursing assessments are appropriate for a patient with sickle-cell anemia?

11.   Briefly describe the nursing care of a patient in sickle-cell crisis.

12.   Develop a patient education plan for a patient with sickle-cell anemia.

13. What are the signs and symptoms of DIC?

Answers to Chapter 14 Study Questions

1.   There are essentially three categories of anemia: 1) loss of RBCs through bleeding (GI bleeding, trauma, excessive menstrual flow are common causes); 2) decreased production of RBCs (hypoproliferative—inadequate numbers of RBCs are produced to meet the body's needs); and 3) increased destruction of RBCs (hemolytic—RBCs are prematurely destroyed).

2.   Women lose iron during menstruation, which is the most common cause of iron-deficiency anemia in women. GI bleeding is a common cause for anemia in men. The use of aspirin products and nonsteroidal anti-inflammatory drugs also can lead to GI irritation, blood loss, and anemia. The GI bleeding is usually occult (can not be seen by the eye) and chronic in nature, but only a small amount of daily chronic blood loss can lead to the development of anemia. Iron absorption can also be decreased if there is an alteration in the mucosa of the small intestine. Chronic alcoholism can cause anemia due to GI irritation and blood loss.

3.   Laboratory tests are conducted, including hemoglobin, hematocrit, and red blood cell count, all of which will be low. The mean corpuscular volume (MCV), mean corpuscular hemoglobin (MCH), and mean corpuscular hemoglobin concentration (MCHC) will be decreased. Serum iron level, total iron-binding capacity (TIBC), iron saturation, and ferritin levels are also obtained. These levels will usually be decreased, with the exception of the TIBC, which will be increased.

4.   Food sources that are high in iron include leafy green vegetables, organ meat (liver), lean meats, beans, egg yolks, carrots, apricots, and raisins.

5.   In pernicious anemia, the intrinsic factor that enables oral vitamin B_{12} to be absorbed is missing. The intrinsic factor is normally secreted from the gastric mucosal cells; it binds with vitamin B_{12} and carries it to the ileum, where the vitamin is subsequently absorbed. Vitamin B_{12} is one of the vitamins required for erythropoiesis (the development of RBCs). A lack of vitamin B_{12} will decrease the formation of RBCs, leading to the development of anemia.

6.   Clinical manifestations of pernicious anemia do not develop until the body's store of vitamin B_{12} is depleted. Onset of manifestations is gradual. The patient may complain of weakness, fatigue, and lethargy. Skin pallor is common. In pernicious anemia, the gastrointestinal tract and the nervous system are particularly affected. The patient develops diarrhea and a smooth, red, sore tongue. Numbness and tingling of the lower legs and feet are common. The patient may experience a loss of balance and demonstrate confusion. Congestive heart failure can develop as the disorder progresses. Pernicious anemia can be fatal if untreated.

7.   Patients who are diagnosed with pernicious anemia need a lifetime replacement of vitamin B_{12}. Monthly intramuscular injections of the vitamin will be necessary.

Response to the injections is usually rapid, with the patient demonstrating fewer symptoms within seventy-two hours. Even with treatment, severe neuropathy may remain, leading to a permanent disability.

8. Sickle-cell anemia is a chronic, hereditary hemolytic anemia. Individuals inherit a sickle hemoglobin gene (HbS). In sickle-cell anemia, the HbS gene causes red blood cells to become crescent-shaped ("sickle") when the oxygen level in the blood decreases. When the cells sickle, they lose their round, flexible shape and become rigid and deformed. This rigid, deformed shape causes the cells to become lodged in small vessels, obstructing blood flow and leading to hypoxia. The viscosity of the blood also increases, causing blood flow to get sluggish. Ischemia, infarction, and necrosis develop in the areas where the blood flow is obstructed. Areas most likely to be affected by infarction and necrosis are the kidneys, brain, bone marrow, and spleen.

9. Examples of some factors are infection, stress, alcohol, smoking, overexertion, cold weather, dehydration, and high altitudes.

10. Subjective data that is gathered by the nurse includes information about the patient's understanding of the disease process and knowledge of self-care activities. Feelings of powerlessness, hopelessness, and lowered self-esteem may be expressed. The nurse should assess pain characteristics and methods of pain control. The nurse should explore the impact of the disease on the patient's ability to carry out the activities of daily living. Objective data collection focuses on vital signs; integumentary findings (swollen, painful joints, leg ulcers); respiratory findings (dyspnea, chest pain, breath sounds, cyanosis); and cardiac status (arrhythmias, murmurs, tachycardia, enlarged heart, edema). The patient's renal functioning should also be monitored through BUN and creatinine laboratory values. The patient should be assessed for signs of dehydration. Urinary output, presence of edema, skin turgor, and examination of mucous membranes can provide information about the fluid status of the patient. The patient should also be assessed for indications of cerebral hypoxia. While these assessments are pertinent at any point in the patient's care, they are especially important during an episode of sickle-cell crisis.

11. Nursing care will vary depending upon the patient's condition and the presence of complications. During an acute sickle-cell crisis, the nurse's main goal is to manage the patient's pain, which can be severe. Prompt administration of analgesics is necessary. Supportive measures to be used in conjunction with pain medication include relaxation techniques, distraction, and breathing exercises. Swollen, painful joints should be carefully supported and elevated. Aggressive fluid replacement may be necessary to prevent dehydration and minimize blood viscosity and sluggish blood flow. Unless contraindicated, the patient should receive six to eight liters of fluid a day during a crisis. This fluid can be oral or intravenous. Preventing infection is another important aspect of care. The patient should be monitored carefully for early signs of an infection, especially

respiratory or urinary tract. Activity is encouraged within the patient's level of tolerance and should be balanced with periods of rest to minimize dyspnea and fatigue.

12.   Patient and family education is an essential aspect of the nursing care. Genetic counseling and family planning should be recommended for the patient and significant others to consider. The nurse can help the patient locate appropriate community resources to help guide decision making in these areas. The patient should also be taught appropriate self-care activities. Avoiding smoking and alcohol and effective stress management are positive lifestyle adjustments. The patient should maintain an adequate fluid intake, minimize exposure to infection, and avoid overexertion. Patients may find support groups helpful and should be encouraged to discuss their concerns.

13.   The onset of DIC is sudden. Initially, the signs and symptoms are related to the presence of thrombosis in different organs. Signs and symptoms can include chest pain, tachycardia, dyspnea, tachypnea, pulmonary emboli, confusion, decreased alertness, cyanosis, decreased peripheral pulses, gastric pain, and decreased urinary output with increased BUN and creatinine. As DIC progresses, bleeding begins. At first, the bleeding is minimal, but can eventually develop into hemorrhage. Frank bleeding can occur in all organs and tissues, and the patient will exhibit multiple sites of bleeding: oral, integumentary, gastrointestinal, genitourinary, cerebrovascular, and respiratory. Bleeding from wound sites and puncture sites, as well as from around inserted lines and catheters, will develop.

Chapter 15: Nursing Care for Shock

Key Terms

Cardiogenic shock
Distributive shock
    Neurogenic
    Septic
    Anaphylactic
Hypovolemic shock
Stages of shock
    Compensatory
    Progressive
    Irreversible (refractory)

Introduction

This chapter discusses care of the patient with shock. **Shock** is a syndrome that is caused by many different factors. Regardless of the etiology of the shock syndrome, the resulting outcome is impaired tissue perfusion due to an inadequate amount of oxygen and nutrients. The decrease in tissue perfusion leads to impaired cellular metabolism. The signs and symptoms of shock are numerous. It is important that the nurse be able to recognize these signs and symptoms promptly, so that early intervention can be implemented. Lack of prompt intervention can lead to the death of the patient. The elderly patient has a higher mortality rate due to shock than younger patients.

Types of Shock

Shock can be classified according to disruptions in the following:

1.   Vascular tone
2.   Heart pumping ability
3.   Intravascular volume

Table 15.1 identifies the various types of shock and some common etiologies. Each type is discussed in more detail below.

Table 15.1 Types of Shock	
Pathophysiological disruption	**Type of shock and common etiologies**
Disruption in vascular tone leads to an increase in the size of the vascular space while circulating blood volume remains unchanged.	Distributive shock (three types): • Anaphylactic shock—allergic reaction • Neurogenic shock—spinal cord injury • Septic shock—infection
Disruption in the heart's ability to pump effectively results in decreased circulation of blood volume.	Cardiogenic shock—arrhythmias, acute MI, tension pneumothorax, pulmonary embolus
Disruption in the intravascular volume results in a decrease in the amount of blood volume available to circulate.	Hypovolemic shock—hemorrhage, burns, dehydration

Distributive Shock

Distributive shock is caused by massive vasodilation of blood vessels. There is no change in the amount of blood volume; rather, the vascular space has been greatly expanded. Distributive shock is further subdivided into three types: neurogenic, anaphylactic, and septic shock.

- **Neurogenic shock** develops when there is an impairment of the autonomic nervous system and the sympathetic vasoconstriction of the vessels is lost, resulting in vasodilation. This leads to pooling of the blood, with a decrease in venous return, cardiac output, tissue perfusion, and cellular metabolism. A common cause of neurogenic shock is cervical spinal cord injuries. Other causes include vasomotor center depression and spinal, epidural, or general anesthesia.

- **Anaphylactic shock** is an acute, massive, systemic allergic reaction to a substance. Common causes of anaphylactic reactions are bee stings, antibiotics, nonsteroidal anti-inflammatories, and food allergies. Chemical mediators, such as histamine, prostaglandins, and leukotrienes, are released from the cells, causing systemic vasodilation, bronchospasms, and laryngeal edema, as well as urticaria. Anaphylactic shock leads to cardiovascular collapse and respiratory failure if not promptly treated.

- **Septic shock** is caused by an infection. The infection may originate from anywhere, but common causes include urinary tract infections, respiratory infections, and indwelling intravenous lines and catheters. Any organism can cause septic shock, but the organisms most responsible for the development of septic shock are gram-negative bacteria. The organisms release endotoxins into the bloodstream, causing massive vasodilation. The elderly and immunocompromised patients are at particular risk for the development of septic shock. There is a mortality rate of approximately 50 percent associated with septic shock.

Cardiogenic Shock

Cardiogenic shock is caused by failure of the heart to pump effectively. The most common cause of cardiogenic shock is left ventricular dysfunction, usually caused by acute myocardial infarction. Decreased left ventricular function leads to a decreased cardiac output, which eventually results in decreased oxygen supply, tissue perfusion, and cellular metabolism. Right-sided heart failure and pulmonary edema may also develop due to a backup of blood into the pulmonary circulation. Another potential cause of cardiogenic shock is mechanical obstruction of blood flow to or from the heart, leading to decreased cardiac output. This mechanical obstruction can be caused by pulmonary emboli, tension pneumothorax, or cardiac tamponade.

Hypovolemic Shock

Hypovolemic shock develops as a result of a decrease in circulating blood volume. A decrease in circulating blood volume can be caused by actual blood loss through hemorrhage. Other causes include burns, which produce a loss of intravascular volume through a fluid shift to the interstitial spaces, and dehydration. Children and the elderly are most susceptible to the development of dehydration. Regardless of the cause, the decrease in circulating blood volume leads to decreased venous return, stroke volume, and cardiac output. Tissue perfusion is impaired, and there is a lack of oxygen available for cellular metabolism.

Stages of Shock

The stages of shock can be classified in several different ways. For the purposes of this study guide, the stages of shock are described as follows:

1. Compensated stage
2. Progressive stage
3. Irreversible or refractory stage

Regardless of the type or cause of shock, and with a few exceptions that are identified in the discussion, these stages of shock can be applied to any patient's clinical situation.

Shock may develop gradually or suddenly, depending upon the severity of the cause and the ability of the body to compensate for the insult. An individual who is chronically ill, in contrast to a healthy individual, would be less likely to have the compensatory mechanisms necessary to respond adequately to the shock syndrome. How quickly the patient's condition advances through the various stages of stock can be highly variable.

Compensated Stage

In the early stage of shock, called the **compensated stage**, the body systems are usually able to compensate for the reduction in vasomotor tone or circulating blood volume. As a result, the metabolic needs of the body's tissues are still met. A decrease in the cardiac output leads to the stimulation of the sympathetic nervous system, and epinephrine and norepinephrine are released, leading to vasoconstriction. Due to this stimulation, there is an accompanying increase in heart rate and myocardial contraction force, causing an increase in cardiac output. Blood pressure is also maintained because of the increase in vascular resistance. The result of this early compensatory action is the maintenance of adequate tissue perfusion.

There are a couple of exceptions to the above sequence of events:

1.   Vasoconstriction and tachycardia will not occur in neurogenic shock due to the disruption of the autonomic nervous system and the inability to stimulate the sympathetic nervous system. Patients experiencing neurogenic shock exhibit hypotension and bradycardia.
2.   In septic shock, the vasoconstriction that occurs in the compensated stage of shock is usually not sufficient to overcome the massive vasodilation that has developed.

The clinical manifestations that develop in the compensated stage of shock are frequently subtle and may be missed. One of the earliest indications of shock in the compensatory stage may be a change in the patient's level of consciousness—restlessness, apprehension, or irritability. This change in level of consciousness is likely due to cerebral hypoxia. The patient is oriented. Neurological changes are the best indicator of the adequacy of cerebral blood flow.

A narrowing of pulse pressure (the difference between the systolic and diastolic blood pressure) is another early indication of compensatory shock. However, the overall blood pressure remains normal or only slightly decreased due to the compensation. A slight increase in pulse occurs. The peripheral pulses are thready, or bounding in the case of septic shock. Respiratory rate and depth are slightly increased.

Urinary output remains normal. Skin is pale and cool, with the exception of septic shock, in which it is warm and flushed. Bowel sounds remain normal or may be hypoactive.

At this point, if treatment of the underlying cause of shock is implemented, the shock is usually reversible. If treatment is not implemented or is unsuccessful, the shock will continue to progress.

Progressive Stage

In the **progressive stage** of shock, the compensation mechanisms become ineffective and decompensation develops. The sympathetic nervous system response causes profound systemic vasoconstriction, leading to occlusion of selected peripheral vascular beds. Because of the vasoconstriction, renal ischemia develops. There is a decreased venous blood flow to the heart, and myocardial function begins to deteriorate, leading to a decrease in cardiac output. Tissue hypoxia develops, and tissue cells begin to undergo anaerobic metabolism. Lactic acid is produced as a by-product of anaerobic metabolism, leading to lactic acid excess and the development of metabolic acidosis.

Clinical manifestations of the progressive stage of shock include continued changes in the patient's level of consciousness. The patient can be apathetic, listless, confused, or agitated. The patient may experience a decreased response to painful stimuli. Speech may be slowed and orientation affected.

Tachycardia develops, with weak, thready peripheral pulses. Blood pressure begins to fall and hypotension develops. Respirations are rapid.

Urinary output is decreased, with oliguria developing. The patient's skin is cold and clammy, and cyanosis may be evident. Body temperature may be decreased, with the exception of septic shock. The patient will complain of thirst.

It takes aggressive medical management to reverse the shock at this stage of development. If treatment does not reverse the shock, the patient will enter the irreversible stage of shock.

Irreversible (Refractory) Stage

When the patient reaches the **irreversible or refractory stage** of shock, the outcome is irreversible and death is imminent. There are no longer any functioning compensatory mechanisms left in the body. Patients who are resuscitated at this point will likely die of multiple organ dysfunction syndrome (MODS). Massive cellular necrosis throughout the body's organs leads to organ failure.

Due to increasing tissue hypoxia, anaerobic metabolism continues within the cells, producing large amounts of lactic acid. The acidic environment causes increased capillary permeability, with fluid and plasma proteins shifting out of the intravascular compartment into the interstitial spaces. This fluid shift causes hypotension to become even more pronounced. As hypotension and tachycardia increase, the cardiac output continues to decrease. This vicious cycle of decreased tissue hypoxia, increasing accumulation of lactic acid, fluid shifting, increasing hypotension and tachycardia, and decreased cardiac output leading to even more tissue hypoxia repeats itself. Eventually, cerebral ischemia develops and the medullary vasomotor center fails, causing a complete loss of sympathetic tone and vasoconstriction. At this point, respiratory and cardiac arrest occurs, followed by death.

Clinical manifestations show evidence of the decompensation that is occurring in the irreversible stage of shock. The patient is likely to be unconscious and unresponsive to stimuli.

The blood pressure continues to fall, with the diastolic blood pressure reaching zero. There is no response to medical intervention. Eventually, the blood pressure is unobtainable and peripheral pulses are absent. The heart rate becomes slow and irregular. Respiration becomes shallow and irregular; Cheyne-Stokes respirations may develop.

Urinary output is minimal. Skin is cold and clammy, with mottling and cyanosis. Bowel sounds are absent.

General Collaborative Care in the Management of Shock

Medical management focuses on early diagnosis and intervention to prevent the progression of shock and organ damage. Diagnosis of shock will include a history and physical examination along with diagnostic studies. The diagnostic studies will include an assessment of the patient's respiratory status, fluid and electrolyte balance, and organ perfusion. Diagnostic studies typically include chest X ray, ABGs, complete blood count, and blood chemistry. Blood cultures may be indicated for septic shock. An ECG will be obtained, and the patient will be placed on a cardiac monitor. Arterial lines are placed to allow for hemodynamic monitoring. Additional tests may be ordered, depending upon the underlying cause of the shock. The patient will be cared for in an intensive care setting.

Initial Collaborative Care

The nurse should anticipate collaborating with the physician to implement the following initial aspects of medical management for the patient who is in shock:

- Establish a patent airway. Administer oxygen is a priority intervention. It is likely that the patient will require intubation and mechanical ventilation.
- Insert arterial lines to allow for hemodynamic monitoring, and large gauge peripheral IV catheters to provide a mechanism for fluid replacement and drug therapy administration.
- Position the patient supine with legs elevated 45°, trunk horizontal, and head level with chest. The Trendelenburg position is no longer used in the treatment of shock.
- Treat cardiac arrhythmias with drug therapy (see chapter 10).
- Insert indwelling urethral catheter to monitor hourly urinary output.
- Provide enteral or parenteral nutritional support.
- Provide emotional support to the patient and significant others.

Fluid Replacement

Rapid fluid replacement therapy is an important aspect of the treatment of all types of shock, with the exception of cardiogenic shock and neurogenic shock. In these two types of shock, fluid replacement may be a part of the treatment, but the fluid is administered at a slower, more cautious rate.

Fluid replacement therapy may consist of the administration of **crystalloid solutions**, **colloid solutions**, and/or **blood products**.

- **Crystalloids** are electrolyte fluids. They may be hypotonic, isotonic, or hypertonic. The most common IV fluid initially administered for shock resuscitation and fluid volume replacement efforts is normal saline, which is an isotonic crystalloid.

- **Colloids**, such as **plasma protein** and **albumin**, are plasma volume expanders. They draw fluid into the intravascular space and are frequently used to treat shock that results from burns. Colloids can cause circulatory overload and are not used with cardiogenic shock.
- If the patient has experienced blood loss, **blood products** will be administered to replace lost hemoglobin. **Packed red blood cells** or **whole blood** may be given.

A pulmonary artery catheter can provide readings on the pulmonary artery wedge pressure (PAWP) and the cardiac output, and thus measure the effectiveness of fluid replacement therapy. Urinary output can also be used to indicate the adequacy of fluid replacement.

Drug Therapy for Shock

Several categories of drugs are used in the treatment of shock. The primary goal of drug therapy is to restore tissue perfusion. These drugs will be administered intravenously.

- **Sympathomimetic (vasopressor) drugs:** Many of these drugs cause peripheral vasoconstriction. The goal for using these drugs is the treatment of hypotension and maintaining a mean arterial systolic blood pressure of 70 to 80 mm Hg. A blood pressure in this range is sufficient for maintaining vital organ perfusion. These drugs must be used with care because excessive vasoconstriction can further compromise tissue perfusion. It is also essential that vasopressor drugs be administered only after adequate fluid replacement has been achieved, or tissue perfusion will be reduced. Commonly used sympathomimetic drugs include dobutamine, dopamine, epinephrine, and norepinephrine.
- **Vasodilator drugs:** Vasodilators are used in cases where extreme vasoconstriction has developed, leading to poor tissue perfusion and increased cardiac workload. The goal is to maintain a mean arterial blood pressure goal of 70 to 80 mm Hg. In cardiogenic shock, a commonly used vasodilator is nitroglycerin. Nitroprusside is commonly used in noncardiogenic shock.
- **Corticosteroids:** Corticosteroids may be used in anaphylactic shock to inhibit the inflammatory process. They are not administered in other forms of shock. Commonly prescribed corticosteroids include dexamethasone, hydrocortisone, and methylprednisolone.
- **Antibiotics:** Antibiotics are used primarily in the treatment of septic shock. However, patients with shock are susceptible to acquiring nosocomial infections due to the many invasive lines that are used in their treatment, and antibiotics would be ordered to treat any acquired infection.

Nutritional Therapy for the Patient in Shock

Adequate nutrition is key to decreasing the morbidity associated with shock. Patients can develop protein-calorie malnutrition if nutritional needs are not met. Some form of nutritional intake is usually implemented within the first twenty-four hours of treatment. Continual enteral feedings, unless contraindicated, are usually the form of nutrition that is provided. Parenteral nutrition may be ordered if enteral feedings cannot be used.

Specific Measures of Care for Different Types of Shock

In addition to the general collaborative care measures already identified, the different types of shock have specific measures of care that should be implemented.

Neurogenic Shock

The treatment of neurogenic shock will vary depending upon the cause. Careful fluid replacement with normal saline to treat hypotension is usually an aspect of the care. In addition, bradycardia may be treated with atropine, and vasopressors may be given to increase blood pressure.

Anaphylactic Shock

In the treatment of anaphylactic shock, the nurse should immediately stop the infusion of any drug or other substance that may be causing the allergic reaction in order to decrease any further absorption. Anaphylactic shock requires immediate intervention with drug therapy. The patient is usually experiencing bronchospasms and laryngeal edema, with severe respiratory distress. First and foremost, the drug of choice for treatment of anaphylactic shock is epinephrine. In addition, bronchodilators and corticosteroids may be administered. Fluid resuscitation is usually required. Following fluid replacement, vasopressors may be administered.

Septic Shock

Treatment of septic shock requires extensive fluid replacement therapy, usually using both crystalloids and colloids. The source of the infection must be identified and the organism cultured. Antibiotic therapy will be started with broad-spectrum antibiotics, until specific antibiotics that the organism will be sensitive to can be identified. Cardiotonic drugs may also be administered.

Cardiogenic Shock

The primary goal of treatment of cardiogenic shock is to restore adequate blood flow to the myocardium and maintain tissue perfusion. Depending upon the underlying cause of the shock, this may require treatment of arrhythmias, cardiac catheterization and angioplasty, or thrombolytic therapy. Drug therapy such as inotropics (norepinephrine), vasodilators, diuretics, beta-blockers, and cardiotonics are examples of drugs that may be administered. Fluids are administered with care to avoid circulatory overload.

Hypovolemic Shock

The major goal of treatment in hypovolemic shock is to provide fluid replacement. This may be accomplished with the administration of crystalloids, colloids, and/or blood products. If the patient is hemorrhaging, surgery may be required to stop blood loss.

Nursing Care of the Patient in Shock

Nursing care of the patient in shock is challenging and complex. The patient's condition requires close monitoring and immediate intervention when necessary.

Nursing Process: Assessment

Nursing assessment focuses on evaluating the quality of tissue perfusion. Skin color and temperature, vital signs, urine output, and level of consciousness are all important factors to assess. The clinical manifestations related to the patient's neurological, respiratory, cardiovascular, gastrointestinal, and urinary status (identified in the section on the stages of shock) are areas that the nurse needs to assess as often as hourly, or even every fifteen to thirty minutes, depending upon the stability of the patient's condition.

Nursing Process: Diagnosis and Planning

The **nursing diagnoses** that are associated with caring for patients in shock are numerous. Some of the most likely nursing diagnoses include, but are not limited to, the following:

- Impaired gas exchange
- Ineffective breathing pattern
- Altered tissue perfusion
- Decreased cardiac output
- Fluid volume deficit
- Anxiety and fear
- Altered nutrition, less than body requirements
- Infection, risk for
- Ineffective family coping

Primary goals for the plan of care are to:

- Restore adequate tissue perfusion
- Meet the body's metabolic demands
- Prevent further injury and complications
- Promote effective coping by patient and family

Nursing Process: Implementation

As mentioned earlier, much of the nursing care of a patient in shock centers on the continuous assessment of the patient, knowing that the respiratory and cardiovascular status of the patient can change rapidly. The nurse must document all assessment findings concisely and promptly so that an accurate baseline of the patient's condition is available to all care providers. While the nurse must monitor the functioning of numerous pieces of equipment, it is essential that the nurse not rely solely upon the numbers provided by the various monitors. Direct physical assessment of the patient is critical. Changes in the patient's condition must be reported promptly.

The nurse works closely with other members of the health-care team to provide the comprehensive care that the patient requires. The section above on general collaborative care describes much of the nursing care required. In addition, the nurse must implement a plan of care to prevent the development of complications as a result of the patient's immobility. Frequent position changes, use of special beds and alternating mattresses, and meticulous skin care are necessary to decrease the likelihood of skin breakdown. If tolerated, passive ROM is implemented several times a day to maintain joint mobility. Frequent oral hygiene is important because of the likelihood of the patient having dry oral mucous membranes. It is also essential that meticulous asepsis be used when caring for the patient and manipulating the many invasive lines; these patients are at a high risk for developing a nosocomial infection.

Emotional support of the patient and family members must not be overlooked. The patient is in a life-threatening position and very dependent upon the nursing staff. The monitors, ventilators, and other medical equipment can be very frightening and intimidating. It is important for the nurse to explain every procedure and treatment to the patient and family members, and answer any questions. If the patient cannot talk, alternate forms of communication should be established. Even if the patient is unconscious, the nurse should continually inform the patient of what is being done to help him or her. The patient's privacy should be maintained.

Nursing Process: Evaluation

The effectiveness of nursing interventions can be evaluated by the achievement of the following **expected outcomes**:

- Return of adequate tissue perfusion
- Evidence of adequate gas exchange in the lungs
- Evidence of normal cardiac output
- Expressed relief of anxiety and fear
- Avoidance of complications

Chapter 15 Study Questions

1.   Describe the three basic pathophysiological disruptions that can lead to shock.

2.   Define the three types of distributive shock.

3.   Define cardiogenic shock.

4.   Define hypovolemic shock.

5. What are the clinical manifestations of a patient who is in the compensated stage of shock?

6. What are the clinical manifestations of a patient who is in the progressive stage of shock?

7. In the irreversible stage of shock, the client will exhibit what signs and symptoms?

8. Identify the initial steps the nurse should anticipate implementing when caring for a patient who is in shock.

9. What is the purpose of administering vasopressor drugs in the patient with shock?

10. What is the drug of choice for a patient in anaphylactic shock?

11. Identify four nursing diagnoses that would be appropriate for the patient in shock.

Answers to Chapter 15 Study Questions

1.   Distribution in vascular tone leads to an increase in the size of the vascular space while circulating blood volume remains unchanged; disruption in the heart's ability to pump effectively results in decreased circulation of blood volume; and disruption in the intravascular volume results in a decrease in the amount of blood volume available to circulate.

2.   Neurogenic shock develops when there is an impairment of the autonomic nervous system and the sympathetic vasoconstriction of the vessels is lost, resulting in vasodilation. This leads to pooling of the blood, with a decrease in venous return, cardiac output, tissue perfusion, and cellular metabolism. Anaphylactic shock is an acute, massive, systemic allergic reaction to a substance. Septic shock is caused by an infection.

3.   Cardiogenic shock is caused by failure of the heart to pump effectively.

4.   Hypovolemic shock develops as a result of a decrease in circulating blood volume.

5.   One of the earliest indications of shock in the compensatory stage may be a change in the patient's level of consciousness, such as restlessness, apprehension, or irritability. This change in level of consciousness is likely due to cerebral hypoxia. The patient is oriented. Neurological changes are the best indicator of the adequacy of cerebral blood flow. A narrowing of pulse pressure is another early indication of compensatory shock. However, the overall blood pressure remains normal or only slightly decreased due to the compensation. A slight increase in pulse occurs. The peripheral pulses are thready, or bounding in the case of septic shock. Respiratory rate and depth are slightly increased. Urinary output remains normal. Skin is pale and cool, with the exception of septic shock, in which it is warm and flushed. Bowel sounds remain normal or may be hypoactive.

6.   Clinical manifestations of the progressive stage of shock include continued changes in the patient's level of consciousness. The patient can be apathetic, listless, confused, or agitated. The patient may experience a decreased response to painful stimuli. Speech may be slowed and orientation affected. Tachycardia develops, with weak, thready peripheral pulses. Blood pressure begins to fall and hypotension develops. Respirations are rapid. Urinary output is decreased, with oliguria developing. The patient's skin is cold and clammy, and cyanosis may be evident. Body temperature may be decreased, with the exception of septic shock. The patient will complain of thirst.

7.   Clinical manifestations show evidence of the decompensation that is occurring in the irreversible stage of shock. The patient is likely to be unconscious and unresponsive to stimuli. The blood pressure continues to fall, with the diastolic

blood pressure reaching zero. There is no response to medical intervention. Eventually, the blood pressure is unobtainable and peripheral pulses are absent. The heart rate becomes slow and irregular. Respiration becomes shallow and irregular; Cheyne-Stokes respirations may develop. Urinary output is minimal. Skin is cold and clammy, with mottling and cyanosis. Bowel sounds are absent.

8.   The nurse should anticipate collaborating with the physician to implement the following initial aspects of medical management for the patient who is in shock:

- Establishing a patent airway and administering oxygen is a priority intervention. It is likely that the patient will require intubation and mechanical ventilation.
- Inserting arterial lines to allow for hemodynamic monitoring, and large gauge peripheral IV catheters to provide a mechanism for fluid replacement and drug therapy administration
- Positioning the patient supine with legs elevated 45°, trunk horizontal, and head level with chest. The Trendelenburg position is no longer used in the treatment of shock.
- Treating cardiac arrhythmias with drug therapy
- Inserting indwelling urethral catheter to monitor hourly urinary output
- Providing enteral or parenteral nutritional support
- Providing emotional support to the patient and significant others

9.   The goal for using these drugs is the treatment of hypotension and maintaining a mean arterial systolic blood pressure of 70 to 80 mm Hg. A blood pressure in this range is sufficient for maintaining vital organ perfusion. These drugs must be used with care because excessive vasoconstriction can further compromise tissue perfusion. It is also essential that vasopressor drugs be administered only after adequate fluid replacement has been achieved, or tissue perfusion will be reduced.

10.   First and foremost, the drug of choice for treatment of anaphylactic shock is epinephrine. In addition, bronchodilators and corticosteroids may be administered. Fluid resuscitation is usually required. Following fluid replacement, vasopressors may be administered.

11.   The nursing diagnoses that are associated with caring for patients in shock are numerous. Some of the most likely nursing diagnoses include, but are not limited to impaired gas exchange; ineffective breathing pattern; altered tissue perfusion; decreased cardiac output; fluid volume deficit; anxiety and fear; altered nutrition: less than body requirements; risk for infection; and ineffective family coping.

UNIT IV: ABNORMAL CELLULAR GROWTH
Chapter 16: An Overview of Abnormal Cellular Growth

Key Terms

Benign
Cancer
Cellular proliferation
Cellular differentiation
Ewing's sarcoma
Fibrocystic breast disease
Gestational trophoblastic neoplasia
Hypertrophy
Leukemia
Lymphoma (Hodgkin's and Non-Hodgkin's)
Malignant
Metastasize
Neoplasm
Neuroblastoma
Osteogenic sarcoma
Prostatic hypertrophy
Pyloric stenosis
Uterine fibroids
Wilms' tumor

Introduction

Cellular growth in the body is normally a carefully regulated process of cellular proliferation and differentiation.

- **Cellular proliferation** is the process of cell division that usually occurs to replace old or dying cells.
- **Cellular differentiation** is the process by which new cells develop specialized function and structure.

Alterations in the process of cellular proliferation and differentiation result in abnormal cellular growth. Abnormal cellular growth can cause many different problems for the patient, depending upon the type and location of the abnormal cellular growth.

Types of Abnormal Cellular Growth

There are several types of abnormal cellular growth. The three types that will be discussed in this study guide are **hypertrophy, benign** abnormal cellular growth, and **malignant** abnormal cellular growth. Each has characteristics that result in different types of problems for the patient.

Characteristics of Hypertrophied Tissue

Hypertrophy is the overgrowth of normal tissue due to an increase in cell size. The etiology of most disorders caused by hypertrophied tissue is unknown. The tissue cells enlarge in size, but retain their normal purpose and function. The most common clinical problems that result from hypertrophied tissue are problems related to **constriction** or **obstruction**.

An example of a patient problem resulting from hypertrophied tissue is **pyloric stenosis.** Pyloric stenosis is a disorder of early infancy that results from a hypertrophied pyloric sphincter. This hypertrophy creates a stricture, or narrowing, between the stomach and the duodenum. This stricture causes the infant to develop projectile vomiting, which prevents the infant from getting necessary nutrients and fluids. Pyloric stenosis can be treated successfully with surgery.

Another example of a patient problem that can result from tissue hypertrophy is **prostatic hypertrophy.** In this disorder, prostatic tissue hypertrophies, leading to an enlarged prostate. The enlarged prostate constricts the urethra, which causes urine retention. Prostatic hypertrophy occurs in middle-aged and elderly males and is typically treated with surgery.

Characteristics of Benign Neoplasms

The term **neoplasm,** which means "new growth," refers to the process of abnormal cellular growth. The word **tumor** is sometimes used interchangeably with the word neoplasm. Neoplasms consist of tissue that has no useful purpose or function. Neoplasms may be benign or malignant. Benign and malignant neoplasms have different characteristics.

Benign neoplasms consist of well-differentiated, structured cells that resemble normal tissue cells and have a slow rate of growth. The term **differentiation** is used to identify how closely neoplastic cells resemble the original cell structure. Benign neoplasms expand as they grow; they do not infiltrate into the surrounding normal tissues. They are also localized and do not **metastasize** (spread). Benign neoplasms can occur in epithelial, connective, muscle, or nerve tissue. Benign neoplasms are not fatal to the patient unless their location creates unrelieved pressure on vital structures. An example of this would be a benign brain tumor that is inoperable due to its location.

Additional examples of patient problems resulting from benign abnormal cellular growth include uterine fibroids and fibrocystic breast disease. **Uterine fibroids** are benign tumors that develop in the myometrium of the uterus. They can be asymptomatic depending upon their size and location. Bleeding is the most common symptom. **Fibrocystic breast disease** is a benign breast disorder in which a woman develops cysts of various sizes, usually bilaterally. This may result in pain and nipple discharge. Fibrocystic breast disease is treated symptomatically.

Another example of a benign abnormal cellular growth problem is **gestational trophoblastic neoplasia (GTN)**, a term used to describe related disorders such as hydatidiform mole. GTN is an abnormal pregnancy that results in abnormal growth of placental tissue. The fetus does not develop normally and dies. Trophoblastic placental tissue causes rapid uterine growth, resulting in bleeding. This condition may be a precursor to a malignancy. It is treated by surgical removal of the molar pregnancy.

Characteristics of Malignant Neoplasms

A **malignant** neoplasm, also known as **cancer**, has characteristics that are very different from a benign neoplasm. Malignant neoplasms are poorly differentiated or undifferentiated, bearing little resemblance to normal tissue cells. They also grow rapidly and infiltrate surrounding tissues as they grow. Malignant neoplasms can **metastasize**, or spread, to distant sites in the body through the bloodstream or lymphatic system. They cause damage and death to normal tissues by using the nutrients needed by the normal tissues to sustain life and by releasing substances that are toxic to the tissues. The patient will ultimately die as a result of most malignancies if the malignancy is not treated successfully. A malignant neoplasm, or cancer, can develop at any time across the life span, but it tends to occur more commonly in children or in the elderly.

Examples of common childhood malignancies include Wilms' tumor, neuroblastoma, and sarcoma. **Wilms' tumor** is the most common childhood malignancy of the kidney, occurring in infancy and early childhood. It may be genetically inherited, but there is currently no way to identify gene carriers. An abdominal mass, which is usually unilateral, is the most common clinical manifestation of a Wilms' tumor. Treatment consists of the surgical removal of the affected kidney (nephrectomy) followed by radiation and chemotherapy. Prognosis is good with early detection.

Neuroblastomas are malignant tumors that originate in the adrenal glands or the sympathetic nervous system. Approximately 70 percent of neuroblastomas are not diagnosed until metastasis has already occurred, leading to a poor prognosis. Signs and symptoms of a neuroblastoma are dependent upon the location of the malignancy and the area of the metastasis. Common sites of metastasis are the lymph nodes, bone marrow, skeletal system, skin, or liver. Treatment includes surgery in the early stages of the disease, and radiation and chemotherapy for treatment of extensive disease.

Sarcomas are primary bone cancers. **Osteogenic sarcoma** is the most frequently occurring bone cancer, usually affecting the lower extremities. The tumor develops in the metaphysis of the long bones. The child may complain of pain, sometimes severe, in the affected area and may develop a limp. There may be a noticeable mass or swelling.

Treatment is surgery that consists of resection of the tumor with salvage of the limb or amputation. Chemotherapy may be used before and after surgery.

Ewing's sarcoma is a highly malignant bone cancer that develops in the shafts of the long bones. Signs and symptoms are similar to osteogenic sarcoma. Treatment consists of radiation and chemotherapy. The prognosis for both of these cancers is poor if metastasis occurs. Metastasis typically occurs to the lungs.

Examples of common malignancies that occur in adults include cancer of the brain, lungs, breast, intestines, stomach, liver, ovaries, prostate, uterus, bladder, and skin. The most commonly occurring forms of cancers in males are prostate (43 percent) and lung (13 percent) cancer. In females, the most commonly occurring forms of cancer are breast (30 percent) and lung (13 percent) cancer. Lung cancer is the leading cause of cancer deaths for both males and females.

Other forms of cancer include those that have a **hematological** origin. **Leukemia** is a malignant hematological disorder that occurs in both children and adults. Leukemia affects the bone marrow and lymph nodes and is characterized by uncontrolled proliferation of immature, poorly differentiated white blood cells. This production of immature, nonfunctioning white blood cells places the patient in an immunocompromised state and increases the patient's risk of infection.

Lymphomas are malignant disorders of the lymph nodes. **Hodgkin's disease** is a form of lymphoma that most commonly occurs in individuals who are in their thirties. It can occur in children, however, typically in their teenage years. **Non-Hodgkin's disease** is a broad category of lymphoid malignancies that occur in both adults and children. Enlarged lymph nodes, fatigue, fever, night sweats, and anorexia are typical clinical manifestations of lymphoma.

Clinical Manifestations of Abnormal Cellular Growth

The clinical manifestations of abnormal cellular growth vary depending upon the type and location of the abnormal cellular growth. Alterations in cell size, rate of growth, and cell function can produce local and/or systemic effects.

Localized Effects of Abnormal Cellular Growth

Hypertrophy of tissue cells produces localized signs and symptoms that result from the alteration in cell size. As demonstrated in the discussion of pyloric stenosis and prostatic hypertrophy, hypertrophy of tissue cells can result in signs of obstruction. Benign and malignant neoplasms can also cause signs and symptoms of obstruction, depending upon the location of the neoplasm.

Benign and malignant neoplasms typically produce localized effects related to the specific tissue or organ affected. Abnormal cellular growth, especially malignancies, can alter an organ's ability to carry out the functions normally associated with the organ.

Malignancies can cause tissue destruction and place pressure on surrounding tissues through invasive growth, leading to pain.

Loss of function can also occur if the neoplasm places pressure on surrounding structures. A patient who has a brain tumor, for example, may experience behavioral changes as a result of pressure being placed on the brain tissue. These behavioral changes may include an alteration in thought processes, confusion, or slurred speech. As another example, a patient who has a bone tumor may have a loss of mobility and function due to pain.

Systemic Effects of Abnormal Cellular Growth

In addition to localized effects, malignant neoplasms also produce systemic effects, especially if metastasis occurs. Patients with a malignancy may be more susceptible to bleeding, infection, nutritional deficiencies, fatigue, and psychosocial alterations.

Common target organs for metastasis include the lungs, brain, liver, and bone. When metastasis occurs, the patient will experience localized signs and symptoms related to the primary site of malignant cellular growth, as well as systemic effects resulting from invasion of the metastasized site.

Chapter 16 Study Questions

1. Define cellular proliferation and cellular differentiation.

2. Define hypertrophy and describe the clinical problems that can result from hypertrophied tissue.

3. Describe two examples of health problems that result from hypertrophied tissue.

4. Define the term "neoplasm."

5. Identify the characteristics of a benign neoplasm.

6.   Describe three examples of health problems that can result from benign abnormal cellular growth.

7.   Identify the characteristics of a malignant neoplasm.

8.   Define Wilms' tumor, neuroblastomas, and sarcomas.

9.   Which malignancies are most common in men and women?

10.   Define leukemia.

11.   Define lymphoma.

12.   Give examples of localized signs and symptoms related to benign and malignant abnormal cellular growth.

13.   Give examples of systemic effects related to malignant cellular growth.

Answers to Chapter 16 Study Questions

1.   Cellular proliferation is the process of cell division that usually occurs to replace old or dying cells. Cellular differentiation is the process by which new cells develop specialized functions and structures.

2.   Hypertrophy is the overgrowth of normal tissue due to an increase in cell size. The tissue cells retain their normal purpose and function. The most common clinical problems that result from hypertrophied tissue are problems that are related to constriction or obstruction.

3.   An example of a patient problem resulting from hypertrophied tissue is pyloric stenosis. Pyloric stenosis is a disorder of early infancy that results from a hypertrophied pyloric sphincter. This hypertrophy creates a stricture, or narrowing, between the stomach and the duodenum. This stricture causes the infant to develop projectile vomiting and prevents the infant from getting necessary nutrients and fluids. Pyloric stenosis can be treated successfully with surgery. Another example of a patient problem that can result from tissue hypertrophy is prostatic hypertrophy. In this disorder, prostatic tissue hypertrophies, leading to an enlarged prostate. The enlarged prostate constricts the urethra, causing urinary retention. Prostatic hypertrophy occurs in middle-aged and elderly males and is typically treated with surgery.

4.   The term "neoplasm," which means "new growth," refers to the process of abnormal cellular growth. The word "tumor" is sometimes used interchangeably with the word neoplasm. Neoplasms consist of tissue that has no useful purpose or function. Neoplasms may be may be benign or malignant.

5.   Benign neoplasms consist of well-differentiated cells that have a slow rate of growth. Benign neoplasms expand as they grow; they do not infiltrate into the surrounding normal tissues. They are also localized and do not metastasize. Benign neoplasms are not fatal to the patient, unless their location creates unrelieved pressure on vital structures. An example of this would be a benign brain tumor that is inoperable due to its location.

6.   Examples of patient problems resulting from benign abnormal cellular growth include uterine fibroids and fibrocystic breast disease. Uterine fibroids are benign tumors that develop in the myometrium of the uterus. They can be asymptomatic depending upon their size and location. Bleeding is the most common symptom. Fibrocystic breast disease is a benign breast disorder in which a woman develops cysts of various sizes, usually bilaterally. This may result in pain and nipple discharge. Fibrocystic breast disease is treated symptomatically. Another example of a benign abnormal cellular growth problem is gestational trophoblastic neoplasia, a term used to describe related disorders such as hydatidiform mole. GTN is an abnormal pregnancy that results in abnormal growth of placental tissue. The fetus does not develop normally and dies.

Trophoblastic placental tissue causes rapid uterine growth, resulting in bleeding. This condition may be a precursor to a malignancy. It is treated by surgical removal of the molar pregnancy.

7.   A malignant neoplasm, also known as cancer, has characteristics that are very different from a benign neoplasm. Malignant neoplasms are poorly differentiated, grow rapidly, and infiltrate surrounding tissues as they grow. Malignant neoplasms can metastasize to distant sites in the body through the bloodstream or lymphatic system. They cause damage and death to normal tissues by using the nutrients needed by the normal tissues to sustain life and by releasing substances that are toxic to the tissues. The patient will ultimately die as a result of most malignancies if the malignancy is not treated successfully. A malignant neoplasm, or cancer, can develop at any time across the life span, but tends to occur more commonly in children or in older adults.

8.   Examples of common childhood malignancies include Wilms' tumor, neuroblastoma, and sarcoma. Wilms' tumor is the most common childhood malignancy of the kidney, occurring in infancy and early childhood. Neuroblastomas are malignant tumors that originate in the adrenal glands or the sympathetic nervous system. Sarcomas are primary bone cancers. Osteogenic sarcoma is the most frequently occurring bone cancer, usually affecting the lower extremities. The tumor develops in the metaphysis of the long bones.

9.   Examples of common malignancies that occur in adults include cancer of the brain, lungs, breast, intestines, stomach, liver, prostate, uterus, bladder, and skin. The most commonly occurring forms of cancers in males are prostate (43 percent) and lung (13 percent) cancer. In females, the most commonly occurring forms of cancer are breast (30 percent) and lung (13 percent) cancer. Lung cancer is the leading cause of cancer deaths for both males and females.

10. Leukemia is a malignant hematological disorder that occurs in both children and adults. Leukemia affects the bone marrow and lymph nodes, and is characterized by uncontrolled proliferation of immature white blood cells. This increase in immature white blood cells places the patient in an immunocompromised state and increases the risk of infection.

11. Lymphomas are malignant disorders of the lymph nodes. Hodgkin's disease is a form of lymphoma that most commonly occurs in individuals who are in their thirties. It can occur in children, however, typically in their teenage years. Non-Hodgkin's disease is a broad category of lymphoid malignancies that occur in both adults and children. Enlarged lymph nodes, fatigue, fever, night sweats, and anorexia are typical clinical manifestations of lymphoma.

12. Benign abnormal cellular growth typically produces localized effects related to the specific tissue or organ affected. For example, local effects of benign cellular growth include pain that results from tissue destruction and pressure of the

neoplasm on surrounding tissues. Loss of function can also occur if the benign neoplasm places pressure on surrounding structures. A patient who has a benign brain tumor, for example, may experience behavioral changes as a result of pressure being placed on the brain tissue. These behavioral changes may include an alteration in thought processes, confusion, or slurred speech. A malignant abnormal cellular growth can produce these same localized signs and symptoms, depending upon the location of the growth.

13.   Patients with a malignancy may be more susceptible to bleeding, infection, nutritional deficiencies, fatigue, and psychosocial alterations. Common target organs for metastasis include the lungs, brain, liver, and bone. When metastasis occurs, the patient will experience the localized signs and symptoms related to the primary site of malignant cellular growth, as well as systemic effects resulting from the metastasized site.

                                           NC4 113001 v1.0

Chapter 17: Factors That Influence Patient Susceptibility and Response to Abnormal Cellular Growth

Key Terms

Carcinogen
Extrinsic or environmental factors
Intrinsic factors
Immunocompromised

Introduction

Many factors can influence the patient's susceptibility and response to abnormal cellular growth. These factors may be **intrinsic** (internal) to the patient or **extrinsic** (external, or environmental) factors. Many of these factors are most commonly associated with malignant abnormal cellular growth, although some have an influence on the hypertrophy of tissues.

Intrinsic Factors

Some intrinsic factors that influence the patient's response to abnormal cellular growth are age and physiological factors, such as immunological functioning, the presence of other illnesses, and the site and degree of involvement of the growth. Genetic predispositions and psychological factors may influence a patient's response as well.

Age

Age is a risk factor for the development of malignancies; many cancers have an increased incidence in older people. The effectiveness of the immune system decreases with age, which causes people to be more susceptible to the development of cancer. In addition, the longer we live, the more exposure we have to carcinogens through our lifestyle habits and in the environment, thus increasing the chances of developing cancer.

There are also numerous cancers that occur primarily in children. In the United States, cancer is the primary cause of death from disease in children who are past the age of infancy. Examples of childhood cancers include Ewing's sarcoma, Wilms' tumor, and retinoblastoma. **Acute lymphoid leukemia** (ALL) and **acute myelogenous leukemia** (AML) are two forms of leukemia that occur in children. Some childhood cancers, such as Wilms' tumor and retinoblastoma, are thought to have a genetic or hereditary component.

Disorders that are caused by tissue hypertrophy can also be age-related. Two examples of disorders that are age-related are benign prostatic hypertrophy and pyloric stenosis.

Benign prostatic hypertrophy (BPH) occurs primarily in middle-aged males, while pyloric stenosis occurs in newborn infants around the age of four to six weeks.

Immunological Functioning

In addition to the previously mentioned age-related immune system inefficiencies, patients who are immunocompromised are also more susceptible to developing a malignant abnormal cellular growth. This may occur in individuals who are taking medications to suppress the immune system (e.g., organ transplant recipients to prevent organ rejection) or those who are immunocompromised from another disease, such as AIDS.

Preexisting Illness

The presence of preexisting illnesses can also influence the patient's susceptibility and response to abnormal cellular growths. Some preexisting conditions can increase the patient's risk of developing a malignant cellular growth. For example, patients with inflammatory bowel disease, Gardner's syndrome, Crohn's disease, familial polyposis, or a long history (over ten years) of ulcerative colitis have a higher risk of developing colon cancer. Women with genital herpes virus or human papilloma virus infection may be at a higher risk for cervical cancer.

The presence of other illnesses can also negatively affect the patient's ability to respond to a malignant abnormal cellular growth. A patient who is already in poor health because of another illness will be more susceptible to the effects of a malignancy. In addition, the presence of other illnesses can affect the patient's ability to tolerate the treatment that is prescribed for the malignancy.

Site of Growth and Degree of Involvement

The site of the abnormal cell growth and the degree of involvement are other significant factors that influence the patient's response to abnormal cellular growth. A localized growth that is benign and accessible to treatment may be easily treated with minimal side effects. A growth that is malignant and has spread to distant sites will demand more extensive treatment and will likely produce local and systemic side effects.

Genetic and Familial Factors

Genetic and familial factors can also influence a patient's response to abnormal cellular growth. Certain types of cancers, such as breast, ovarian, and colon cancers, have demonstrated familial predispositions. Other cancers that result from specific genetic abnormalities include acute leukemias, neuroblastomas, Wilms' tumors, and skin cancers.

Psychological Factors

There is some evidence to suggest that psychological factors, such as stress, can influence a patient's response to abnormal cellular growth. Chronic physical or emotional stress can alter the body's hormone secretions and immune system effectiveness. These changes can either lead to an increase in the growth of malignant cells or the body's inability to detect and stop the growth of abnormal cells in the early stages. In addition, an individual's coping behaviors will influence how they respond to abnormal cellular changes, especially if they are faced with the potential diagnosis of cancer. Fear, anxiety, and depression are the most common psychological responses to a cancer diagnosis. The nurse can provide support by helping the patient cope effectively with the situation by encouraging the patient to verbalize feelings. The nurse can listen to the patient's fears and concerns, and answer questions. The nurse can also help the patient and family identify resources for support, such as counselors, support groups, social workers, and clergy.

Extrinsic or Environmental Factors

Extrinsic or environmental factors can also cause abnormal cellular growth and influence how a patient responds. It is believed that about 85 percent of all cancers are related to extrinsic or environmental factors. These factors include physical and chemical agents, socioeconomic status, cultural factors, and dietary factors.

Physical and Chemical Agents

An individual's exposure to certain physical and chemical agents can influence the development of abnormal cellular growth. Exposure to such physical agents as sunlight, radiation, or chronic inflammation or irritation of tissues can lead to the development of abnormal cellular growth due to cellular damage. Individuals can take preventive action to avoid excessive exposure to either sunlight or sources of radiation, and they can take precautions to eliminate chronic irritants, such as chewing tobacco or pipes.

Tobacco smoke is the most prominent chemical **carcinogen**. A carcinogen is a substance that promotes cellular alterations that cause cancer. Other common carcinogenic chemical substances include alcohol, asbestos, various dyes and pesticides, soot and tar, and toxic chemical compounds that pollute our air and water supplies. Many of these substances can be found in or near the workplace environment.

Socioeconomic Status and Cultural Factors

Socioeconomic status and cultural factors can also influence an individual's response to abnormal cellular growth. For example, an individual's occupation may expose him or her to certain carcinogenic agents. Heavily industrialized areas may have higher incidences of lung cancer due to air pollutants. Farmers may be more prone to skin cancer due to excessive sun exposure. Cultural factors that influence health habits and beliefs, dietary customs, and other lifestyle behaviors may predispose an individual to certain abnormal cellular changes or protect an individual from these cellular changes if the habits are healthy, positive ones.

Individuals who are less educated and have a lower income tend to have a higher incidence of cancer and a higher death rate. This higher incidence of cancer and subsequent higher death rate are frequently attributed to environmental and social factors.

An individual's lack of knowledge may influence the lack of health-promoting behaviors. Lack of insurance and access to health care are also significant problems for many individuals from lower socioeconomic backgrounds, and this can affect how quickly a patient is able to seek health care that would provide screening, early diagnosis, and treatment of a malignancy. Minority populations may be at a higher risk for cancer due to these socioeconomic factors. For example, African-Americans, especially males, have a higher incidence rate of cancer and death due to cancer than do Caucasians.

Dietary Factors and Nutritional Status

Dietary factors and the nutritional status of the individual may also affect a patient's response to abnormal cellular growth. Certain dietary factors are associated with a higher incidence of malignant growths. Fat and nitrites are substances that have been associated with malignancies such as colon, prostate, and breast cancers. Alcohol intake has been associated with head, neck, and liver cancers. Obesity may also increase the risk of certain types of cancer, such as colon cancer.

Other dietary habits have a positive, healthy effect and are associated with decreasing the likelihood of a malignancy. Foods that appear to decrease the risk of cancer include high-fiber diets, cruciferous vegetables, and foods containing carotenoids.

The patient's nutritional status will influence how the patient responds to malignant abnormal cellular growth. An impaired nutritional status can adversely affect the patient's immune system, increase the potential for infection, delay healing, and decrease functional ability. It may also promote further growth of the malignancy. A poor nutritional status can also decrease the patient's ability to undergo surgery, chemotherapy, or radiation treatment for the malignancy.

It is important for the nurse to closely assess the patient's nutritional status and develop a plan of care that will support an adequate nutritional intake. The nurse should work with the patient to identify foods that the patient can tolerate. It is important that the patient eat a high-calorie, high-protein diet. Usually the patient will tolerate smaller, more frequent feedings. Frequent oral hygiene can also stimulate the patient's appetite.

Chapter 17 Study Questions

1.   Give examples of intrinsic factors that can influence a patient's response to abnormal cellular growth.

2.   Describe how psychological factors can influence a patient's response to abnormal cellular growth.

3.   Give examples of extrinsic factors that can influence a patient's response to abnormal cellular growth.

4.   Define carcinogen.

5.   What is the most prominent chemical carcinogen?

6. How does socioeconomic status influence an individual's response to abnormal cellular growth?

7. Describe dietary factors that have been associated with a higher incidence of malignant growths.

8. How can an impaired nutritional status influence a patient's response to malignant cellular growth?

Answers to Chapter 17 Study Questions

1. Some intrinsic factors that influence the patient's response to abnormal cellular growth are age and physiological factors, such as immunological functioning, the presence of other illnesses, and the site and degree of involvement of the growth. Genetic and familial predispositions and psychological factors may also influence a patient's response as well.

2. Some evidence suggests that stress can influence a patient's response to abnormal cellular growth. Chronic physical or emotional stress can alter the body's hormone secretions and the effectiveness of the immune system. These changes can either lead to an increase in the growth of malignant cells or the body's inability to detect and stop the growth of abnormal cells in the early stages. In addition, an individual's coping behaviors will influence how they respond to abnormal cellular changes, especially if they are faced with the potential diagnosis of cancer. Fear, anxiety, and depression are the most common psychological responses to a cancer diagnosis.

3. It is believed that about 85 percent of all cancers are related to extrinsic (environmental) factors. These factors include physical and chemical agents, socioeconomic status, cultural factors, and dietary factors.

4. A carcinogen is a substance that promotes cellular alterations that cause cancer.

5. Tobacco smoke is the most prominent chemical carcinogen.

6. Individuals who are less educated and have a lower income tend to have a higher incidence of cancer and a higher death rate. Lack of access to health care is a significant problem for many individuals from lower socioeconomic backgrounds and can affect how a patient responds to an abnormal cellular growth.

7. Certain dietary factors are associated with a higher incidence of malignant growths. Fat, alcohol, and nitrites are substances that have been associated with malignancies. Obesity may also increase the risk of certain types of cancer, such as colon cancer.

8. An impaired nutritional status can adversely affect the patient's immune system, increase the potential for infection, delay healing, and decrease functional ability. It may also promote further growth of the malignancy. A poor nutritional status can also decrease the patient's ability to undergo surgery, chemotherapy, or radiation treatment for the malignancy.

Chapter 18: Therapeutic Interventions for Abnormal Cellular Growth

Key Terms

Analgesics
    Nonopioid
    Opioid
Antineoplastic agents
Biologic response modifiers
Biotherapy
Bone marrow transplant
Breast self-examination
Chemotherapy
    Cell-cycle phase specific
    Cell-cycle phase nonspecific
Colostomy
Cytotoxic
Hormonal therapy
Ileal conduit
Immunotherapy
Intestinal resection
Laryngectomy
Mastectomy
Prostatectomy
Radiation therapy
Steroids
Surgical intervention
    Diagnosis and staging
    Curative
    Palliation
    Adjuvant therapy
Testicular self-examination

Introduction

Therapeutic interventions related to the care of a patient with an abnormal cellular growth will vary depending on the nature of the cellular growth, the client's condition, and the goal of the therapy. Therapeutic interventions can include medications, surgery, chemotherapy, radiation therapy, biotherapy, and bone marrow transplant. These interventions may be used singly or in combination with each other. This chapter describes these interventions and the theoretical basis for their use in treating patients with an abnormal cellular growth.

Medications

The categories of medications that are most commonly used as treatment interventions for abnormal cellular growth include antineoplastic agents, steroids, analgesics, and hormonal therapy. The drugs of choice will depend on the type of cellular growth.

Antineoplastic Agents

Antineoplastic agents have a **cytotoxic effect** and are used to kill malignant tumor cells. They act in several ways, but primarily by interfering with cellular reproduction, inhibiting DNA and RNA formation, and inhibiting protein formation. Antineoplastic agents are also referred to as **chemotherapy**. They may be used as the sole treatment in some forms of cancer, such as leukemia, or in combination with surgery and radiation. Antineoplastic agents may be administered preoperatively to shrink a tumor or postoperatively to eradicate any malignant cells not removed by surgery.

Steroids

Steroids may also be used in treatment of abnormal cellular growth for their anti-inflammatory and selective cytotoxic effect. For example, steroids may be prescribed to treat cerebral edema caused by a benign or malignant brain tumor or spinal cord compression caused by a tumor. Adrenal corticosteroid hormones, such as hydrocortisone, are toxic to lymphocytic cells and can also be used to treat some cancers of the lymph system.

Analgesics

Analgesics are used to control pain caused by the pressure and inflammation created by abnormal cellular growths, especially malignant growths. Analgesics may be administered by many different routes, including the oral, intramuscular, intravenous, transdermal, or epidural routes. Intravenous patient-controlled analgesia may be used to provide the patient with a maximum of self-control for treatment of pain.

Nonopioid analgesics, such as nonsteroidal anti-inflammatory medications or aspirin, may be administered to patients experiencing mild to moderate pain. Nonopioid analgesics act primarily by inhibiting prostaglandin synthesis and decreasing inflammation, and/or by blocking peripheral pain impulses. Acetaminophen may also be used for its analgesic effects, but it does not have any anti-inflammatory action. **Opioid analgesics**, or narcotics, are given for more severe pain. Opioid analgesics alter pain perception by acting upon the central nervous system.

Regardless of the type of analgesics used, it is important that the medications be administered on a regular schedule to effectively control the severe pain that can result from cancer. The patient should be encouraged to take prescribed analgesics even if they are not experiencing pain at the time.

Some patients will refuse to take opioid analgesics in the mistaken belief that they will become addicted to the drugs. Health-care professionals may also have this same concern and may be reluctant to prescribe and administer the medication as frequently as it should be to effectively control pain. Patients who are taking opioid analgesics for pain relief, and not the psychological effects of the drug, do not need to fear becoming addicted. It is the responsibility of the nurse to be knowledgeable about pain management and to address the patient's concerns and questions about this issue.

Hormonal Therapy

Hormonal therapy refers to the use of hormones or hormone-blocking agents to affect the growth of malignant abnormal cellular growth. There are some malignancies that grow in response to hormone stimulation. The cancers most frequently identified as being responsive to hormonal manipulation include some forms of breast, prostate, uterine, and adrenal gland cancers. Estrogens, androgens, and progestins are hormones that are commonly used to treat hormone-receptive tumors. Hormone-blocking agents, such as the anti-estrogen drugs used to treat some forms of breast cancer, can also be used. The hormones used for treatment are chosen based upon the type of cancer being treated and which hormones stimulate the abnormal growth of the cells. The goal is to alter the hormonal stimulus of the cancer and retard the growth of the malignancy.

Surgical Intervention

Surgery is the most common intervention used to treat abnormal cellular growth. There are several reasons why surgery is used to treat health problems associated with abnormal cellular growth. Surgery may be diagnostic, curative, palliative, or reconstructive. In the case of a malignant neoplasm, surgery can be used alone or in combination with chemotherapy and radiation.

Diagnostic Surgery

Surgery is frequently used initially to **diagnose and stage** a disease. A needle or surgical **biopsy** can be performed to take a tissue sample for analysis, thus confirming a diagnosis. A more extensive surgery is performed to stage a disease, allowing the surgeon to remove lymph glands for pathology examination and to visually inspect the tissues and structures surrounding the abnormal cellular growth. If the growth is a malignancy, staging the disease through surgery helps to determine if metastasis has occurred.

Curative Surgery

Surgery may also be **curative**. This means that the growth, either benign or malignant, is completely resectable or removable through surgery. Surgery may be used to remove hypertrophied tissue, as in prostatic hypertrophy or the correction of a pyloric stenosis, or it may be used to remove a benign or malignant neoplasm. Examples of surgeries that may be performed to achieve a cure include laryngectomy, mastectomy, colon resection with or without a colostomy, cystectomy with the creation of an ileal conduit, and prostatectomy. Some of these surgeries, while they may cure the patient of cancer, leave the patient with irreversible changes in body functioning that will require lifelong management.

Palliative Surgery

In some cases, surgery is performed as a **palliative** measure to reduce the patient's symptoms or to provide a means for additional treatment. This type of surgery is usually used in patients who have an advanced form of cancer. For example, palliative surgery may be performed to reduce the size of a tumor that cannot be completely resected to decrease pain and other symptoms related to obstruction and pressure. A gastrostomy tube may be inserted to provide nutrition to a patient who cannot swallow comfortably due to a head and neck tumor; this is an example of palliative surgery that provides additional treatment.

Reconstructive Surgery

Surgery may also be **reconstructive** following other surgery, often for cosmetic reasons or to improve function. Breast reconstruction following a mastectomy is an example of reconstructive surgery. Reconstructive surgery may also be used in skin cancers or head and neck cancers.

Nursing Care Related to Surgery

Preoperative Care

Preoperatively, it is important for the nurse to provide support to the patient and family. The potential diagnosis of cancer produces uncertainty, fear, and anxiety in everyone. The patient may feel overwhelmed by the diagnostic tests and procedures, some of which will cause discomfort. The parents of a child who is undergoing diagnostic testing for a potentially malignant disease frequently will express feelings of disbelief. It is the nurse's responsibility to establish a trusting relationship with open communication with the patient and family, keeping them as informed as possible. The nurse can best accomplish this by listening to the patient's concerns and answering questions.

At this time, the nurse is also assessing the patient for factors that will affect the patient's response to surgery. The patient's age, level of functional ability prior to surgery, and the presence of any preexisting health conditions will have an impact on the patient's recovery postoperatively. Laboratory values will be assessed to determine electrolyte and other blood chemistry values.

A complete blood count (CBC) will also be done to determine the need for the administration of any blood products prior to surgery. For example, a patient who is anemic may require an infusion of red blood cells to increase hemoglobin and hematocrit levels. Platelet counts and white blood cell counts will also be evaluated to determine if the patient is at risk for developing bleeding (related to low platelet counts) or infection (related to low white blood cell counts).

An assessment of the nutritional status of the patient is another important factor to be considered prior to surgery. If the patient is nutritionally deficient, nutritional supplements will be provided preoperatively. These may be oral supplements, or if the patient cannot ingest enough nutrients orally, total parenteral nutrition (TPN) will be administered. TPN is infused through a central intravenous line and provides all of the patient's nutritional needs through the infusion of fluids that provide carbohydrates, lipids, electrolytes, vitamins, and trace minerals. It is important that the patient have an adequate nutritional status to support wound healing and recovery after surgery.

Preoperative teaching will focus on what the patient needs to know about the surgical procedure and the anticipated postoperative care. Some surgical procedures will lead to changes in body function and/or appearance that the patient will have to adapt to postoperatively. The ability to communicate, swallow, and breathe normally may be altered by a **laryngectomy**. A **colostomy** that results from a colon resection produces changes in bowel elimination, and the removal of the bladder (**cystectomy**) with an **ileal conduit** produces changes in urinary elimination. A **mastectomy**, the removal of a breast, may affect a woman's body image. A **prostatectomy** can produce sexual dysfunction.

Anticipating such physiological changes, in addition to coping with a diagnosis of cancer, can be emotionally very stressful for the patient. Answering the patient's questions and encouraging the patient to express any fears and concerns is an important nursing function during the preoperative time. Many patients are concerned about how their life will be changed following surgery, especially their relationships with their significant others. Family members may also have many questions, which they may be afraid to ask in front of the patient. The nurse should assess needs and provide emotional support to both the patient and the patient's family.

Postoperative Care

Postoperatively, the nurse provides general postoperative care and monitors the patient for complications. Priorities of care following surgery include providing pain control and comfort, promoting adequate nutrition, preventing infection, and meeting the emotional needs of the patient and the family. Patients who have a cancer diagnosis may already be immunodeficient and nutritionally deprived prior to surgery as a result of the disease. The nurse must pay particular attention to preventing infection and promoting nutrition so that recovery from surgery is not delayed. Many patients may also be facing additional treatment with chemotherapy and/or radiation therapy, so it is important that they avoid complications that may delay further life-supporting therapy. Specific nursing measures related to postoperative care are further discussed in the following chapters on nursing care.

Chemotherapy

Chemotherapy involves the use of **antineoplastic agents (drugs)** to treat cancer. Chemotherapy drugs are frequently administered to the patient in a clinic setting. They may be given orally, intravenously, intrathecally, or infused directly into a body cavity.

Chemotherapy drugs affect normal cells as well as malignant cells, and they can produce serious systemic side effects that affect all body systems. Nausea, vomiting, and bone marrow suppression are the most common side effects experienced by patients receiving chemotherapy. Common side effects associated with chemotherapy are the following:

- Anorexia
- Nausea and vomiting
- Stomatitis and mucositis
- Alopecia
- Bone marrow suppression

Chemotherapy is most often used in combination with other treatment modalities, such as surgery and radiation therapy. The development of chemotherapy has greatly improved the overall survival rate of patients and has actually led to the cure of some forms of cancer.

A malignant abnormal cellular growth's response to chemotherapy varies based upon the type of malignancy. Chemotherapy may be **curative** or **palliative**.

- **Curative** chemotherapy actually produces a cure of the cancer; this may be with the use of chemotherapy alone or in combination with other treatment modalities. Examples of some cancers that may be cured with the use of chemotherapy include gestational trophoblastic tumors, Wilms' tumor, osteogenic sarcoma, testicular cancer, Hodgkin's disease, acute lymphoblastic leukemia (ALL), and acute myeloblastic leukemia (AML).
- **Palliative** chemotherapy does not produce a cure, but is instead used to relieve the patient's symptoms. Unfortunately for some cancers, chemotherapy is completely ineffective. Some common forms of cancer that demonstrate little to no response to chemotherapy drugs include melanoma, head and neck, pancreas, stomach, and nonsmall cell lung cancers.

Chemotherapy drugs work by interfering with the phases of the cell cycle. The drugs can be placed into two classifications according to when they effectively target the cell cycle: cell-cycle phase specific drugs and cell-cycle phase nonspecific drugs.

- **Cell-cycle phase specific drugs** are effective when the cells are dividing.
- **Cell-cycle phase nonspecific drugs** are effective during all stages of the cell phases, whether the cell is dividing or resting.

Most chemotherapy drugs are administered in combination to take advantage of the different cell-cycle effects produced by the various medications. In addition, combination chemotherapy can also decrease the likelihood of the tumor developing drug resistance. The classification and action of chemotherapeutic agents is summarized in Table 18.1.

Table 18.1 Classification and Action of Chemotherapeutic Agents		
Classification	**Action**	**Examples**
Alkylating agents	• Cell-cycle phase nonspecific • Interfere with nucleic acid duplication, preventing mitosis	• Mechlorethamine (Mustargen; nitrogen mustard) • Cyclophosphamide (Cytoxan); cisplatin (Platinol)
Antibiotic (antitumor) drugs	• Cell-cycle phase nonspecific • Inhibit DNA and RNA synthesis	Doxorubicin (Adriamycin)
Vinca plant alkaloids (miotic inhibitors)	• Cell-cycle phase specific • Bind to cellular proteins, blocking cells' ability to divide	• Vincristine (Oncovin) • Vinblastine (Velban)
Antimetabolites	• Cell-cycle phase specific • Block essential enzymes necessary for DNA synthesis or act as an "imposter" building block for cell, interfering with production of DNA	• Fluorouracil (5-FU) • Methotrexate (Mexate)
Miscellaneous drugs	• Act through a variety of mechanisms • May be cell-cycle phase specific or nonspecific	• Asparaginase (Elspar) • Hydroxyurea (Hydrea) • Paclitaxel (Taxol)

The nursing management of the patient receiving chemotherapy is complex and multifaceted. The care of the patient receiving chemotherapy, including management of side effects, is addressed in the following chapters on nursing care.

Radiation Therapy

Radiation therapy (radiotherapy) involves the use of radioactive agents to kill malignant cells. It is a localized treatment specifically directed to an identified tumor. The goal of the therapy is to destroy as many cancer cells as possible while minimizing the effect on the surrounding normal tissues. Radiation therapy works by damaging cell DNA and affecting the cell's ability to grow and multiply. Radiation therapy may be used alone or in combination with surgery and chemotherapy. Radiation therapy may also be used palliatively to shrink the size of a tumor and decrease any symptoms related to tumor pressure. Radiation therapy is particularly effective in treating Hodgkin's disease and early stage breast, cervical, larynx, and prostate cancers. It is commonly used as adjuvant therapy in the treatment of bladder, later stage breast, head and neck, lung, brain, esophageal, and rectum cancers. Osteogenic sarcoma, liver, renal, and pancreatic cancers are not responsive to radiation therapy.

Tissue Radiosensitivity

Tissue radiosensitivity depends on several factors. Cells that are actively and rapidly dividing, poorly differentiated, and well oxygenated are more susceptible to radiation. These factors apply to both normal and malignant cells. Tissues such as bone marrow, gastrointestinal tract, and skin divide frequently and are especially sensitive to radiation. Because of this sensitivity, the side effects of radiation therapy frequently involve the skin, bone marrow, and gastrointestinal tracts. The most common side effects associated with radiation therapy are the following:

- Skin reactions
- Fatigue
- Nausea
- Anorexia
- Bone marrow suppression

External and Internal Radiation Therapy

There are two types of radiation therapy—external and internal. **External radiation** therapy is the most common form. External radiation is delivered by a linear accelerator machine that produces high-energy X rays that are delivered to deep body structures with a minimum of scattering. In external radiation, the rays are directed to a specific area of the body that has been carefully measured and outlined prior to the initiation of the therapy. Visible ink markings are placed on the patients to mark the areas of treatment. Special radiation-blocking molds may also be customized to the patient to shield organs from the radiation. For children especially, who may find it difficult to lie still and maintain a certain position, molds and other devices may be used to immobilize and protect the patient during treatment.

The length of the treatment will vary depending upon the type of cancer being treated and the dosage that needs to be delivered. Most treatment lasts from a period of two to eight weeks, with patients receiving a treatment daily, Monday through Friday. The actual treatment period is brief, taking about two to three minutes, and is painless.

Internal radiation therapy, which is used less frequently than external radiation, involves the actual placement of a radioactive substance in or near the tumor site. These radioactive substances are placed in a body cavity (e.g., cervix or rectum) or within the tissue itself (e.g., breast or prostate). The time the radioactive substances are in place varies, ranging from hours to several days. Individuals coming in contact with the patient during this time must be protected from exposure to the radiation by using a lead shield, maintaining a distance, and limiting the time spent in the presence of the patient.

Another form of internal radiation therapy is a liquid form radioisotope that may be taken orally, administered intravenously, or instilled into a body cavity. The radioisotope will be gradually eliminated from the body through the patient's urine, feces, or perspiration. Traces may also be found in emesis or wound drainage. Special precautions may need to be implemented to handle these body fluids during the time of radioactivity. The length of radioactivity depends on the half-life of the isotope.

The nursing management of the patient receiving radiation therapy, including management of side effects, is addressed in the following chapters on nursing care.

Biotherapy

Biotherapy has become the fourth modality used to treat cancer. As with the other treatments, biotherapy may be used alone or in combination with surgery, chemotherapy, or radiation.

Biotherapy is the use of **biologic response modifiers (BRMs)** to manipulate the immune system of the patient and alter the patient's biological response to cancer. BRMs can be naturally occurring cells or cell products, or they may be genetically engineered drugs. Manipulating the immune system through the use of BRMs can decrease the abnormal cellular growth of cancer, destroy cancer cells, interfere with the metastasis of cancer cells, or stimulate the growth of certain types of blood cells to support treatment efforts. The most common BRMs are monoclonal antibodies, interferons, interleukins, and colony-stimulating factors.

- **Monoclonal antibodies** are antibodies that are grown to target specific types of malignant cells. Monoclonal antibodies are currently used to help diagnose ovarian and colorectal cancer. Applications to other forms of cancer are under investigation.
- **Interferons (IFNs)** are classified as **cytokines**. Cytokines are proteins that are used to manipulate immune function. Interferons are glucoproteins that are produced by leukocytes. Interferons have antiviral and antitumor properties. They are used to facilitate cellular destruction and to inhibit cell multiplication.
- **Interleukins (ILs)**, which are also classified as cytokines, are produced primarily by the lymphocytes and monocytes. They appear to act by stimulating activity among the cells of the immune system, especially leukocytes.
- **Colony-stimulating factors (CSFs)** are also known as **hematopoietic growth factors**. CSFs are glycoprotein cytokines that are used to stimulate the growth of various blood cells. CSFs are primarily used to treat the bone marrow suppression side effects of other cancer treatment modalities such as chemotherapy and radiation therapy. For example, GM-CSF and G-CSF are used to treat neutropenia. Erythropoietin (EPO) is used to treat anemia. The use of CSFs to stimulate bone marrow recovery from treatment with chemotherapy helps decrease the incidence of life-threatening infections and allows for chemotherapy treatments to continue with less interruption.

Immunotherapy is a subcategory of biotherapy; its goal is to stimulate immune response through the use of nonspecific immunotherapy agents. It is considered to be an investigative form of biotherapy, but early clinical trials failed to produce the anticipated results. One area that has shown some promise, however, is the use of bacille Calmette-Guérin (BCG) in the treatment of localized malignant melanoma and bladder cancer. Research into immunotherapy is ongoing.

Because biotherapy can actually alter the patient's response to cancer, it is thought to demonstrate much promise for the future treatment of cancer. As the research of BRMs continues, this treatment modality will expand and become more common. It is the nurse's responsibility to be knowledgeable about biotherapy, as this treatment modality evolves and becomes more commonplace, and to provide the patient with education and support. Keeping up-to-date with current medical and nursing literature and research is important for nurses.

It is also important for the nurse to monitor the patient for the therapeutic and adverse effects of biotherapy. Side effects of biotherapy vary depending upon the agent used; however, frequent side effects include flu-like symptoms, fatigue, and signs of neurological toxicity. Management of the side effects includes providing a restful environment and treating the occurrence of flu-like symptoms with acetaminophen.

Bone Marrow Transplant

Bone marrow transplantation is used to treat a variety of cancers, including hematological cancers such as leukemias and lymphomas. In bone marrow transplantation, the patient receives high doses of chemotherapy and/or radiation therapy that is sufficient to destroy the malignant cells and the bone marrow. Then, harvested bone marrow is infused into the patient to reestablish a normally functioning bone marrow system that is capable of producing white blood cells, platelets, and red blood cells. Colony-stimulating factors are used to stimulate the return of normal bone marrow function.

The bone marrow that is to be transplanted is most commonly harvested three different ways:

1. **Allogeneic** (from an unrelated donor)
2. **Autologous** (from the patient)
3. **Syngeneic** (from an identical twin)

Another method, **peripheral blood stem cell bone marrow transplantation**, is relatively new and involves stimulating the production of the patient's stem cells through the use of colony-stimulating factors. The stem cells are then collected from the patient and stored for reinfusion later, after the cancerous bone marrow has been eradicated.

The period between when the patient's bone marrow is eradicated and replaced by new, normally functioning bone marrow that can produce new blood cells is called **engraftment**. Engraftment takes about two to four weeks to complete. This is a very difficult time for patients, and they require very close monitoring and skilled nursing care. First of all, the high doses of chemotherapy and/or radiation produce side effects that are intensified due to the high doses. These side effects include nausea, vomiting, stomatitis, diarrhea, and alopecia, as well as chronic liver, lung, and cardiac complications. Until engraftment is accomplished, patients are at a high risk for experiencing infection, sepsis, and bleeding. These complications may be fatal. Family members also require much support during these critical days.

Bone marrow transplantation is expensive, and many insurance companies do not cover the expenses. It is also a very complex, stressful procedure, and patients who are considered candidates for bone marrow transplantation must be very carefully assessed physically and psychologically before consenting to the treatment. The social support systems and financial resources of patients are also a consideration.

Health Teaching

In recent years, health-care research has indicated that emphasizing the prevention and early detection of cancer is believed to be the best way to decrease cancer mortality. The nurse has a significant role in the primary and secondary prevention of cancer. **Primary prevention** of cancer involves an emphasis on activities that prevent an individual's exposure to risk factors that might lead to the development of cancer. Nurses are in a key position to teach individuals how to minimize the risk factors for cancer:

- Decrease dietary fat.
- Increase dietary fiber.
- Increase amounts of fresh vegetables and fruits.
- Avoid obesity.
- Practice moderation with intake of smoked, salt-cured and nitrate-cured foods.
- Minimize alcohol intake.
- Do not smoke or chew tobacco.

The **secondary prevention** of cancer emphasizes the early detection and prompt treatment of cancer. Individuals must be educated about the early warning signs of cancer (Table 18.2).

Table 18.2 The Seven Warning Signs of Cancer
Change in bowel and bladder habits
A sore that does not heal
Unusual bleeding or discharge
Thickening or lump in breast or elsewhere
Indigestion or difficulty in swallowing
Obvious change in wart or mole
Nagging cough or hoarseness

In addition, screening to detect cancer is an important component of secondary prevention. Instructing women on the importance of doing monthly breast self-examination, obtaining mammograms as indicated, and to have annual Papanicolaou's tests is important in detecting breast and uterine cancer. Men should be instructed in monthly testicular self-examination to detect testicular cancer, and annual prostate examinations after age fifty, including a rectal examination and PSA analysis, to detect prostate cancer.

Men and women alike should be instructed about the importance of annual digital rectal examinations (after age forty), annual fecal occult blood tests (after age fifty), and sigmoidoscopy examination every five years after age fifty for the early detection of colorectal cancer.

The nurse's role in health education is an important one. Whether the nurse practices in the community, an acute care setting, or an office setting, health education about cancer prevention and early detection should be incorporated into the nurse's practice. Nurses can also model positive lifestyle behaviors through their own personal habits and choices.

Chapter 18 Study Questions

1. Identify six treatment modalities that can be used to treat abnormal cellular growth.

2. Describe the primary action of antineoplastic agents.

3. Why are steroids used to treat abnormal cellular growth?

4. Describe the primary actions of nonopioid and opioid analgesics.

5.   Explain why hormonal therapy can be used to treat malignant abnormal growths.

6.   Identify three reasons surgical intervention may be used to treat abnormal cellular growth.

7.   What are the general priorities of postoperative care following surgery for a malignancy?

8.   Describe the differences between curative chemotherapy and palliative chemotherapy.

9.   Describe what is meant by cell-cycle phase specific chemotherapy drugs and cell-cycle phase nonspecific drugs.

10.   What factors make tissue cells more sensitive to radiation therapy?

11.   Define external and internal radiation therapy.

12.   Describe biotherapy.

13. Describe the four most common biologic response modifiers (BRMs) used in biotherapy.

14. Describe the process used for bone marrow transplantation.

15. Explain the differences between primary and secondary prevention of cancer.

Answers to Chapter 18 Study Questions

1. Treatment modalities include medications, surgery, chemotherapy, radiation therapy, biotherapy, and bone marrow transplant.

2. Antineoplastic agents have a cytotoxic effect and are used to kill malignant tumor cells. They act in several ways, but primarily by interfering with cellular reproduction, inhibiting DNA and RNA formation, and inhibiting protein formation.

3. Steroids may be used in treatment of abnormal cellular growth for their anti-inflammatory and selective cytotoxic effect.

4. Nonopioid analgesics act primarily by inhibiting prostaglandin synthesis and decreasing inflammation, and/or by blocking peripheral pain impulses. Opioid analgesics alter pain perception by acting upon the central nervous system.

5. Hormonal therapy refers to the use of hormones or hormone-blocking agents to affect the growth of malignant abnormal cellular growth. There are some malignancies that grow in response to hormone stimulation. The cancers most frequently identified as being responsive to hormonal manipulation include some forms of breast, prostate, uterine, and adrenal gland cancers. Estrogens, androgens, and progestins are hormones that are commonly used to treat hormone-receptive tumors. Hormone-blocking agents, such as the anti-estrogen drugs used to treat some forms of breast cancer, can also be used. The hormones used for treatment are chosen based upon the type of cancer being treated and which hormones stimulate the abnormal growth of the cells. The goal is to alter the hormonal stimulus of the cancer and retard the growth of the malignancy.

6. Surgery is frequently used initially to diagnose and stage a disease. Surgery may also be curative. This means that the growth, either benign or malignant, is completely resectable, or removable, through surgery. In some cases, surgery is performed as a palliative measure to reduce the patient's symptoms or to provide a means for additional treatment.

7. Postoperatively, the nurse provides general postoperative care and monitors the patient for complications. Priorities of care following surgery include providing pain control and comfort, promoting adequate nutrition, preventing infection, and meeting the emotional needs of the patient and the family.

8. Curative chemotherapy actually produces a cure of the cancer; this may be with the use of chemotherapy alone or in combination with other treatment modalities. Palliative chemotherapy does not produce a cure, but is instead used to relieve the patient's symptoms.

9.   Chemotherapy drugs work by interfering with the phases of the cell cycle. The drugs can be placed into two classifications according to when they effectively target the cell cycle: cell-cycle phase specific drugs and cell-cycle phase nonspecific drugs. Cell-cycle phase specific drugs are effective when the cells are dividing. Cell-cycle phase nonspecific drugs are effective during all stages of the cell phases, whether the cell is dividing or resting.

10.   Tissue radiosensitivity varies depending on several factors. Actively and rapidly dividing, poorly differentiated, and well-oxygenated cells are more susceptible to radiation. These factors apply to both normal and malignant cells. Tissues such as bone marrow, gastrointestinal tract, and skin divide frequently and are especially sensitive to radiation. Because of this sensitivity, the side effects of radiation therapy frequently involve the skin, bone marrow, and gastrointestinal tracts.

11.   There are two types of radiation therapy—external and internal. External radiation therapy is the most common form and is delivered by a linear accelerator. In external radiation, the rays are directed to a specific area of the body that has been carefully measured and outlined prior to the initiation of the therapy. Internal radiation therapy, which is used less frequently than external radiation, involves the actual placement of a radioactive substance in or near the tumor site. These radioactive substances are placed in a body cavity (e.g., cervix or rectum) or within the tissue itself (e.g., breast or prostate). Another form of internal radiation therapy is a liquid form radioisotope that may be taken orally, administered intravenously, or instilled into a body cavity.

12.   Biotherapy is the use of biologic response modifiers (BRMs) to manipulate the immune system of the patient and alter the patient's biological response to cancer. Manipulating the immune system through the use of BRMs can decrease the abnormal cellular growth of cancer, destroy cancer cells, interfere with the metastasis of cancer cells, or stimulate the growth of certain types of blood cells to support treatment efforts. BRMs may be naturally occurring cells or cell products, or they may be genetically engineered drugs.

13.   The most common BRMs are monoclonal antibodies, interferons, interleukins, and colony-stimulating factors. Monoclonal antibodies are antibodies that are grown to target specific types of malignant cells. Interferons (IFNs) are classified as cytokines. Cytokines are proteins that are used to manipulate immune function. Interferons are glucoproteins that are produced by leukocytes. Interferons have antiviral and antitumor properties. They are used to facilitate cellular destruction and to inhibit cell multiplication. Interleukins (ILs) are also classified as cytokines, and are produced primarily by the lymphocytes and monocytes. They appear to act by stimulating activity among the cells of the immune system, especially leukocytes. Colony-stimulating factors (CSFs) are also known as hematopoietic growth factors. CSFs are glycoprotein cytokines that are used to stimulate the growth of various blood cells.

14.   In bone marrow transplantation, the patient receives high doses of chemotherapy and/or radiation therapy in order to destroy the malignant cells and the bone marrow. Harvested bone marrow is then infused into the patient to reestablish a normally functioning bone marrow system that is capable of producing white blood cells, platelets, and red blood cells. Colony-stimulating factors are used to stimulate the return of normal bone marrow function.

15.   Primary prevention of cancer involves an emphasis on activities that prevent an individual's exposure to risk factors that might lead to the development of cancer. The secondary prevention of cancer emphasizes the early detection and prompt treatment of cancer.

Chapter 19: Nursing Care for Tissue Hypertrophy

Key Terms

Benign prostatic hypertrophy (BPH)
Continuous bladder irrigation
Hypertrophic pyloric stenosis (HPS)
Transurethral resection of the prostate (TURP)

Introduction

This chapter will focus on nursing care of the patient with selected problems related to tissue hypertrophy. Most of the health problems experienced by patients with hypertrophied tissue are problems that are related to obstruction. Surgical intervention is frequently required to relieve symptoms and treat these cases, so the nurse should anticipate providing preoperative and postoperative care. Nursing care related to two common conditions resulting from hypertrophied tissues, hypertrophied pyloric stenosis and benign prostatic hypertrophy, will be discussed in this chapter.

Hypertrophic Pyloric Stenosis

Hypertrophic pyloric stenosis (HPS) is a congenital disorder of early infancy that results from hypertrophy of the pylorus muscle. It is one of the most common surgical disorders in infants. The cause is unknown, although there is a genetic predisposition towards the disorder. It is more common in males and in Caucasians.

Pathophysiology

In HPS, the pyloric muscle hypertrophies, causing a narrowing and partial obstruction of the pyloric channel that connects the stomach to the duodenum. Eventually, as the hypertrophied muscle enlarges, this narrowing can lead to complete obstruction of the pyloric channel. The stomach can become dilated as a result of the obstruction.

Clinical Manifestations

Initial indications of HPS at approximately two to four weeks of age may only be regurgitation of the infant's feeding or occasional nonprojectile vomiting. As the hypertrophied muscle continues to enlarge, the clinical manifestations of HPS include projectile vomiting after a feeding, signs of hunger, weight loss, and dehydration. Palpation of the abdomen reveals a small mass in the area of the epigastrium, and visible peristaltic waves may be seen as the stomach attempts to move the feeding through the area of obstruction. These later signs and symptoms are usually evident by the time the infant is six weeks old.

Diagnostic Tests

In addition to the above clinical manifestations, an upper GI X ray or ultrasound may be done. These tests will demonstrate the narrowed pyloric channel and delayed gastric emptying that are characteristic of HPS. Serum electrolytes will also be assessed to determine if there has been any electrolyte depletion as a result of the vomiting.

Medical Management

The infant who has been diagnosed with HPS will be treated surgically to relieve the pyloric obstruction. A **pyloromyotomy**, in which an incision is made in the upper right abdominal quadrant, may be performed to relieve the obstruction and remove the hypertrophied tissue.

More recently, laparoscopic surgery has been successful in treating HPS. With the use of the laparoscope, a smaller incision is used. This lessens the time spent in surgery and quickens recovery time. Prognosis is good for the infant, regardless of which surgical intervention is used.

Prior to surgery, the fluid and electrolyte status of the infant will be established. If the infant has become dehydrated, intravenous fluids and electrolytes will be infused to correct any fluid and electrolyte imbalances that have developed. The infant can develop hyponatremia and hypokalemia. Metabolic alkalosis can also develop.

Nursing Process: Assessment

The nurse will focus the assessment on the infant's history of feeding followed by vomiting. Evidence of weight loss and dehydration will also be gathered. The nurse will assess the infant's weight, frequency and amount of emesis, urinary output, and the infant's vital signs. Tachycardia, tachypnea, and hypotension may be present, indicating dehydration. The infant's fontanel should also be assessed; if shrunken, this is further evidence of dehydration. The color and moisture of mucous membranes should be assessed; dry, pale membranes are indicative of dehydration.

Nursing Process: Nursing Diagnosis and Planning

Based upon an analysis of the gathered data, the following **nursing diagnoses** may be appropriate for the infant with HPS:

- Fluid volume deficit (risk for) related to persistent vomiting
- Altered nutrition, less than body requirements related to persistent vomiting

Primary goals for the infant with HPS include the following:

- Demonstrates no signs of dehydration
- Has an adequate intake of fluids
- Demonstrates no sign of vomiting

- Tolerates and retains adequate amounts of feedings
- Parents are supported and informed of infant's care

Nursing Process: Implementation

Preoperative nursing care of the infant will involve the following nursing measures:

- Restoring and maintaining fluid and electrolyte balance through IV infusion
- Monitoring intake and output, including urinary specific gravity
- Assessing vital signs, skin turgor, and oral mucous membranes
- Measuring weight daily
- Maintaining nasogastric tube patency (if one is inserted) to decompress the stomach and decrease vomiting
- Providing support and information to the parents about the infant's condition and treatment

Postoperatively, the following nursing measures will receive priority:

- Monitoring IV fluids and patency of nasogastric tube if inserted
- Measuring intake and output
- Administering analgesics to control pain
- Resuming feedings with clear liquids within four to six hours postoperatively, in frequent, small amounts; progressing to breast milk or formula, as tolerated
- Positioning infant with head elevated
- Observing for signs of wound inflammation/infection
- Providing wound care
- Providing support and education for the parents
- Encouraging the parents to be involved in the infant's care

Nursing Process: Evaluation

The effectiveness of nursing interventions can be measured by the achievement of the following **expected outcomes** by the infant and family:

- Demonstrates no signs of dehydration
- Demonstrates adequate intake of fluids
- Demonstrates no sign of vomiting
- Tolerates and retains adequate amounts of feeding
- Recovers from surgery with no postoperative complications
- Family expresses understanding of and involvement in infant's care

Benign Prostatic Hypertrophy (BPH)

Benign prostatic hypertrophy (BPH) is a common disorder in men over age fifty. It is the most common reproductive system problem occurring in males, with 75 percent of men over age seventy developing the condition. Surgery can be performed to treat BPH if symptoms are serious enough. Developing BPH does not predispose a man to cancer of the prostate.

Pathophysiology

BPH is caused by enlargement of prostatic tissue. It is believed that the enlargement of tissue is the result of endocrine changes caused by increased levels of androgen. The enlarged prostate gland encircles and constricts the urethra. This constriction obstructs the flow of urine from the bladder. The bladder becomes irritable as a result of the urine retention, and over a period of time, the bladder muscle can hypertrophy. Prolonged retention of urine can result in urinary tract infections and hydronephrosis from urine reflux into the kidneys.

Clinical Manifestations

The most common clinical manifestations of BPH are related to urine obstruction. The severity of the symptoms of obstruction will vary, depending upon the location of the enlarged tissue. The patient typically complains of frequency of urination with incomplete bladder emptying. Hesitancy and difficulty starting the urine stream are also common, as is nocturia. The patient is likely to experience a decrease in the force and volume of urination. Dribbling may occur after voiding. Hematuria may also develop.

Diagnostic Tests

Diagnosis of BPH is usually made through the use of a digital rectal examination that reveals the presence of an enlarged prostate gland. Other diagnostic procedures may include a transrectal ultrasound of the prostate and a cystoscopy. In addition, a urinalysis with a culture is usually obtained to determine the presence of bacteria. Renal function studies, such as a BUN and creatinine, may be checked to detect any renal impairment. The BUN and creatinine are elevated if renal function has been affected by prolonged urinary retention. A prostate-specific antigen (PSA) level is obtained to rule out prostate cancer.

Medical Management

Initially, if the symptoms are mild, the BPH will be monitored without treatment. If treatment is necessary, pharmacological therapy may first be tried as a conservative treatment. Since BPH is thought to be due to an excess of androgen, the drug finasteride (Proscar) is prescribed to suppress dihydrotestosterone (androgens).

If conservative therapy is not successful, patients will undergo surgery to remove the hypertrophied tissue. The most common surgical procedure for treatment of a hypertrophied prostate is a **transurethral resection of the prostate (TURP)**. An endoscope is inserted through the urethra into the prostate; the prostate tissue is then removed through the scope. There is no surgical incision. Other procedures, which require an incision, include the **suprapubic prostatectomy**, **perineal prostatectomy**, and **retropubic prostatectomy**. These procedures are used for large hypertrophied prostates and allow for greater exploration of the surrounding tissues and organs.

Nursing Process: Assessment

The nurse will focus the assessment upon the patient's urinary pattern and clinical manifestations. The nurse should assess for the presence of urinary frequency, urgency, diminished stream, dribbling, and retention. The presence of nocturia can affect the patient's sleep pattern. Some patients will also decrease fluid intake to decrease urinary discomfort. The nurse should also assess the patient for any anxiety related to impending surgical procedures and the potential for sexual dysfunction. The bladder should be palpated for distention.

Nursing Process: Nursing Diagnosis and Planning

Prior to treatment of the BPH, the **primary nursing diagnoses** are as follows:

- Urinary retention related to urethral blockage secondary to enlarged prostate
- Pain related to bladder distention due to inability to void
- Anxiety related to lack of knowledge about potential surgical procedure and impact on sexual functioning

If surgical treatment is necessary, potential **postoperative nursing diagnoses** include the following:

- Pain related to bladder spasms
- Risk for urinary tract infection related to indwelling catheter
- Urge incontinence and dribbling related to altered sphincter control
- Anxiety related to concerns about altered sexual functioning

Primary goals for the patient following a TURP include the following:

- Relief of bladder pain from bladder spasms
- Absence of urinary tract infection
- Return of normal urinary elimination pattern
- Decreased anxiety about effect of surgery on sexual functioning

Nursing Process: Implementation

Nursing measures are similar following all prostate surgical procedures. The nursing measures discussed in this study guide focus on the care of the patient who has had a TURP, as this is the most common surgical procedure used to treat BPH.

The patient may have an indwelling urinary catheter in place prior to surgery to relieve urinary retention. Preoperatively, the nurse will answer the patient's questions and provide instruction about anticipated postoperative care. The nurse should instruct the patient to expect to have an indwelling catheter in place after surgery. **Continuous**

bladder irrigation may also be implemented. The patient should be instructed to anticipate hematuria and some blood clots. The nurse should answer any questions the patient may have about sexual functioning following surgery.

Postoperatively, nursing care for the patient with a TURP will focus on the following areas:

- Relieving pain
- Maintaining a patent urinary catheter
- Monitoring the patient for complications

Pain relief is a priority nursing measure following a TURP. Patients may experience bladder spasms due to bladder irritability. When patients experience bladder spasms, they frequently complain about having an urge to urinate and a sensation of bladder fullness, even though they have a catheter in place. The nurse may note the expression of blood and urine from around the catheter where it is inserted into the urethra. The nurse's first action should be to assess the patency of the catheter and to irrigate it if necessary. If the catheter is patent, the nurse can administer analgesics and medication that relaxes smooth muscle to relieve the bladder spasms. Sitz baths may also relieve the spasms.

Maintaining a patent urinary catheter is another priority nursing action. After a TURP, the catheter may become obstructed with a blood clot, thus interfering with urinary drainage. Retention of urine causes the patient great discomfort and can cause hemorrhage. The nurse must assess the urinary drainage system frequently and irrigate as necessary to ensure patency.

A **continuous bladder irrigation system** may be used following a TURP. This system consists of a three-way catheter with a bag of irrigating fluid attached to continuously irrigate the bladder and prevent clot formation. It is important for the nurse to maintain an accurate record of intake and output, including the amount of irrigating fluid that is instilled. The irrigating fluid that is inserted into the bladder must be returned into the drainage bag to prevent overdistention of the bladder.

The nurse should also monitor the patient for complications. The patient who has had a TURP is at risk for hemorrhage, deep vein thrombosis, and urinary tract infections.

- **Hemorrhage** is a potentially major complication following a TURP due to the vascular nature of the prostate tissue. The nurse should closely monitor the patient for signs of hemorrhage and shock. Frequent vital sign checks are necessary, and the patient should be checked carefully for signs of shock. Close observation of the color of the urinary drainage is also essential. Initially the drainage is a reddish pink. Within twenty-four hours of surgery, the urine color should begin to clear to a light pink. Bright red bleeding should be reported to the surgeon.

- **Deep vein thrombosis (DVT)** is another potential problem. The nurse should assess the patient carefully for signs of DVT and encourage the patient to ambulate.
- **Urinary tract infection** is another potential complication due to the insertion of the Foley catheter.

Nursing Process: Evaluation

The effectiveness of nursing interventions can be measured by the achievement of the following **expected outcomes** by the patient:

- Return of normal urinary functioning with no incontinence
- Demonstrates no signs of urinary tract infection
- Avoids complications post surgery

Chapter 19 Study Questions

1.   Describe the pathophysiology and clinical manifestations of hypertrophic pyloric stenosis.

2.   Describe the nursing assessments appropriate for an infant suspected of having hypertrophic pyloric stenosis.

3.   The nurse is caring for an infant who is scheduled to have a pyloromyotomy. What nursing measures are appropriate for the infant's preoperative care?

4.   The infant's mother asks when her baby can resume feeding following a pyloromyotomy. How should the nurse respond?

5.   Identify expected outcomes of care for an infant who has had surgery for hypertrophic pyloric stenosis.

6.   Describe the pathophysiology and clinical manifestations of benign prostatic hypertrophy.

7.   The nurse is caring for a patient who is suspected of having benign prostatic hypertrophy. What nursing assessments would be appropriate for this patient?

8.   Identify potential nursing diagnoses for a patient following a TURP.

9.   Describe two priority nursing measures for care of a patient following a TURP.

10.   Describe a continuous bladder irrigation (CBI) system and the accompanying nursing care.

11.   Identify patient complications commonly associated with TURP surgery.

Answers to Chapter 19 Study Questions

1. In HPS, the pyloric muscle hypertrophies, causing a narrowing and partial obstruction of the pyloric channel that connects the stomach to the duodenum. Eventually, as the hypertrophied muscle enlarges, this narrowing can lead to a complete obstruction of the pyloric channel. The stomach can become dilated as a result of the obstruction. Initial indications of HPS at approximately two to four weeks of age may only be regurgitation of the infant's feeding or occasional nonprojectile vomiting. As the hypertrophied muscle continues to enlarge, the clinical manifestations of HPS include projectile vomiting after a feeding, signs of hunger, weight loss, and dehydration. Palpation of the abdomen reveals a small mass in the area of the epigastrium, and visible peristaltic waves may be seen as the stomach attempts to move the feeding through the area of obstruction. These later signs and symptoms are usually evident by the time the infant is six weeks old.

2. The nurse will focus the assessment on the infant's history of feeding followed by vomiting. Evidence of weight loss and dehydration will also be gathered. The nurse will assess the infant's weight, frequency and amount of emesis, urinary output, and vital signs. Tachycardia, tachypnea, and hypotension may be present, indicating dehydration. The infant's fontanel should also be assessed; if shrunken, this is further evidence of dehydration. The color and moisture of mucous membranes should be assessed, with dry, pale membranes indicative of dehydration.

3. Preoperative nursing care of the infant will involve the following nursing measures: restoring and maintaining fluid and electrolyte balance through IV infusion; monitoring intake and output, including urinary specific gravity; assessing vital signs, skin turgor, and oral mucous membranes; measuring weight daily; maintaining nasogastric tube patency if one is inserted to decompress the stomach and decrease vomiting; providing support and information to the parents about the infant's condition and treatment.

4. The nurse should tell the mother that the infant can resume feedings with clear liquids within four to six hours postoperatively, in frequent, small amounts, progressing to breast milk or formula, as tolerated.

5. The effectiveness of nursing interventions can be measured by the achievement of the following expected outcomes by the infant and family: demonstrates no signs of dehydration; demonstrates adequate intake of fluids; demonstrates no sign of vomiting; tolerates and retains adequate amounts of feeding; recovers from surgery with no postoperative complications; and the family expresses understanding of and involvement in infant's care.

6. BPH is caused by enlargement of prostatic tissue. It is believed that the enlargement of tissue is the result of endocrine changes caused by increased levels

of androgen. The enlarged prostate gland encircles and constricts the urethra. This constriction obstructs the flow of urine from the bladder. The bladder becomes irritable as a result of the urine retention and over a period of time, the bladder muscle can hypertrophy. Prolonged retention of urine can result in urinary tract infections and hydronephrosis from urine reflux into the kidneys. The most common clinical manifestations of BPH are related to urine obstruction. The severity of the symptoms of obstruction will vary, depending upon the location of the enlarged tissue. The patient typically complains of frequency of urination with incomplete bladder emptying. Hesitancy and difficulty starting the urine stream are also common, as is nocturia. The patient is likely to experience a decrease in the force and volume of urination. Dribbling may occur after voiding. Hematuria may also develop.

7. The nurse will focus the assessment upon the patient's urinary pattern and clinical manifestations. The nurse should assess for the presence of urinary frequency, urgency, diminished stream, dribbling, and retention. The presence of nocturia can affect the patient's sleep pattern. Some patients will also decrease fluid intake to decrease urinary discomfort. The nurse should also assess the patient for any anxiety related to impending surgical procedures and the potential for sexual dysfunction. The bladder should be palpated for distention.

8. Potential nursing diagnoses for TURP are as follows: pain related to bladder spasms; risk for urinary tract infection related to indwelling catheter; urge incontinence and dribbling related to altered sphincter control; and anxiety related to concerns about altered sexual functioning.

9. Pain relief is a priority nursing measure following a TURP. Patients may experience bladder spasms due to bladder irritability. When patients experience bladder spasms, they frequently complain about having an urge to urinate and a sensation of bladder fullness, even though they have a catheter in place. The nurse may note the expression of blood and urine from around the catheter where it is inserted into the urethra. The nurse's first action should be to assess the patency of the catheter and to irrigate it, if necessary. If the catheter is patent, the nurse can administer analgesics and medication that relaxes smooth muscle to relieve the bladder spasms. Sitz baths may also help.

Maintaining a patent urinary catheter is another priority nursing action. After a TURP, the catheter may become obstructed with a blood clot, thus interfering with urinary drainage. Retention of urine causes the patient great discomfort and can cause hemorrhage. The nurse must assess the urinary drainage system frequently and irrigate as necessary to ensure patency.

10. A continuous bladder irrigation system may be used following a TURP. This system consists of a three-way catheter with a bag of irrigating fluid attached to continuously irrigate the bladder and prevent clot formation. It is important for the nurse to maintain an accurate record of intake and output, including the

amount of irrigating fluid that is instilled. The irrigating fluid that is inserted into the bladder must be returned into the drainage bag to prevent overdistention of the bladder.

11. The patient who has had a TURP is at risk for hemorrhage, deep vein thrombosis, and urinary tract infections.

Chapter 20: Nursing Care for Benign Abnormal Cellular Growths

Key Terms

Fibrocystic breast disease
Gestational trophoblastic neoplasia
    Hydatidiform mole
Uterine fibroids
Leiomyomas

Introduction

This chapter will focus on nursing care of the patient with selected problems related to benign abnormal cellular growth. A benign abnormal cellular growth is a well-differentiated, localized growth that usually produces symptoms related to pressure on surrounding tissues. Examples of common patient problems resulting from benign abnormal cellular growth include **uterine fibroids** and **fibrocystic breast disease**. Another example of a benign abnormal cellular growth problem is **gestational trophoblastic neoplasia (GTN)**, a term used to describe related disorders such as hydatidiform mole. The nursing care related to these health problems is discussed.

Uterine Fibroids

Uterine fibroids, or **leiomyomas**, are benign tumors that develop in the myometrium of the uterus. They are the most commonly occurring benign tumors of the pelvis. Fibroids occur more frequently in African-American women than Caucasian women.

Pathophysiology

The cause of fibroids is unknown, although their growth appears to be stimulated by estrogen. They are composed of smooth muscle cells and can develop in any of the layers of the uterus. Uterine fibroids tend to shrink in size as the woman enters menopause. Uterine fibroids do not predispose a woman to uterine cancer.

Clinical Manifestations

Uterine fibroids are frequently asymptomatic, depending upon their size and location. When symptoms do develop, bleeding is most common. Other symptoms include feelings of bladder, rectal, and pelvic pressure. Because of the bladder and rectal pressure, the patient may complain of urinary frequency or retention, and constipation. If the fibroid is large, the abdomen may be enlarged. The patient may also experience painful intercourse (**dyspareunia**) or problems with infertility. With the chronic loss of blood, some women develop iron-deficiency anemia.

Diagnostic Tests

Uterine fibroids are usually diagnosed through a pelvic examination that demonstrates an enlarged uterus with the presence of nodular tumors. CT scans, MRI, or sonography can also be used to confirm the diagnosis and determine the size and location of the tumors. An endometrial biopsy may also be done to confirm the diagnosis and rule out the presence of cancer.

Medical Management

If the fibroids are asymptomatic, they will be monitored without any treatment. As the woman approaches menopause and estrogen levels decrease, the fibroids will shrink. If the fibroids are symptomatic, surgical treatment may become necessary. In some cases, laser therapy may be used to resect the fibroid. In other cases, a **myomectomy** may be performed. A myomectomy allows for removal of the fibroid, leaving the uterus intact. However, fibroids are the most common cause for a woman to have a **hysterectomy**. In a hysterectomy, the entire uterus is removed. Either a vaginal or abdominal hysterectomy will be performed. The decision to perform a hysterectomy is influenced by several factors. These factors include the severity of the symptoms, the age of the patient, and the patient's desire to retain her ability to bear children.

Nursing Process: Assessment

The nurse assesses the patient's history of unusual bleeding and any complaints of bladder, rectal, or pelvic pressure. The nurse should determine if the patient has any difficulty with urinary frequency or retention. The nurse should also assess for the presence of constipation, which may occur as a result of rectal pressure from the fibroid. A woman who is anemic may complain of fatigue and a lack of ability in carrying out normal activities of daily living. The nurse should also ask the patient if she experiences painful intercourse. If the patient is scheduled for surgery, the nurse will assess the patient's understanding of the surgical procedure and will address any concerns the patient may have.

Nursing Process: Nursing Diagnoses and Planning

Prior to treatment for symptomatic uterine fibroids, the primary potential or actual **nursing diagnoses** include the following:

- Urinary elimination, altered, secondary to bladder pressure from uterine fibroid tumor
- Constipation secondary to rectal pressure from uterine fibroid tumor
- Potential for fatigue secondary to chronic blood loss and anemia
- Anxiety related to lack of knowledge about hysterectomy and impact on sexual functioning
- Sexuality patterns, altered, related to experiencing pain during intercourse

If the patient has a hysterectomy (vaginal or abdominal) as a result of the uterine fibroids, **postoperative nursing diagnoses** will include the following:

- Pain related to surgical intervention
- Urinary retention related to edema, loss of bladder tone, and pain
- Constipation related to surgical manipulation of bowel
- Sexuality patterns, altered, related to perceived feelings of undesirability and fear of partner rejection
- Potential for body image disturbance related to loss of uterus and childbearing ability

Primary goals of care following a hysterectomy include the following:

- Relief of pain
- Return of normal urinary elimination pattern
- Return of normal bowel elimination pattern
- Decreased anxiety about effect of surgery on sexual functioning
- Return of positive body image

Nursing Process: Implementation

Preoperative nursing care includes patient teaching to prepare the patient for surgery and address any concerns the patient may have about altered sexual functioning following surgery. The nurse should instruct the patient to expect an indwelling urinary catheter following surgery. If the patient is to have an abdominal hysterectomy, an abdominal incision will be present. Pain management will also need to be addressed and the importance of early ambulation emphasized.

Postoperatively, the nurse will administer analgesics to relieve pain. The nurse will provide catheter care, as the patient will likely have an indwelling catheter for the first twenty-four hours following surgery. Upon removal of the catheter, the patient's urinary elimination pattern will be monitored. It is common for patients to have some initial difficulty voiding, so the nurse should closely monitor the patient for urinary retention. The nurse should also closely assess for any indication of a urinary tract infection.

Early ambulation will be important to avoid the common postoperative complication of thrombophlebitis. Antiembolic compression stockings may be ordered to promote the return of peripheral circulation. Early ambulation also encourages the return of normal peristaltic activity. Complaints of abdominal pain due to gas are common, especially following an abdominal hysterectomy due to the surgical manipulation of the intestines.

For a patient who has had a vaginal hysterectomy, perineal care will be a necessity. Sitz baths and heat lamps may be used to promote healing and provide comfort.

Discharge teaching includes teaching the patient how to identify the signs of a urinary tract infection. Patients who have had an abdominal hysterectomy also need to know how to care for the incision; typically, the incision needs to be kept clean and dry, and is left open to air after the physician removes the surgical dressing. The patient should also be encouraged to continue mild exercise (walking) and to avoid prolonged sitting or long car rides. Heavy lifting should also be avoided. The patient can usually resume sexual intercourse approximately six weeks after surgery.

Nursing Process: Evaluation

The effectiveness of nursing interventions can be measured by the achievement of the following **expected outcomes** by the patient:

- Verbalizes relief of pain
- Demonstrates ability to urinate without difficulty
- Experiences return of normal peristaltic activity
- Verbalizes positive feelings related to body image and sexual functioning
- Avoids postoperative complications (wound infection, urinary tract infection, thrombophlebitis, paralytic ileus)

Fibrocystic Breast Disease

Fibrocystic breast disease is a benign breast disorder in which a woman develops cysts of various sizes, usually bilaterally. This may result in pain and nipple discharge. Fibrocystic breast disease is treated symptomatically. Fibrocystic breast disease can occur at any age, but it is especially common in women between the ages of forty and fifty. It is the most common breast disorder.

Pathophysiology

The cause of fibrocystic breast disease is not completely understood. However, it is believed the disorder is due to estrogen and progesterone hormone level changes. Fibrocystic breast disease does not predispose a woman to breast cancer; however, cystic breast changes may make it difficult to detect a cancerous lump if one should develop.

Clinical Manifestations

Cysts of varying sizes develop, and are soft and freely movable. The cysts increase and shrink in size, sometimes rapidly. Breast tenderness and pain increases before or during menstruation. The cysts almost always occur bilaterally and are most often found in the upper, outer quadrant of the breasts. Nipple discharge may also occur. The discharge may be milky, yellow, green, or dark brown in color.

Diagnostic Tests

When a breast mass is discovered, it is usually further examined by either biopsy or aspiration to determine if it is a cyst or a malignancy. It is important that women be taught how to conduct breast self-examination so that they can monitor the status of their breast tissue on a monthly basis. Any changes in symptoms should be promptly reported to a health-care professional for further evaluation. Regular mammography is also important.

Medical Management

Much of the medical management suggested for fibrocystic breast disease is not supported with scientific evidence. However, women do seem to obtain some relief by implementing the following suggestions:

- A good support bra is important to decreasing discomfort.
- Recommended dietary changes include eliminating methylxanthines, which are found in coffee, tea, chocolate, and cola, and decreasing salt intake. Vitamin E may be beneficial.
- Pharmacological therapy can include the use of danazol (Danocrine), which is an androgen that is used to decrease estrogen production, thus reducing symptoms.
- A mild analgesic may be prescribed.
- Stress reduction may also help reduce breast discomfort.

Nursing Process

When caring for a woman with fibrocystic breast disease, the nurse's primary responsibility is one of patient education. The nurse should help the patient understand the nature of the disorder and the recommended treatment. It is important for the nurse to teach the patient how to conduct monthly breast self-examination and emphasize the necessity of reporting any noted changes to a health-care professional.

Gestational Trophoblastic Neoplasia

Gestational trophoblastic neoplasia (GTN) represents several neoplastic diseases that result in an abnormal growth of the chorionic portion of the placenta. It is a tumor of the placenta. Some of the neoplasias are malignant and some are benign. A benign form of GTN is **hydatidiform mole**.

Pathophysiology

Hydatidiform mole is relatively uncommon, occurring in approximately 1 out of every 2,000 pregnancies. It is also referred to as a **molar pregnancy**, and may be characterized as partial or complete.

- In a **partial hydatidiform mole**, a fetus is present but does not develop normally and usually dies within the first three months of conception.
- In a **complete hydatidiform mole**, there is no fetal tissue present.

In hydatidiform mole, edematous villi proliferate. The mole takes on a grapelike appearance, and is attached to the lining of the uterus. The placenta continues to grow, without the presence of a fetus. Trophoblastic placental tissue causes rapid uterine growth, eventually resulting in bleeding. Hydatidiform mole is believed to be caused by genetic abnormalities that prevent normal fetal development and progression of the pregnancy.

Clinical Manifestations

At first, the pregnancy may appear to be normal, although the uterus may appear to be larger than expected. Vaginal bleeding is a common symptom of hydatidiform mole. The patient develops nausea and vomiting, which may be severe. Fetal heart tones will be absent. Blood and urine B-hCG levels will be higher than anticipated for the gestational age of the pregnancy. Patients may develop pre-eclampsia.

Diagnostic Tests

The diagnosis of a hydatidiform mole is usually made with an ultrasound that displays the characteristic appearance of the mole without the presence of a fetus.

Medical Management

Treatment of a gestational trophoblastic neoplasia is a dilatation and curettage (D & C) to remove the placental tumor. The patient's B-hCG levels will continue to be monitored to detect any malignant trophoblastic changes that may develop. The B-hCG levels should return to normal within six weeks of the D & C. The patient will be advised to avoid pregnancy for at least one year following the occurrence of the neoplasm and followed closely for the development of a potential malignancy.

Nursing Process: Assessment

The nurse will obtain a thorough health history from the patient. The physical examination will include a measurement of the fundal height, which will likely be greater than that anticipated for the gestational age, and auscultation for fetal heart sounds. Since the patient will likely report severe nausea and vomiting, the nurse should also assess for fluid and electrolyte imbalances. Vital signs should be noted, especially blood pressure. A patient who is pre-eclampsic will have an elevated blood pressure. The nurse should make note of any vaginal bleeding and look for evidence of clear, fluid-filled vesicles that may be noted in the vaginal discharge.

Nursing Process: Nursing Diagnosis and Planning

Based upon an analysis of gathered data, the following **nursing diagnoses** may be appropriate for the patient with gestational trophoblastic neoplasia:

- Fluid volume deficit related to excessive vomiting
- Anticipatory grieving related to pregnancy loss

Primary goals for the patient with gestational trophoblastic neoplasia include the following:

- Knowledge of gestational trophoblastic neoplasia and follow-up treatment
- Elimination of vomiting
- Maintenance of normal fluid balance
- Verbalization of feelings of loss and grief

Nursing Process: Implementation

Nursing measures will include preparing for the patient for a D & C and providing follow-up care. A primary nursing intervention will be providing patient instruction regarding the need for contraception and avoidance of pregnancy for at least one year. The nurse should also provide the patient with an opportunity to express her feelings about the loss of her pregnancy. It is also essential that the patient understand the need for follow-up medical care to detect any possible developments of a malignancy.

Nursing Process: Evaluation

The effectiveness of nursing interventions can be measured by the achievement of the following **expected outcomes** by the patient:

- Expresses understanding of disease process and treatment
- Expresses feelings of loss and grief
- Avoids complications

Chapter 20 Study Questions

1.   Identify potential nursing diagnoses for a patient who has symptomatic uterine fibroids.

2.   The nurse is caring for a patient who has had a vaginal hysterectomy because of uterine fibroids. Develop a care plan for this patient.

3.   The nurse is developing a teaching plan for a patient who has fibrocystic breast disease. What information should the nurse include in this plan?

4.   What are the clinical manifestations of a hydatidiform mole?

5.   What nursing assessments are appropriate for a patient suspected of having a hydatidiform mole?

6.   Describe appropriate nursing care for a patient with a hydatidiform mole.

Answers to Chapter 20 Study Questions

1.   Prior to treatment for symptomatic uterine fibroids, the primary potential or actual
      nursing diagnoses include the following: altered urinary elimination secondary to
      bladder pressure from uterine fibroid tumor; constipation secondary to rectal
      pressure from uterine fibroid tumor; potential for fatigue secondary to chronic
      blood loss and anemia; anxiety related to lack of knowledge about hysterectomy
      and impact on sexual functioning; and altered sexuality patterns related to
      experiencing pain during intercourse.

2.   Postoperatively, the nurse will administer analgesics to relieve pain. The nurse
      will provide catheter care, as the patient will likely have an indwelling catheter for
      the first twenty-four hours following surgery. Upon removal of the catheter, the
      patient's urinary elimination pattern will be monitored. It is common for patients
      to have some initial difficulty voiding, so the nurse should closely monitor the
      patient for urinary retention. The nurse should also closely assess for any
      indication of a urinary tract infection. Early ambulation will be important to
      avoid the common postoperative complication of thrombophlebitis. Antiembolic
      compression stockings may be ordered to promote the return of peripheral
      circulation. Early ambulation also encourages the return of normal peristaltic
      activity. For a patient who has had a vaginal hysterectomy, perineal care will be a
      necessity. Sitz baths and heat lamps may be used to promote healing and provide
      comfort. Discharge teaching includes teaching the patient how to identify the
      signs of a urinary tract infection. The patient should also be encouraged to
      continue mild exercise (walking) and to avoid prolonged sitting or long car rides.
      Heavy lifting should also be avoided. The patient can usually resume sexual
      intercourse approximately six weeks after surgery.

3.   A good support bra is important to decreasing discomfort. Recommended dietary
      changes include eliminating methylxanthines, which are found in coffee, tea,
      chocolate, and cola, and decreasing salt intake. Vitamin E may be beneficial. A
      mild analgesic may help breast discomfort. Stress reduction may also help reduce
      breast discomfort. The nurse should help the patient understand the nature of the
      disorder and the recommended treatment. It is important for the nurse to teach the
      patient how to conduct monthly breast self-examination and emphasize the
      necessity of reporting any noted changes to a health-care professional.

4.   At first, the pregnancy may appear to be normal, although the uterus may appear
      to be larger than expected. Vaginal bleeding is a common symptom of
      hydatidiform mole. The patient develops nausea and vomiting, which may be
      severe. Fetal heart tones will be absent. Blood and urine B-hCG levels will be
      higher than anticipated for the gestational age of the pregnancy. Patients may
      develop pre-eclampsia.

5.   The nurse will obtain a thorough health history from the patient. The physical examination will include a measurement of the fundal height, which will likely be greater than that anticipated for the gestational age, and auscultation for fetal heart sounds. Since the patient will likely report severe nausea and vomiting, the nurse should also assess for fluid and electrolyte imbalances. Vital signs should be noted, especially blood pressure. A patient who is pre-eclampsic will have an elevated blood pressure. The nurse should make note of any vaginal bleeding and look for evidence of clear, fluid-filled vesicles that may be noted in the vaginal discharge.

6.   Nursing measures will include preparing for the patient for a D & C and providing follow-up care. A primary nursing intervention will be providing patient instruction regarding the need for contraception and avoidance of pregnancy for at least one year. The nurse should also provide the patient with an opportunity to express her feelings about the loss of her pregnancy. It is also essential that the patient understand the need for follow-up medical care to detect any possible developments of a malignancy.

Chapter 21: Nursing Care for Cancer Patients

Key Terms

Alopecia
Bone marrow suppression
Cachexia
Fatigue
Leukopenia
Pain assessment scales
    Visual analogue scales
Pain management
Skin reaction
Stomatitis
Thrombocytopenia

Introduction

When caring for a patient who has been diagnosed with cancer and is undergoing treatment, the nurse must be aware of the common problems that patients with cancer can experience, regardless of the type of cancer. The problems may be a result of the underlying disease or may result from the cancer treatment of surgery, chemotherapy, and radiation therapy. These common problems include pain, infection, bleeding tendencies, impaired nutritional status, disruptions in skin and tissue integrity, fatigue, and psychosocial issues. It is important for the nurse to remain vigilant in his or her assessment of these potential problems and to implement an appropriate plan of care. Nursing measures for promoting patient comfort, tissue integrity, optimal nutrition, safety from bleeding and infection, and spiritual and emotional support will be covered in this chapter. These nursing measures are appropriate for all patients and family members, regardless of age or type of cancer.

Managing Pain

The majority of patients who have been diagnosed with cancer will experience pain and discomfort. This pain may be acute and/or chronic in nature; most frequently it is characterized as chronic. Pain may occur as a result of the disease process, or it may occur as a side effect of treatment. It affects every aspect of the patient's life, and quality of life becomes an issue.

With appropriate assessment and symptom management, the patient's pain can be controlled. Inadequate pain control is most likely the result of a poor understanding of pain management and misconceptions about the use of drug therapy by the health-care providers, the patient, and family members. It is seldom the case that adequate pain control cannot be achieved to provide the patient with an acceptable quality of life.

Nursing Process: Assessment

Adequate pain control begins with accurate pain assessment by the nurse. The nurse should assess the site, source, duration, and intensity level of the patient's pain. Aggravating and alleviating factors should be identified. Other factors to assess include the patient's religious and cultural beliefs, past experiences with pain, how the pain is interfering with activities of daily living, and how effectively the patient is coping with the pain. Psychosocial factors such as the presence of anxiety, fear, or fatigue, cultural beliefs, and spirituality can influence how a patient responds to pain and should also be carefully assessed by discussing these issues with the patient and family.

A **pain assessment scale** can be used to assess the pain and to also determine the effectiveness of interventions. Pain assessment scales provide a method by which the patient can rate the severity of pain, usually on a scale from zero to ten. These are referred to as **visual analogue scales** (**VAS**) and are used in many institutions. Some pain scales include pictures of facial expressions ("happy" face to "crying, sad" face) that patients can select from to rate the amount of pain they are experiencing. These are particularly effective with children, but are used with patients of all ages.

Nursing Process: Nursing Diagnosis and Planning

It is the nurse's responsibility to prevent, relieve, or control the patient's pain by implementing nursing measures that include pharmacological and nonpharmacological methods of management. The nurse should work with the patient to develop goals related to the control of pain. The patient may have a goal of eliminating pain. For many patients, a more realistic goal may be to decrease and control the intensity of the pain. Many patients also want to balance the control of pain and discomfort with being able to participate in activities that are meaningful to them. Keeping the patient's goals in mind and working collaboratively with the patient, the nurse can develop an effective plan for pain management.

The nurse should discuss pain management with the patient and identify what the patient's expectations are in relation to pain relief. From this information, mutually agreed upon goals for care can be established. Potential **nursing diagnoses** for a patient who is experiencing pain may include the following:

- Alteration in comfort, pain related to disease process and treatment
- Self-care deficit related to pain
- Activity intolerance related to pain
- Fatigue related to chronic cancer pain
- Ineffective management of therapeutic regimen related to lack of knowledge of pain management principles

Primary goals for the patient who has cancer pain include the following:

- Relief or satisfactory control of pain
- Maintenance of self-care activities at an acceptable level

- Increased tolerance of activity
- Relief from fatigue
- Increased knowledge of pain management

Nursing Process: Implementation

Pharmacological Interventions

The pharmacological interventions used for pain management will vary depending upon the extent of the patient's pain. The World Health Organization (WHO) has developed a **three-step approach** to managing cancer pain. Essentially, as the patient's pain increases, the strength of the analgesics used to treat the pain is also increased. For patients who are experiencing mild pain, nonopioid analgesics, such as NSAIDs and acetaminophen, are used. For moderate pain, weak opioids are used, and for severe pain, stronger opioids will be prescribed. **Adjuvant medications** may be used in conjunction with analgesics at any step in the process to enhance the effect of the analgesic. Examples of common adjuvant medications that are used to promote patient comfort include antidepressants, antiemetics, and stimulants.

For pain control to be most effective, it is important to administer the analgesics on a regularly scheduled basis, not a PRN ("as needed") basis. Routine administration of pain medication maintains therapeutic blood levels of the drugs and promotes more consistent pain control. Analgesics may be administered by various routes: orally, rectally, transdermally, parenterally, or intraspinally. The route chosen will be based upon the patient's condition and needs. In addition to receiving pain medication on a regularly prescribed schedule, patients will also receive medication for any "breakthrough" pain that may occur before the next regularly scheduled dose.

One method of administering analgesia is through the use of **patient-controlled analgesia (PCA)**. The goal of patient-controlled analgesia is to allow patients to self-medicate themselves within prescribed safety parameters. For the administration of parenteral medications, a PCA pump is used to deliver the medication. The pump can be used to deliver pain medication continually with boluses of the drug, as needed or intermittently. The patient pushes a button to deliver the medication when needed. The amount of medication that is delivered is preset by the nurse and controlled by the pump. Research has indicated that patients who use PCA achieve better pain control and may in fact require less medication than patients who are medicated PRN.

Patients who are experiencing severe pain may benefit from an intraspinal infusion of opioids. With the intraspinal route, a catheter is inserted into the subarachnoid or epidural space and medications are administered through the catheter. Directly administering pain medication into the subarachnoid space provides rapid pain relief with fewer side effects than systemically administered analgesics. The patient should be monitored closely for respiratory depression.

The nurse should be prepared to have a frank discussion with the patient, family members, and other health-care providers about the need for patients to take pain medication, even when they are not experiencing pain. Remember, that is why the patient is not experiencing pain—because they are being routinely medicated to prevent and control the pain! Not administering the medication will place the patient on a vicious cycle of inadequate pain control, making it impossible to achieve an optimum level of comfort for the patient. To withhold pain medication because of fears that the patient will become "addicted" is misguided and unethical.

Unfortunately, these fears have led to inadequate pain management for many. Over a period of time, the patient will likely develop a **tolerance** for opioids and will require increases of the dosages to maintain a therapeutic effect. Patients can also develop a **physical dependence** on opioids over a period of time. Neither tolerance nor physical dependence indicates that the patient is addicted. **Addiction** is the need, or compulsion, to take a drug for the psychological benefits it provides. Addiction is such a rare occurrence in patients who receive opioids for therapeutic management of pain that concerns about addiction should never be used as a reason to not provide pain relief to patients.

Nonpharmacological Interventions

Nonpharmacological methods can be used in conjunction with pain medication to control pain and promote comfort. The application of heat or cold, massage, therapeutic touch, and transcutaneous electrical nerve stimulation (TENS) are noninvasive methods that can be used. Relaxation techniques, music, distraction, imagery, humor, and prayer are additional methods. The nurse should explore these various techniques with the patient to determine which work most effectively for the patient.

Nursing Process: Evaluation

Expected patient outcomes related to the relief of pain include the following:

- Expresses feelings of decreased pain and discomfort to a tolerable, manageable level
- Expresses satisfaction with participation in activities of daily living
- Verbalizes increased knowledge about pain management
- Experiences relief from fatigue

Preventing Infection and Bleeding

Patients who have cancer are in a compromised state from the disease and treatment. They are particularly susceptible to developing complications, such as bleeding and infection, that can be life threatening. Bleeding and infection are the two most common life-threatening complications that the patient with cancer faces. The nurse has a prominent role in promoting patient safety and preventing the development of these complications through vigilant assessment, prompt intervention, and patient education.

Nursing Process: Assessment

Patients with cancer are at an increased risk for infections. In fact, infection is the leading cause of death in patients with cancer. Nurses should be alert to assessing for early indications of infection. Common sites for infection include the lungs, urinary tract, throat, perianal area, and skin. Infection may occur as a result of the malignancy, invasive procedures, skin/mucous membrane impairment, or malnutrition. Patients may also be predisposed to infection as a result of treatment. Chemotherapy, radiation therapy, and some biologic response modifiers can all cause bone marrow suppression, leading to leukopenia (decreased white blood cells).

The patient with cancer should also be carefully assessed for signs of bleeding. A common cause of bleeding is bone marrow suppression resulting from chemotherapy and radiation therapy. Medications may also interfere with coagulation. Mucous membranes, gastrointestinal, urinary, and respiratory tracts are common sites of bleeding. Patients should be closely assessed for ecchymosis (bruising), petechiae, change in mental status, and the presence of blood in the stools, urine, emesis, or sputum.

Nursing Process: Nursing Diagnosis and Planning

Potential **nursing diagnoses** for the patient are the following:

- Infection, risk for, related to decreased immune response
- Bleeding, risk for, related to disease process and treatment

A **primary goal** of the patient is to avoid the complications of infection and bleeding.

Nursing Process: Implementation

A significant complication of chemotherapy and radiation therapy is bone marrow suppression that can cause decreased platelets (thrombocytopenia) and white blood cells (leukopenia). Some forms of cancer, such as leukemia and lymphoma, also lead to the development of thrombocytopenia and leukopenia. Nurses must be careful to implement safety measures to help prevent the development of bleeding or hemorrhage that can result from thrombocytopenia and infection that can develop because of leukopenia.

The nurse should monitor laboratory values carefully to detect **thrombocytopenia**. When platelet counts are between 20,000 and 50,000 mm^3, the patient is at a moderate risk for bleeding; below that, the patient is placed at a severe risk for bleeding. The patient should be assessed closely for change in mental status that can indicate cerebral bleeding, petechiae, ecchymosis, bleeding gums, hematuria, hematemesis, and blood in the stools. The patient should also be assessed for prolonged bleeding from any venipuncture or injection sites, or slight cuts.

To decrease the chances of bleeding, the patient should be instructed to use an electric shaver instead of a straight razor, and a soft toothbrush should be used for oral hygiene. To minimize oral tissue trauma, the patient should avoid foods that are hard to chew and any substance, such as commercial mouthwash, that may be drying to the mucosa. In addition, invasive procedures should be avoided as much as possible. All puncture sites must have direct pressure applied for a minimum of five minutes. The patient should be instructed to avoid the Valsalva maneuver, forceful nose blowing, and coughing, as these actions can cause bleeding. Rectal medications and temperatures should also be avoided to prevent rectal tissue trauma. Stool softeners are used to prevent constipation and prevent straining. Water-based lubricants are recommended for use during sexual intercourse to decrease friction and trauma. Medications that can interfere with clotting (e.g., aspirin) must be avoided. If the patient is at a severe risk for bleeding, strenuous activity should be avoided to decrease risk of injury.

The nurse should also closely monitor the patient for **leukopenia (decreased WBCs)** and implement safety measures to prevent infection. In addition to monitoring the patient for leukopenia, the **absolute neutrophil count (ANC)** is monitored. A decreased concentration of neutrophils further increases the patient's risk for infection. Bone marrow suppression is an expected side effect of chemotherapy and radiation therapy. **Nadir** is the term used when the ANC has reached its lowest level following therapy.

Vital signs are taken every four hours and WBC and ANC values are monitored daily. The patient should be monitored closely for signs of infection, including the presence of a temperature or chills. Any elevation in temperature over 101° Fahrenheit should be promptly reported. The patient is encouraged to cough and deep breathe every two hours to prevent the development of atelectasis and respiratory infections. Strict asepsis is used when performing any invasive procedures and manipulating any intravenous lines, urethral catheters, or any other invasive lines. These invasive lines are common sources of nosocomial infections in immunosuppressed patients.

Good hand washing is important for all individuals coming in contact with the patient, and good personal hygiene is important for the patient as well. Rectal and vaginal examinations are avoided to decrease trauma and chance of infection. Fresh flowers, vegetables, and fruits are avoided, as they can carry bacteria to which the immunosuppressed patient may be susceptible. A private room may be desirable and visitors limited. If patients are severely immunosuppressed (absolute WBC of less than 1000/mm^3), they may be placed in protective isolation.

Nursing Process: Evaluation

Expected patient outcomes related to the potential complications of bleeding and infection are as follows:

- Has no evidence of infection
- Has no evidence of bleeding, petechiae, or ecchymosis

Promoting Nutritional Status

Nursing Process: Assessment

Assessing the patient's nutritional status is an important nursing responsibility when caring for the patient with cancer. An impaired nutritional status can delay healing, delay treatment, cause immune incompetence, and lead to generalized debility of the patient. Weight loss and cachexia, which is emaciation, are common nutritional problems. Anorexia, nausea and vomiting, stomatitis, difficulty with chewing and swallowing, and diarrhea are problems that can affect the patient's nutritional intake. These problems can also lead to a fluid volume deficit. The nurse should closely monitor the patient's diet, fluid intake, caloric intake, and weight.

Nursing Process: Nursing Diagnosis and Planning

Potential **nursing diagnoses** related to nutritional status are as follows:

- Altered nutrition, less than body requirements related to anorexia, nausea and vomiting, cachexia, and/or stomatitis
- Fluid volume deficit, risk for, related to side effects of chemotherapy drugs (nausea, vomiting, diarrhea)

Primary goals of the patient are to:

- Maintain optimal nutritional intake
- Minimize weight loss to 10 percent of pretreatment weight
- Maintain adequate fluid intake

Nursing Process: Implementation

Anorexia, nausea, vomiting, and cachexia are common problems for patients with cancer. Anorexia, nausea, and vomiting are frequently caused by cancer treatment, especially chemotherapy. Radiation therapy, particularly to the head and neck region, can cause anorexia, nausea, vomiting, and taste impairment. These problems make it difficult for the patient to maintain an optimal nutritional and fluid intake. Cachexia develops during advanced disease, due to the increasing metabolic and competing nutritional demands of the tumor accompanied by a decreased nutritional intake. Inadequate nutrition and decreased fluid intake can lead to weight loss, impair skin integrity, contribute to fatigue, and impede the healing process.

There are numerous nursing measures that can help promote optimal nutrition. These nursing measures include the following:

- Providing frequent oral hygiene prior to meals and throughout the day
- Relieving pain, especially before mealtime
- Serving small, frequent feedings throughout the day
- Providing a high-calorie, high-protein diet with bland foods

- Providing nutritional supplements
- Maintaining a quiet environment, free of odors, during mealtime
- Encouraging fluid intake
- Administering antiemetic medications to control nausea and vomiting; during chemotherapy treatments these medications are administered **prior** to the patient developing any symptoms of nausea or vomiting
- Increasing activity level as tolerated

If the patient is not able to take in enough food orally to maintain adequate nutrition, other nutritional interventions will be necessary. Continuous enteral feedings or total parenteral nutrition (TPN) may be implemented. Intravenous fluids can also be administered to replace fluid volume and electrolytes.

Nursing Process: Evaluation

Expected patient outcomes related to the maintenance of optimal nutrition and fluid intake include the following:

- Experiences decreased incidences of anorexia, nausea and vomiting, diarrhea
- Maintains body weight
- Demonstrates no signs of dehydration
- Maintains normal elimination patterns

Preserving Skin and Tissue Integrity

The patient may experience disruptions in skin and tissue integrity due to side effects of chemotherapy and radiation therapy, and poor nutrition. Invasive procedures also disrupt tissue integrity, predisposing the patient to infection.

Nursing Process: Assessment

The nurse should carefully assess the oral mucous membranes of the patient, as this is a common site for disruption of tissue integrity. The gastrointestinal tract is particularly sensitive to chemotherapy and radiation therapy, resulting in the side effects of anorexia, nausea and vomiting, and diarrhea. **Alopecia** (hair loss) also occurs as a result of chemotherapy or radiation therapy and may affect the patient psychologically. Radiation may also cause a disruption of skin integrity in the area being irradiated and requires special care of the skin.

Nursing Process: Nursing Diagnosis and Planning

Potential **nursing diagnoses** related to skin and tissue integrity include:

- Altered oral mucous membranes related to treatment stomatitis
- Impaired tissue integrity related to effects of radiation therapy treatments and disease

A **primary goal** for the patient is to maintain tissue integrity.

Nursing Process: Implementation

Specific problems of tissue integrity include stomatitis, alopecia, and skin reactions from radiation therapy. There are several nursing measures that can be implemented to promote tissue integrity.

Stomatitis

Stomatitis, which is inflammation of the oral tissues, can cause the patient to have difficulty eating due to the pain caused by the inflammation and ulcerations that can develop. Chemotherapy may cause stomatitis due to bone marrow suppression, which increases the patient's risk for infection. Radiation therapy in the head and neck area can also lead to stomatitis.

Good oral hygiene can help prevent the development of stomatitis. A soft-bristled toothbrush is used to minimize irritation. Flossing and rinsing with normal saline or water every two hours while awake is also encouraged. Flossing is discouraged if the patient's platelet count is low, as bleeding may occur. Lips should be lubricated to avoid dryness. Other measures include avoiding irritating substances, such as alcohol-based mouthwashes. Foods should be easy to chew, nonspicy, and not too hot. Applying topical anesthetics like viscous lidocaine can help minimize discomfort during mealtimes and oral hygiene.

Alopecia

Alopecia (hair loss) develops in response to chemotherapy and radiation therapy. For most individuals, hair loss will begin about two to three weeks after treatment is started. The hair becomes brittle and begins to break off and fall out. This hair loss can cause anxiety, depression, and lead to an altered body image. Provide time to allow the patient to verbalize fears and concerns about hair loss. Telling the patient that the hair will grow back after treatment is completed may help the patient cope with the change.

Hair usually begins to grow back about two months after the last treatment. The hair may have a different color and texture. Care of the scalp includes gentle cleansing of the scalp and protecting the scalp from exposure to heat and cold. Wigs, scarves, and hats may be used to cover the scalp while the hair grows back. It is important to cover the scalp to protect it from the sun and temperature extremes. Wigs and hairpieces should be purchased before hair loss occurs to help the individual cope with the impending hair loss.

Skin Reactions

Skin reactions due to radiation therapy can develop during treatment. The patient should be taught how to carefully protect the skin to prevent irritation and dryness. Radiation skin care varies from agency to agency, so the nurse should be familiar with the policies of the institution. Typical care includes gentle daily cleansing of the skin with lukewarm water. The area should be patted dry and not rubbed. Lotions, perfumes, deodorants, harsh soaps, and powders are not applied to the area that is being radiated. Only prescribed creams or ointments should be applied to the skin. Restrictive clothing should be avoided over the area, as that can promote skin irritation. The skin should be protected from the sun and the cold. Straight-edged razors should not be used over the area. Heating pads, hot water bottles, and ice can further damage the skin and should be avoided. **Wet desquamation**, which is the formation of blisters and weeping skin, can develop. Skin that begins weeping should be cared for carefully to avoid introducing an infection. Blisters should not be broken. Moisture dressings and topical antibiotics may be prescribed for use on the area.

Nursing Process: Evaluation

Expected patient outcomes related to the maintenance of skin and tissue integrity include the following:

- Avoids oral mucous membrane infections
- Maintains intact oral mucosa
- Maintains skin integrity

Relieving Fatigue

Fatigue is a common problem of patients with cancer, most often occurring in association with chemotherapy and radiation therapy. The fatigue is chronic and can be overwhelming for the patient, seriously affecting quality of life.

Nursing Process: Assessment

The nurse should assess the patient carefully for signs of fatigue and note the impact of fatigue on the patient's ability to carry out activities of daily living. The nurse should also assess the patient for other factors that can contribute to fatigue, including pain, anxiety, and poor nutrition.

Nursing Process: Nursing Diagnosis and Planning

Potential **nursing diagnoses** related to fatigue include the following:

- Fatigue related to disease process and treatment
- Activity intolerance related to fatigue

Primary goals for the patient include the following:

- Management of fatigue
- Increased activity tolerance
- Participation in activities of daily living

Nursing Process: Implementation

The nurse should collaborate with the patient to develop a plan of care that will minimize the effects of the fatigue. The following are measures that might help with fatigue:

- Alternating activity with frequent rest periods throughout the day is essential, as are increased hours of nighttime sleep.
- Mild exercise, such as yoga and walking, can be effective in combating fatigue, as can relaxation exercises. Diversionary activities are helpful as well.
- Nutritional intake should be examined to ensure an adequate amount of protein and calorie intake.
- The patient may need to consider accepting assistance from others to help with carrying out roles and responsibilities.
- Coping with fatigue can be challenging, so the nurse should provide time for the patient to express frustration and explore ways to increase coping skills.

Nursing Process: Evaluation

Expected outcomes related to the management of fatigue are as follows:

- Expresses decreased fatigue levels
- Maintains a satisfactory level of involvement in activities of daily living

Providing Psychosocial Support

Nursing Process: Assessment

The psychosocial issues are many when caring for a patient with cancer. For example, the nurse needs to carefully assess the impact of the disease and treatment on the patient. Anger, fear, and anxiety are common feelings associated with a life-threatening illness. Body image and self-esteem changes can be significant, especially when faced with some of the life-altering changes in body functioning and appearance that occur as a result of surgery and treatment. The patient's self-concept is affected as roles and responsibilities change and the possibility of death is considered. It is important that the nurse assess the patient's and family's ability to cope with the effects of the disease and its treatment.

The nurse should also assess where the patient and family are with the grieving process. Kübler-Ross identified five stages of grieving: denial, anger, bargaining, depression, and acceptance. Is the patient or family in denial about the diagnosis of cancer, or are there feelings of anger, hostility, or depression? If the patient is a child, how are the parents coping with anticipatory grief over the loss of the child? Is there communication between the patient and family members, or are they avoiding discussion of the diagnosis and its implications? Has the patient accepted the diagnosis, but the family members are still in denial? The nurse must remember that working through the stages of grief is highly individualized and variable.

Nursing Process: Nursing Diagnosis and Planning

Potential **nursing diagnoses** related to psychosocial concerns are as follows:

- Grieving related to anticipated loss and altered role function
- Body image disturbance related to changes in appearance and role function
- Altered family processes related to having a family member with a life-threatening illness
- Anticipatory grieving related to perceived loss of a child
- Diversionary activity deficit related to hospitalization and restricted environment

Primary goals for the patient who has cancer include the following:

- Provision of emotional and spiritual support
- Progression through the grieving process
- Maintenance of body image and self-concept
- Demonstration of effective coping skills

Nursing Process: Implementation

Patients who have been diagnosed with cancer require a significant amount of support to assist them in coping with the diagnosis, as does their family. The nurse needs to be sensitive to providing the patient and family with opportunities to share their fears and concerns. The nurse can also foster open, honest communication between the patient and family. The nurse can encourage the patient and family to discuss their concerns and express their feelings, whether they are feelings of anger, fear, guilt, depression, or hopelessness. Patients and family members may need to be told that their feelings are valid and normal. It is normal for individuals to be at different stages of the grief process.

The patient's support system should be assessed. Social services, counseling, and support groups can be accessed to provide support for the patient and family. The spiritual needs of the patient should be assessed as well, and the appropriate clergy contacted for the patient. Professional counseling may be indicated.

Nursing Process: Evaluation

Expected patient and family outcomes related to psychosocial issues include the following:

- Verbalizes knowledge of disease and treatment
- Progresses appropriately through the stages of the grief process
- Verbalizes acceptance of body appearance and role function changes
- Participates in enjoyable diversionary activities
- Family members verbalize feelings to nurse and each other
- Family members provide support for each other

- Family members express grief
- Family members cope with the potential loss of child

Home Care of the Patient with Cancer

Patients with cancer receive much of their treatment in the home setting and are hospitalized only for acute health problems. Today's advanced technology allows patients to receive intravenous fluids and medications, such as blood products, chemotherapy, pain medication, antiemetics, antibiotics, and nutritional therapy in the home with the support and guidance of the home health nurse. Even with the care provided by the home health nurse, the patient and family assume much of the responsibility for providing care. Thorough teaching is essential to enable the patient and family to safely assume these responsibilities.

The home health care nurse is responsible for evaluating the following:

- Patient's home environment
- Patient and family's knowledge and ability to provide care
- Need for psychological support
- Effectiveness of pain management plan and other therapies

It is the home health nurse's responsibility to coordinate the patient's care between and among other health-care providers. The home health nurse facilitates continuity and coordination of the patient's care. The nurse can also help the patient and family access community resources and support groups.

If the patient is terminal, the nurse will help the patient and family make the decision of when to accept hospice care. Hospice programs support the patient and family through the terminal stages of the patient's illness, helping them to voice their fears and feelings of grief and loss. Helping the patient and family maintain open channels of communication is essential to achieving a peaceful death for the patient. Following the patient's death, families can continue to receive support through hospice as they grieve and cope with the death.

Chapter 21 Study Questions

1.   The nurse is caring for a patient with lung cancer who is experiencing pain.
        Identify some of the factors the nurse should include in an assessment of this
        patient's pain.

2.   Identify potential nursing diagnoses that would be appropriate for a patient
        experiencing pain.

3.   Describe the World Health Organization (WHO) three-step approach to managing
        cancer pain.

4.   What is the most effective means of achieving pain control for patients experiencing chronic cancer pain?

5.   What are the two most common life-threatening complications that can affect patients with cancer?

6.   The nurse is caring for a patient who has thrombocytopenia as a result of chemotherapy. What safety factors should the nurse incorporate into the patient's plan of care?

7.   A patient who has been receiving chemotherapy has a white blood count of $1000/mm^3$. What safety factors should the nurse implement for this patient?

8.   Describe nursing measures that can be used to promote adequate nutrition in a patient who is experiencing anorexia and nausea as a result of radiation therapy.

9.   A patient has bone marrow suppression. What nursing measures should be implemented to prevent the development of stomatitis?

10.   A patient is beginning radiation therapy for breast cancer. What should the nurse tell the patient about skin care for the area receiving radiation?

11.   A patient who is receiving radiation therapy complains of persistent feelings of fatigue and asks the nurse what he should do to relieve the fatigue. How should the nurse respond?

Answers to Chapter 21 Study Questions

1.   Adequate pain control begins with accurate pain assessment by the nurse. The nurse should assess the site, source, duration, and intensity level of the patient's pain. Aggravating and alleviating factors should be identified. Other factors to assess include the patient's religious and cultural beliefs, past experiences with pain, how the pain is interfering with activities of daily living, and how effectively the patient is coping with the pain. Psychosocial factors, such as the presence of anxiety, fear, or fatigue, cultural beliefs, and spirituality, can influence how a patient responds to pain and should also be carefully assessed by discussing these issues with the patient and family.

2.   Nursing diagnoses may include the following: alteration in comfort, pain related to disease process and treatment; self-care deficit related to pain; activity intolerance related to pain; fatigue related to chronic cancer pain; and ineffective management of therapeutic regimen related to lack of knowledge of pain management principles.

3.   The World Health Organization (WHO) has developed a three-step approach to managing cancer pain. Essentially, as the patient's pain increases, the strength of the analgesics used to treat the pain is also increased. With patients who are experiencing mild pain, nonopioid analgesics, such as NSAIDs and acetaminophen, are used. With moderate pain, weak opioids are used, and for severe pain, stronger opioids will be prescribed. Adjuvant medications may be used in conjunction with analgesics at any step in the process to enhance the effect of the analgesic. Examples of common adjuvant medications that are used to promote patient comfort include antidepressants, antiemetics, and stimulants.

4.   For pain control to be most effective, it is important to administer the analgesics on a regularly scheduled basis, not a PRN ("as needed") basis. Routine administration of pain medication maintains therapeutic blood levels of the drugs and promotes more consistent pain control. Analgesics may be administered by various routes: orally, rectally, transdermally, parenterally, or intraspinally. The route chosen will be based upon the patient's condition and needs. In addition to receiving pain medication on a regularly prescribed schedule, patients will also receive medication for any "breakthrough" pain that may occur before the next regularly scheduled dose.

5.   Bleeding and infection are the two most common life-threatening complications that the patient with cancer faces.

6.   To decrease the chances of bleeding, the patient should be instructed to use an electric shaver instead of a straight razor, and a soft toothbrush should be used for oral hygiene. To minimize oral tissue trauma, the patient should avoid foods that are hard to chew and any substance, such as commercial mouthwash, that may be drying to the mucosa. In addition, invasive procedures should be avoided as

much as possible. All puncture sites must have direct pressure applied for a minimum of five minutes. The patient should be instructed to avoid the Valsalva maneuver, forceful nose blowing, and coughing, as these actions can cause bleeding. Rectal medications and temperatures should also be avoided to prevent rectal tissue trauma. Stool softeners are used to prevent constipation and prevent straining. Water-based lubricants are recommended for use during sexual intercourse to decrease friction and trauma. Medications that can interfere with clotting (e.g., aspirin) must be avoided. If the patient is at a severe risk for bleeding, strenuous activity should be avoided to decrease risk of injury.

7.   Vital signs are taken every four hours and WBC counts are monitored daily. The patient should be monitored closely for signs of infection, including the presence of a temperature or chills. Any elevation in temperature over 101° Fahrenheit should be promptly reported. The patient is encouraged to cough and deep breathe every two hours to prevent the development of atelectasis and respiratory infections. Strict asepsis is used when performing any invasive procedures and manipulating any intravenous lines, urethral catheters, or any other invasive lines. These invasive lines are common sources of nosocomial infections in immunosuppressed patients. Good hand washing is important for all individuals coming in contact with the patient, and good personal hygiene is important for the patient as well. Rectal and vaginal examinations are avoided to decrease trauma and chance of infection. Fresh flowers, vegetables, and fruits are avoided, as they can carry bacteria to which the immunosuppressed patient may be susceptible. A private room may be desirable and visitors limited.

8.   Nursing measures include providing frequent oral hygiene prior to meals and throughout the day; relieving pain, especially before mealtime; serving small, frequent feedings throughout the day; providing a high-calorie, high-protein diet with bland foods; providing nutritional supplements; maintaining a quiet environment, free of odors, during mealtime; encouraging fluid intake; administering antiemetic medications to control nausea and vomiting; and increasing activity level as tolerated.

9.   Good oral hygiene can help prevent the development of stomatitis. A soft-bristled toothbrush is used to minimize irritation. Flossing and rinsing with normal saline or water every two hours while awake is also encouraged. Flossing is discouraged if the patient's platelet count is low, as bleeding may occur. Lips should be lubricated to avoid dryness. Other measures include avoiding irritating substances, such as alcohol-based mouthwashes. Foods should be easy to chew, nonspicy, and not too hot. Applying topical anesthetics like viscous lidocaine can help minimize discomfort during mealtimes and oral hygiene.

10.   Skin reaction due to radiation therapy can develop during treatment. The patient should be taught how to carefully protect the skin to prevent irritation and dryness. Radiation skin care varies from agency to agency, so the nurse should be familiar with the policies of the institution. Typical care includes gentle daily

cleansing of the skin with lukewarm water. The area should be patted dry and not rubbed. Lotions, perfumes, deodorants, harsh soaps, and powders are not applied to the area that is being radiated. Only prescribed creams or ointments should be applied to the skin. Restrictive clothing should be avoided over the area, as that can promote skin irritation. The skin should be protected from the sun and the cold. Straight-edged razors should not be used over the area. Heating pads, hot water bottles, and ice can further damage the skin and should be avoided. Wet desquamation, which is the formation of blisters and weeping skin, can develop. Skin that begins weeping should be cared for carefully to avoid introducing an infection. Blisters should not be broken. Moisture dressings and topical antibiotics may be prescribed for use on the area.

11.   The nurse should collaborate with the patient to develop a plan of care that will minimize the effects of the fatigue. Alternating activity with frequent rest periods throughout the day is essential, as are increased hours of nighttime sleep. Mild exercise, such as yoga and walking, can be effective in combating fatigue, as can relaxation exercises. Diversionary activities are helpful as well. Nutritional intake should be examined to ensure an adequate amount of protein and calorie intake. The patient may need to consider accepting assistance from others to help with carrying out roles and responsibilities. Coping with fatigue can be challenging, so the nurse should provide time for the patient to express frustration and explore ways to increase coping skills.

Chapter 22: Nursing Care for Selected Malignancies

Key Terms

Abdominoperineal resection
Acute lymphocytic leukemia (ALL)
Acute myeloid leukemia (AML)
Basal cell carcinoma
Colostomy
Cystectomy
Dumping syndrome
Hodgkin's disease
Ileal conduit
Ileostomy
Lobectomy
Lumpectomy
Lymphedema
Malignant melanoma
Modified radical mastectomy
Neuroblastoma
Osteogenic sarcoma
Pneumectomy
Radical prostatectomy
Squamous cell carcinoma
Stoma
Subtotal gastrectomy
Wilms' tumor

Introduction

Over one million people are diagnosed annually with some form of cancer. Cancer is the second leading cause of death in the United States. In men, the leading causes of death from cancer are lung, prostate, and colon cancer. In women, the leading causes of death are lung, breast, and colon cancer. The most common form of childhood cancer is leukemia. Nurses have a significant role in the prevention, screening, diagnosis, and treatment of cancer. The care of a patient with cancer can be challenging and complex.

This chapter discusses the specific nursing care related to cancers of the bladder, brain, breast, colon, liver, lung, ovaries, prostate, skin, stomach, and uterus. The childhood cancers of Wilms' tumor, neuroblastoma, and osteogenic sarcoma are addressed. Leukemia and lymphoma, which affects children and adults, are also covered. Prevention, screening, diagnosis, treatment, and specific nursing measures for selected malignancies will be covered. The general nursing care principles that were presented in chapter 21 can be applied to the care of patients with the selected malignancies being discussed in this chapter and will not be repeated.

Nursing Assessment

A patient who is suspected of having a malignancy will be thoroughly assessed for any physiologic and functional changes. Extensive diagnostic testing will frequently be included in the assessment. The nurse's responsibility is to gather and synthesize data related to the patient's health status and functional health patterns. This section will discuss potential assessment areas and findings related to a malignancy.

Health History

The first step in gathering assessment data is obtaining the patient's **health history**. The nurse should gather data about the patient's chief complaint and any subjective symptoms the patient may be experiencing. Functional changes should be noted. The nurse should also obtain information about any allergies the patient may have and medications that the patient is taking, including prescribed and over-the-counter medications, as well as vitamin and herbal preparations. Determining the existence of preexisting illnesses is also an important consideration.

Risk Factors

When collecting data during the health history, it is important for the nurse to consider any **risk factors** that can lead to the development of a malignancy and question the patient about health habits related to these risk factors. For example, the nurse should gather information about the patient's history of smoking, chewing tobacco, or using snuff. Alcohol intake should also be assessed. Normal dietary habits should be noted, as well as any recent weight loss or gain. The patient's occupation or other environmental factors may place him or her at risk due to exposure to pollutants or chemicals that are carcinogenic. As some malignancies are genetic or familial in origin, the patient's family history should also be carefully assessed.

Psychosocial Needs

The **psychosocial needs** of the patient and family is another area that deserves special consideration by the nurse. Health beliefs, cultural factors, financial concerns, and social support systems should be carefully assessed.

Growth and Development

The nurse should assess the patient's stage of **growth and development**, and how it has been affected by illness. The diagnosis of cancer can hinder a child's growth and development due to the disease process and treatment regimen. Chronic disease such as cancer can affect the development of the child's mobility and functional ability. Cancer can affect the child's ability to separate from the family to form relationships with peers, progress academically, and participate in age-appropriate recreational activities. Self-concept and self-esteem, especially in the adolescent years, can be threatened. Children may also regress to an earlier developmental stage when they are ill.

The developmental stage of adults can also be affected by a diagnosis of cancer. Leaving home, marrying, starting a career or family are all developmental tasks of a young adult that can be delayed by cancer. Coping with a chronic, possibly life-threatening illness can also affect an adult's feelings of productivity and worthiness. Fatigue, a common side effect of cancer, can seriously challenge the patient's ability to remain independent and engage in self-care activities. Body image and self-esteem can be altered by appearance-altering treatment options. Roles and responsibilities can be significantly changed, altering family relationships. It is important that the nurse allow the patient and family members the opportunity to verbalize their feelings about the life-altering impact of cancer.

Objective Data

In addition to the health history, the nurse will need to gather **objective data** that is related to the malignancy. A systemic head-to-toe assessment should be conducted. Table 22.1 contains clinical manifestations related to common malignancies.

Table 22.1 Clinical Manifestations Related to Common Malignancies	
Malignancy	**Clinical manifestations**
Bladder cancer	Painless hematuria, urgency, dysuria, urinary obstruction
Brain cancer	Headache, vomiting, papilledema, altered thought processes, personality changes, focal symptoms (related to location of brain affected by tumor)
Breast cancer	Irregular fixed lump, dimpling of skin, nipple retraction, nipple discharge
Colon cancer	Change in bowel habits, pencil-shaped stool, occult bleeding, rectal bleeding, abdominal pain, anorexia, weight loss, weakness, fatigue
Liver cancer	Right upper quadrant abdominal mass; abdominal pain; weight loss; fatigue; jaundice; ascites; elevated alkaline phosphate, AST, and ALT
Lung cancer	Cough, hemoptysis, shortness of breath, unilateral wheeze
Ovarian cancer	Enlarged abdomen, ascites; abdominal and back pain; pelvic pressure; change in bowel patterns, flatulence; urinary frequency; irregular or heavy menstrual periods
Prostate cancer	Urinary obstruction: urgency, frequency, retention; hematuria; low back pain; malaise
Skin cancer (malignant melanoma)	Irregular, circular, multicolored lesions, usually located on trunk and lower extremities
Stomach cancer	Anorexia, nausea, vomiting, weight loss, dyspepsia, fatigue, weakness, abdominal pain
Uterine cancer	Abnormal vaginal bleeding; purulent, bloody discharge
Wilms' tumor	Abdominal mass (on one side), fatigue, malaise, fever, weight loss, dyspnea, cough (with lung metastasis)

Table 22.1 Clinical Manifestations Related to Common Malignancies

Malignancy	Clinical manifestations
Neuroblastoma	Firm, irregular abdominal mass (nontender); urinary frequency or retention (tumor compression of GU tract); metastatic symptoms (lymph nodes, bone marrow, bone, liver, skin)
Sarcoma, osteogenic	Pain at affected site, limp

Leukemia
  – acute lymphocytic leukemia (ALL)
  – acute myelogenous (AML)
	Infections, bleeding tendencies, weakness, fatigue, lymphadenopathy, fever

Lymphomas (Hodgkin's disease)	Fatigue, weakness, anorexia, night sweats, fever, lymphadenopathy

Laboratory Tests and Other Diagnostic Data

Patients may need to undergo extensive diagnostic testing to determine the cause of the patient's signs and symptoms. Diagnostic testing is conducted to help determine the presence and type of tumor, the extent of the disease (including metastasis), and the level of functioning of all body systems.

Diagnostic tests that are used include laboratory tests such as the following:

- Blood tests (CBC, serum electrolytes and chemistry)
- Tumor markers (PSA, CEA, AFP)
- Cytology tests
- Urinalysis

Other diagnostic tests include radiological tests such as X rays, magnetic resonance imaging (MRI), computerized tomography (CT scans), radioisotope studies, and ultrasound. Biopsies of suspicious lesions and tumors are also done. An endoscopy procedure may be used to visualize structures and obtain tissue specimens (e.g., bronchoscopy, cystoscopy, gastroscopy, or sigmoidoscopy).

During this time period, patients and their families can experience a considerable amount of anxiety and fear as they await the outcomes of the tests. Some of the anxiety and fear may be related to the diagnostic procedures. The nurse can assist the patient and family by carefully explaining what the patient should expect during the procedures and by answering questions. The nurse can also facilitate communication between the family members and the patient. Table 22.2 lists diagnostic procedures used to diagnose common cancers.

Table 22.2 Diagnostic Procedures for Common Cancers	
Cancer	**Diagnostic procedures**
Bladder	Urinalysis, cystoscopy, biopsy, urine cytology, intravenous pyelogram (IVP), CT scan, MRI, carcinoembryonic antigen (CEA)
Brain	CT scan, MRI, skull X ray, cerebral angiogram
Breast	Mammography, ultrasound, biopsy, estrogen-progesterone receptor assays
Colon	Digital rectal exam, stool guaiac test, sigmoidoscopy, colonoscopy, barium enema, carcinoembryonic antigen (CEA), biopsy, ultrasound, CT scan
Gastric	Upper GI tract X ray, gastroscopy
Leukemia	Bone marrow aspiration/biopsy
Liver	Elevated alkaline phosphate, AST, GGT, lactic hydrogenase; elevated bilirubin; elevated Alpha-fetoprotein (AFP); ultrasound; liver scan; liver biopsy
Lung	Sputum cytology, chest X ray, CT scan, bronchoscopy with biopsy, fine-needle aspiration biopsy
Lymphoma	Lymph node biopsy, bone marrow aspiration, chest X ray, liver/spleen CT scan, lymphangiography
Ovarian	CA-125 (tumor marker), ultrasound, CT scan, MRI
Prostate	Digital rectal exam, elevated alkaline and acid phosphatase, needle aspiration and biopsy, elevated prostate specific antigen (PSA) assay
Skin (malignant melanoma)	Excision and biopsy

The data gathered during the health history, physical examination, and diagnostic testing will be used by the health-care team to determine the patient's health status, medical treatment, and a nursing plan of care.

Bladder Cancer

Incidence and Risk Factors

Bladder cancer is more common in men than women, usually affecting men over the age of fifty. Cigarette smoking is considered the leading cause of bladder cancer.

Clinical Manifestations and Diagnosis

The most common symptom of bladder cancer is painless gross hematuria. The patient may also experience changes in voiding. Dysuria and urgency may develop. Urinary tract infections are common.

Bladder cancer is definitively diagnosed through a **cystoscopy** and **biopsy** of the tumor. A urinalysis, urine cytology, and IVP are additional diagnostic tests that are ordered. CT scans and MRIs may be ordered to determine the presence of possible metastasis.

Treatment

Treatment usually consists of **transurethral resection** of the tumor. If the cancer is invasive, the bladder will likely be removed (**cystectomy**) and a **urinary diversion** created. In a urinary diversion, urine is diverted through an opening in the abdomen. An **ileal conduit** is the most common form of urinary diversion in which a segment of the ileum is used as a passageway to carry urine from the ureters to the opening in the abdomen. A **urostomy** bag, which is attached to the abdomen, is used to collect the urine. The patient will have a permanent alteration in urinary elimination that may cause an alteration in the patient's body image and will require instruction in self-care.

Nursing Measures

Nursing measures related to the care of an ileal conduit include monitoring the urinary output, assessing the stoma, applying the ostomy appliance, and maintaining skin integrity. Immediately postoperatively, **urine output** will be monitored hourly. An output below 30 ml/hour is cause for concern and should be reported. There may be an obstruction or the patient may be dehydrated.

The stoma should be pink to light red in color. A stoma that is dusky in color indicates ischemia. A dark black-brown colored stoma indicates necrosis has developed. An ostomy appliance, or pouch, is applied around the stoma to collect stool or urine. The appliance is carefully fit over peristomal skin that has been gently cleansed and had a skin barrier applied to protect the skin from irritation. Ostomy appliances (collection pouches) are emptied of urine before the pouch gets more than one-third full to prevent disruption of the seal and urinary leakage. Ostomy appliances will usually last up to seven days before requiring to be changed. Instruct the patient to avoid foods that cause a strong odor in the urine to control odor and encourage appliance changes as scheduled.

The nurse is responsible for instructing the patient how to manage self-care upon discharge. The patient is encouraged to drink plenty of fluids to decrease the amount of mucus (from the mucous membrane of the conduit) that will be present in the urine and to decrease the chance of a UTI. Altered body image and anxiety about sexuality are potential nursing diagnoses for the patient. The nurse should encourage the patient to verbalize concerns and fears about the surgery.

Brain Cancer

Incidence and Risk Factors

Brain cancer may be either primary or secondary (metastatic) in nature. The cause of primary brain cancer is unknown. Environmental factors may be influential in the development of brain cancer, and in some cases there may be a familial tendency. Primary brain cancer is more prevalent in children and middle-aged adults. Metastatic brain cancer is most common in adults. Primary cancers that frequently metastasize to the brain are lung, breast, gastrointestinal, renal, and skin.

Brain cancer can take the form of a self-contained spherical mass, or the cancer can be infiltrative in nature and invade surrounding tissue. In either case, the tumor places pressure on surrounding tissue structures causing edema to develop. This pressure and edema leads to increased intracranial pressure. In most cases a spherical tumor is easier to remove surgically than an infiltrating mass.

The most common types of primary brain cancer are gliomas. The most common type of glioma is an **astrocytoma**, which grows slowly, infiltrating surrounding tissues. A highly malignant form of a glioma is a **glioblastoma**.

Clinical Manifestations and Diagnosis

Clinical manifestations will vary, depending upon the location of the tumor. General symptoms include visual disturbances, headache, vomiting, and papilledema. The patient may also experience personality changes, altered thought processes, and seizures. In about 20 percent of the patients, a headache is the only symptom.

Brain cancer is diagnosed by CT scan and MRI to define the size and location of the tumor. Skull X rays may also be performed. Additional diagnostic tests may be conducted as necessary to determine if the cancer is a primary or secondary site.

Treatment

Treatment consists of surgery (craniotomy) to remove tumors that are encapsulated. Surgical techniques are increasingly refined, enabling surgeons to reach areas of the brain that were previously unobtainable. Chemotherapy and/or radiation therapy are implemented following surgery; these therapies are also used to treat inoperable, infiltrating cancers.

Nursing Measures

Nursing management of the patient with brain cancer is dependent upon the type of cancer, stage of the disease, and treatment. In all cases, the nurse will closely monitor the neurological status of the patient. Headache and vomiting can be indicative of increased intracranial pressure and must be promptly reported. Seizure precautions are implemented for patients who have experienced seizure activity. Other safety features must also be implemented if the patient is experiencing altered thought processes or mobility impairment.

Breast Cancer

Incidence and Risk Factors

Women in the United States have a 1 in 8 chance of developing breast cancer. The risk of breast cancer increases with age. There are believed to be a number of factors that contribute to the development of breast cancer. Estrogen is increasingly thought to play a prominent role in the development of some cancers. There is some association with an increased risk for breast cancer in women who are childless, have a child after the age of thirty, or experience early menarche or late menopause. Genetics are also thought to play a role. The presence of a BRCA-1 or BRCA-2 gene mutation has been associated with breast cancer. Another risk factor is a family history of breast cancer. There is a weak association with obesity and alcohol intake.

Clinical Manifestations and Diagnosis

Clinical manifestations of breast cancer include a painless lump, orange-peel appearance of the skin, nipple discharge, and retraction. The lump is usually fixed and hard. The upper outer quadrant of the breast is where most of the lumps are found. Breast cancer can be detected with mammography. A definitive diagnosis is made through a biopsy, such as a fine needle aspiration, excisional, incisional, or stereotactic biopsy.

Routine screening with a mammogram (annually after age forty), clinical breast examination, and self-breast examination are strongly recommended. Mammograms should begin early in women who are at high risk for developing breast cancer. The earlier the tumor is detected, the better the prognosis will be. Prognosis depends to some extent upon whether or not metastasis has occurred. The most common site for early metastasis is the axillary lymph nodes. The most common sites for distance metastasis are bone and lungs. Prognosis also depends upon the histology of the tumor. A tumor that is estrogen or progesterone receptive has a better prognosis than one that is not.

Treatment

Treatment consists of surgery as well as radiation therapy and chemotherapy.

- A **lumpectomy**, which conserves breast tissue, may be performed, followed by radiation therapy. Axillary node dissection may also be done with the lumpectomy. Lumpectomy has been proven to achieve a survival rate that is equivalent to a modified radical mastectomy.
- A **modified radical mastectomy** is the removal of all of the breast tissue along with the axillary nodes.
- **Radiation therapy** and **chemotherapy** may also be used for treatment following surgery. See chapter 21 to review the care of a patient receiving radiation therapy or chemotherapy.
- **Hormonal therapy** may also be used if tissue assays demonstrate that the tumor is estrogen and/or progesterone dependent. If the tumor is hormone dependent, measures will be taken to decrease the production of estrogen to slow growth of the tumor. **Tamoxifen**, an antihormonal agent (estrogen antagonist), is the most commonly prescribed hormone drug used in the treatment of breast cancer.

Nursing Measures

Postoperative nursing care is similar in both surgical procedures because of the removal of the axillary nodes. Pain management is a priority goal of nursing care. Potential complications include fluid accumulation at the site of the incision and wound infection. Typically, small drainage tubes attached to a collection device are inserted at the time of surgery to facilitate drainage. The drain is removed when drainage falls below 30 ml/24 hours. Patients will go home with the drain in place, so the nurse must instruct the patient in incision and drain care.

Arm, shoulder, and hand exercises are encouraged daily to restore full range of motion following surgery. The patient should be instructed to not allow blood pressures to be taken in the arm, nor should injections or blood draws be performed on the arm. Gloves should be worn while gardening to protect the patient from a break in skin integrity that can lead to an infection. Constrictive clothing should not be worn either.

Lymphedema, which is the swelling of the affected arm due to inadequate lymphatic and venous drainage, can also occur. This is a chronic problem that can be managed by arm exercises and the use of an elastic device that provides compression and improves lymphatic and venous flow.

The patient may experience an alteration in body image and self-esteem as a result of having breast surgery, even a lumpectomy. This can have an impact on sexual functioning. Allow the patient time to verbalize fears and concerns. The nurse should promote open communication between the patient and spouse or partner.

Colon Cancer

Incidence and Risk Factors

Colon cancer is the third most common cancer in the United States. Risk factors for colon cancer include increasing age and a history of polyps, inflammatory bowel disease, or familial polyposis. A high-fat, high-protein, and low-fiber diet is also associated with colon cancer. Unfortunately, colon cancer is frequently diagnosed after metastasis has already occurred, so the five-year survival rate is only 40 percent to 50 percent. Metastasis most often occurs to the liver.

Clinical Manifestations and Diagnosis

Clinical manifestations are determined by the location of the tumor. The most common symptom is a change in bowel habits. Bloody stools are the second most common symptom. Other symptoms of colon cancer include anorexia, weight loss, fatigue, and anemia. Tumors that occur in the right side of the colon can cause dark, tarry stools (melena) and dull pain. Tumors that are located on the left side of the colon are most likely to cause cramping abdominal pain, ribbon stools, bright red bleeding, and constipation. Obstruction of the colon may occur.

Diagnostic tests used to diagnose colon cancer include digital rectal exam, testing for fecal occult blood, barium enema, sigmoidoscopy, or colonoscopy with biopsy. Carcinoembryonic antigen (CEA) may also be used to diagnose cancer and track response to treatment. CEA levels will drop as the tumor is eradicated. Elevated CEA levels can indicate the tumor has reoccurred.

Treatment

Treatment includes surgical removal of the tumor. If the patient has experienced an intestinal obstruction prior to surgery, a nasogastric tube will be inserted to decompress the GI tract and intravenous fluids will be administered.

The surgical procedures used to treat colon cancer can vary:

- A **colon resection with anastomosis** may be done. This is where the segment of the colon that contains the tumor is surgically removed and then the colon is reconnected (anastomosis).
- An **abdominoperineal resection with the creation of a permanent colostomy** will be performed for a tumor that is located in the rectum and sigmoid areas. A **colostomy** is the creation of an opening in the colon that is brought to the surface of the abdomen to allow for removal of stool through the opening (stool) into a collection pouch. A colostomy can be either permanent or temporary.
- Chemotherapy or radiation therapy may be used as adjuvant therapy following surgery.

Nursing Measures

Preoperative nursing care prior to colon surgery includes assessing the nutritional status of the patient. If possible, the patient should be encouraged to eat a low-residue, high-calorie, high-protein, and high-carbohydrate diet. A full liquid diet is usually prescribed twenty-four to forty-eight hours prior to surgery. If the patient is not capable of taking nutrients orally, total parenteral nutrition (TPN) may be prescribed. Antibiotics are administered prior to surgery to decrease the bacteria in the bowel. Laxatives and/or enemas are used before surgery to empty the colon.

Postoperative nursing care includes wound care and monitoring the patient closely for infection. Common complications include a paralytic ileus, respiratory infection, and wound infection. The nurse will assess the abdomen for distention and the return of bowel sounds. A vigorous program of preventive respiratory care will be implemented, including deep breathing, turning, coughing, and incentive spirometry at least every two hours. The incision will be observed for redness and drainage. If a colostomy has been created, the nurse will monitor the color of the stoma (opening). A stoma should be pink to light red in color. A stoma that is dusky in color indicates ischemia. A dark black-brown colored stoma indicates necrosis.

An ostomy appliance, or pouch, is applied around the stoma to collect the stool. The colostomy will typically begin to function about three to six days after surgery. The consistency of the stool will depend upon the location of the colostomy. A colostomy that is created in the descending colon will produce stool that is fairly well formed. A transverse colostomy produces stool that is soft and unformed. If a patient has had an **ileostomy** performed, where the stoma is created in the ileum or small intestine, the stool will be liquid.

The appliance is carefully fit over peristomal (around the stoma) skin that has been gently cleansed and had a skin barrier, such as a wafer or paste, applied to protect the skin from irritation. Ostomy appliances are emptied before the pouch gets more than one-third full, to prevent disruption of the seal and leakage of stool. For some patients, the colostomy is easily regulated and a consistent stool evacuation time can be established. For these patients, wearing a pouch may not be a necessity; a simple dressing is used to cover the stoma. Patients who have an **ileostomy** will require a pouch, as the stool cannot be regulated.

Irrigating the Colostomy

Some patients may irrigate their colostomy. This is not routinely done with all patients; rather, it depends upon the location of the colostomy and the patient's preference. Irrigating the colostomy can help establish a regular pattern of evacuation. Some patients may prefer to allow the ostomy to evacuate naturally without the aid of irrigation. This decision should be made in collaboration with the physician.

The nurse will assist the patient in learning how to irrigate the ostomy. Ileostomies are not irrigated. Colostomy irrigation is a clean procedure. Typically, the irrigation will take place with the patient seated on the toilet, although if the patient's condition does not permit activity, the procedure can be performed with the patient in the bed. The patient applies an open-ended irrigating pouch to the ostomy to allow for introduction of the irrigating tube and drainage of the returning liquid into the toilet or bedpan. The open end of the pouch is placed into the toilet or bedpan. A bag of approximately 1000 ml of lukewarm tap water is prepared and placed about twenty inches above the height of the stoma to facilitate the flow of water. The tube, which can be in the form of a catheter or cone, is lubricated with water-soluble jelly, and then gently introduced into the stoma.

The tube should *never* be forced. After introduction of the tube, the water flow is gradually started and water is allowed to flow slowly into the colon. If cramping occurs, the patient should temporarily stop the water flow until the cramping subsides, and then resume the irrigation until all the water has flowed into the colon. The tube is slowly removed; the return of water and stool should begin, with the majority of the return occurring within ten to fifteen minutes. The patient can resume activity, but will want to leave the irrigating pouch on for about forty-five minutes, to collect the remnants of the irrigation return. Following completion of the irrigation procedure, the area is cleansed and gently dried, and a clean pouch or dressing is applied.

The nurse is responsible for teaching the patient how to care for the ostomy in preparation for discharge. Additionally, nutrition and fluid intake should be discussed with the patient. The patient can eat anything that he or she desires, as long as the diet does not cause diarrhea or constipation. Foods that cause gas or odor should be avoided. Such foods include eggs, cabbage, and beans. If the food created GI distress for the patient prior to surgery, it will continue to be a problem for the patient following surgery. Fluid intake should be at least 2000 ml per day.

Potential **nursing diagnoses** for patients who have had colon surgery with or without the creation of a colostomy can include the following:

- Altered nutrition, less than required
- Impaired skin integrity
- Altered body image

Anxiety about sexual functioning is another potential concern of the patient. The presence of a colostomy does not hinder sexual activity, preclude childbearing for women, or necessarily mean impotence will develop. The nurse should allow the patient time to express fears and concerns, and seek out the appropriate guidance to help answer the patient's questions.

Leukemia

Leukemia is caused by the proliferation of white blood cells (WBCs) in the bone marrow. This proliferation is unregulated and "crowds" out the normal cell production. Leukemia may be acute or chronic in nature. Acute forms of leukemia develop rapidly and can result in death within months of diagnosis if not treated aggressively. Chronic forms of leukemia develop more slowly, and progress over a period of time, even years. Chronic forms of leukemia tend to produce more mature WBCs.

Leukemia may also develop from the lymphoid stem cell line or the myeloid stem cell line. Leukemia can strike individuals of all ages. The two forms of leukemia that will be addressed in this study guide are **acute myeloid leukemia (AML)** and **acute lymphocytic leukemia (ALL)**. Chronic forms of both types of leukemia also exist.

Acute Myeloid Leukemia (AML)

Incidence and Risk Factors

AML can affect all age groups, but occurs more commonly in older individuals. There is a defect in the hematopoietic stem cell that affects the normal production of all forms of cells—erythrocytes, monocytes, granulocytes, and platelets. AML is potentially a curable form of leukemia, but the prognosis can vary greatly.

Clinical Manifestations and Diagnosis

The clinical manifestations of AML are related to the insufficient production of blood cells. A lack of erythrocytes leads to anemia, with accompanying fatigue and weakness. The decreased production of normal WBCs (leukopenia) can lead to infection. The decrease in platelets (thrombocytopenia) causes bleeding. The patient may also experience pain from increased pressure in the spleen and bone marrow caused by proliferation of cells. The major cause of death in AML is from infection and bleeding.

Diagnosis of AML is made by CBC and bone marrow aspiration. A CBC will demonstrate a decrease in platelet count and erythrocytes. The leukocyte count can be variable—either high, normal, or low—but there will be a greatly decreased number of normal cells. Bone marrow analysis will demonstrate large numbers of immature blast cells.

Treatment

Medical management of AML consists of trying to achieve remission and returning the bone marrow to normal cell production. Aggressive chemotherapy is used to treat AML, and the treatment produces serious side effects of its own. The patient becomes extremely neutropenic, thrombocytopenic, and anemic during treatment. The patient can develop infections, bleeding, stomatitis, and mucositis during treatment. Blood products such as platelets and RBCs, and stimulating granulocytic growth factors are administered to counteract these effects.

Despite this aggressive approach to chemotherapy, many patients (approximately 70 percent) do not sustain a state of remission and have a relapse. The five-year survival rate after a relapse out of remission is about 5 percent. Bone marrow transplantation (BMT) is another form of aggressive treatment for AML. The complications of BMT are significant and include infection and bleeding.

Nursing Measures

The nursing management of patients with AML focuses on preventing complications and providing supportive care and was covered in chapter 21. It is particularly important that the nurse focus care on the prevention of infection and bleeding.

Acute Lymphocytic Leukemia (ALL)

Incidence and Risk Factors

Acute lymphocytic leukemia (ALL) most commonly occurs in children; the peak age of occurrence is four years old. In ALL, there is an increase in the production of immature lymphocytes. Because of the increased numbers of immature lymphocytes, the production of normal cells such as leukocytes, erythrocytes, and platelets is limited. A CBC and bone marrow analysis will demonstrate these pathophysiological changes.

Clinical Manifestations and Diagnosis

Clinical manifestations are similar to AML; however, patients with ALL tend to exhibit more signs of cellular infiltration into affected organs than other forms of leukemia, resulting in more incidence of bone pain, abdominal pain from enlarged spleen and liver, and headache from meningeal irritation.

Treatment

Treatment is similar to AML, with the goal being remission. Chemotherapy, particularly vinca alkaloids, and corticosteroids are especially effective in treating ALL. Treatment can be complex, but patients tend to respond better to treatment than those with AML. Approximately 80 percent of the children with ALL will achieve a five-year survival rate. Bone marrow transplantation may also be considered.

Nursing Measures

Nursing care of the child with ALL will be guided by the treatment plan. The main focus of care is preventing the complications of infection and bleeding. Providing support to the family is essential, helping them to cope with the diagnosis and addressing their many questions and concerns. See chapter 21 for general nursing care guidelines.

Liver Cancer

Incidence and Risk Factors

Liver cancer is predominately caused by metastasis of the cancer from another site. It is not uncommon for the first evidence of an abdominal cancer, such as colon cancer, to be liver metastasis. Primary liver cancer, when it does occur, is usually related to chronic liver disease such as hepatitis or cirrhosis.

Clinical Manifestations and Diagnosis

The clinical manifestations of liver cancer and the diagnostic tests commonly performed are presented in Tables 22.1 and 22.2. **Alpha-fetoprotein** is a tumor marker that is elevated in about 40 percent of the patients who have liver cancer. When the CEA, which can be an indicator of gastrointestinal cancer, is also elevated, this is an indication of metastatic liver cancer.

Treatment

Treatment of liver cancer is primarily palliative. Surgery is used rarely, generally because of the widespread pathology associated with the cancer and underlying chronic liver disorders. Radiation or chemotherapy can be administered, with the goal of decreasing pain and discomfort and increasing quality of life. At this time, there is no well-defined treatment plan for liver cancer that has proved to be consistently successful.

Nursing Measures

Nursing management is essentially supportive and depends upon the patient's symptoms. General nursing care for the patient with liver cancer is covered in chapter 21.

Lung Cancer

Incidence and Risk Factors

Lung cancer kills more men and women annually in the United States than any other type of cancer. While the incidence of lung cancer in men has remained stable, it is rising in women. It is estimated that 85 percent of all lung cancer is caused by inhalation of cigarette smoke and other carcinogenic chemicals. Risk factors include tobacco smoke, secondhand smoke, and environmental exposure to toxins. There is some familial predisposition to lung cancer. The majority of patients with lung cancer already have metastasis when diagnosed.

Clinical Manifestations and Diagnosis

The signs and symptoms of lung cancer are listed in Table 22.1. The extent of the signs and symptoms will depend upon the size and location of the tumor. The most common symptom of lung cancer is a cough or a cough that changes in character. Pain is a late symptom and is usually related to bone metastasis.

The tests used to diagnose lung cancer are identified in Table 22.2. In addition to those tests, the patient will undergo screening for metastatic disease. Bone scans, liver scans, and CT of the brain are some additional tests that may be performed.

Treatment

Medical management of lung cancer frequently includes surgery in an attempt to provide a cure. Surgery will be performed when the tumor is localized and no metastatic disease has been detected. The most common surgical procedure performed is a **lobectomy**, in which a single lobe of the lung is removed. If the entire lung is removed, it is a **pneumectomy**. Unfortunately, due to the late diagnosis of many cases of lung cancer, many tumors are inoperable.

Radiation therapy can be used in a small percentage of cases to attempt a cure. It is more effective in small cell lung cancers. Radiation therapy is also used preoperatively to shrink a tumor or to provide palliative treatment to relieve symptoms of pressure and obstruction. Chemotherapy is also used as adjuvant therapy to surgery or radiation therapy. Chemotherapy may help decrease symptoms, but it does not cure that patient.

Nursing Measures

Nursing management of the patient with lung cancer includes managing the symptoms of dyspnea and fatigue, and other symptoms that might occur as a result of treatment. Patients who have surgery may have chest tubes inserted. (See chapter 5 to review the care of patients with chest tubes.)

Deep breathing exercises, coughing, and chest physiotherapy will be used to help remove secretions. The patient may require suctioning if the secretions cannot be coughed up. The nurse will help the patient assume a position that facilitates breathing and chest expansion. Bronchodilators may be administered to help dilate the airways and move air around the obstruction caused by the tumor. Nursing measures for helping the patient cope with fatigue and providing psychological support are covered in chapter 21 and are applicable to the patient with lung cancer.

Lymphomas

Incidence and Risk Factors

Lymphomas are malignant neoplasms that originate in the lymph system. Lymphomas usually originate in the lymph nodes, but can also develop in the spleen, bone marrow, liver, or gastrointestinal tract. There are two categories of lymphomas, **Hodgkin's**

disease and **non-Hodgkin's lymphomas**. This study guide will focus discussion on Hodgkin's disease.

Hodgkin's disease occurs more often in men than women. The cause of Hodgkin's is unknown. There is some evidence of a familial tendency. It typically develops in adults in their early twenties or fifties. Some patients who develop Hodgkin's disease also have the Epstein-Barr virus.

Clinical Manifestations and Diagnosis

The hallmark of Hodgkin's disease is the **Reed-Sternberg cell**, which is a large immature malignant lymphoid cell. Diagnosis of Hodgkin's disease is accomplished through excisional lymph node biopsy and identification of the presence of the Reed-Sternberg cell. Through analysis of the pathology of the tumor cells, the disease can be divided into different subgroups.

The clinical manifestations of Hodgkin's disease include the painless enlargement of lymph nodes (lymphadenopathy). Common sites for the enlarged lymph nodes include the supraclavicular, cervical, and mediastinal nodes. The nodes will be firm. Other symptoms can develop depending upon the organs that are invaded by the disease. For example, pulmonary invasion can lead to the development of a cough; hepatic invasion is evidenced by jaundice; and splenomegaly can lead to abdominal pain. Bone pain is another symptom caused by bone infiltration. The patient can also experience fever, night sweats, and weight loss.

In addition to the diagnostic findings of the Reed-Sternberg cell through a biopsy, a CBC, platelet count, and sedimentation rate will be obtained. CBC will reveal a mild anemia. The platelet count is usually normal, while the WBC may be elevated or decreased. Chest X rays, CT scans of the abdomen, pelvis, and lungs, and bone scans may be obtained to detect evidence of further lymphadenopathy and to stage the disease. Liver and renal studies are also assessed.

Treatment

The goal of medical management is to cure the patient. Treatment is dependent upon the staging of the disease, but consists of radiation therapy and chemotherapy. Chemotherapy is sometimes used alone. Hodgkin's disease is considered to be curable.

Nursing Measures

Many patients with Hodgkin's disease are cared for as outpatients, unless complications develop as a result of chemotherapy or radiation therapy treatments. Nursing care of the patient with Hodgkin's disease consists of providing psychological support to the patient and patient education to help the patient avoid the complications of treatment, primarily bone marrow suppression. These patients are particularly susceptible to infection because of the suppressed immune response caused by the disease and as a side effect of treatment. Chapter 21 covers general nursing care principles that can be applied to care of the patient with a lymphoma.

Ovarian Cancer

Incidence and Risk Factors

Ovarian cancer most commonly occurs in women who are in their fifties and is usually not diagnosed until the disease is in its advanced stages. Because of the lateness of diagnosis, the mortality rate is high. Risk factors include infertility, nulliparity, and heredity. Genetic research continues on BRCA-1 and BRCA-2 genetic mutations, which appear to predispose the woman to both ovarian and breast cancer.

Clinical Manifestations and Diagnosis

The clinical manifestations of ovarian cancer are subtle and vague. Most commonly, the woman will complain of an enlarged abdomen, abdominal pain, ascites, back pain, pelvic pressure, and a change in bowel patterns. Flatulence may also occur. Urinary frequency or stress incontinence may also occur and the woman's menstrual period may become irregular or heavier in flow.

Ovarian cancer is difficult to diagnose definitively in the early stages and is not detectable by a pelvic examination. There are no useful screening diagnostic studies available. Ultrasounds, CT scans, and MRI may be used. CA-125, a tumor marker, may also be evaluated, but once again, it is not used for a definitive diagnosis. A laparotomy is performed to confirm diagnosis.

Treatment

Surgery consisting of a total abdominal hysterectomy with bilateral salpingo-oophorectomy is performed to remove the tumor. Following surgery, the patient will receive chemotherapy. Common chemotherapy drugs used to treat ovarian cancer include paclitaxel and cisplatin.

Nursing Measures

Nursing care of the patient with ovarian cancer includes care following abdominal surgery. The patient will require significant emotional support as she copes with the diagnosis, surgery, and aggressive chemotherapy. As the disease progresses, the nurse will focus care on providing adequate nutritional support, fluid intake, and pain relief. The family and patient will require ongoing support as the prognosis is usually poor.

Prostate Cancer

Incidence and Risk Factors

Prostate cancer is the most common cancer in men, especially African-American males. Risk factors for prostate cancer include increasing age and a diet that is high in fat.

Clinical Manifestations and Diagnosis

Prostate cancer is usually asymptomatic in its early stages. Common signs and symptoms are presented in Table 22.1. Signs of urinary obstruction are late indicators of the disease. Back pain is indicative of bone metastasis, which commonly occurs in prostate cancer.

If prostate cancer is diagnosed early, the chances of a cure are high. Routine rectal examination of the prostate is recommended annually after the age of forty. The tests used to diagnose prostate cancer are listed in Table 22.2. It should be noted that an elevated prostate-specific antigen (PSA) is indicative of an increased amount of prostate tissue, not necessarily a malignancy. The PSA is frequently used to measure the patient's response to treatment and monitor for reoccurrence of the tumor. Bone scans are also frequently conducted to detect the presence of metastasis.

Treatment

Medical management of prostate cancer is based upon the patient's age and stage of disease, and may include surgery, radiation therapy, or hormonal therapy.

- A **radical prostatectomy**, in which the prostate gland is removed, may be performed. This will result in sexual impotence. Some men will develop problems with urinary incontinence as well.
- Radiation therapy may be curative in early stages of the disease. The therapy may be delivered via linear accelerator or through an implant of radioactive seeds.
- Hormone therapy may be used to control the cancer, but not cure. **Antiandrogen agents** are administered to suppress androgen production and slow the growth of the tumor. Common hormonal medications used to achieve androgen suppression include the administration of diethylstilbestrol (DES), luteinizing hormone-releasing hormone (LHRH), and flutamide.

Nursing Measures

Nursing management of the patient with prostate cancer includes preoperative and postoperative care for the patient who is undergoing a prostatectomy. The nursing care is similar to the care of a patient undergoing a TURP, which was presented in chapter 19. In addition to the nursing measures covered in chapter 19 and depending upon the surgical approach taken, there may be a perineal incision or an abdominal incision that will require care. The opportunity for wound infection is great, especially in the perineal incision, so careful aseptic technique with dressing changes and meticulous perineal cleansing is essential. Sitz baths and heat lamps may be used to promote healing of the perineal incision.

Following the removal of a urethral catheter, perineal exercises will be started to increase the patient's urinary control and decrease episodes of incontinence. It may take up to one year for the "dribbling" of urine to stop. In addition to the physical aspects of care, it is important that the nurse allow the patient an opportunity to express his concerns about impotence and discuss his options for resuming sexual activity.

Skin Cancer

Incidence and Risk Factors

In the United States, skin cancer is the most prevalent form of cancer. It is usually one of the most successfully treated forms of cancer. The leading risk factor for the development of skin cancer is exposure to the sun. Other risk factors include exposure to toxins, aging, immunosuppression, and genetic factors. Fair-skinned, blue-eyed, and fair-haired individuals are more prone to developing skin cancer.

Clinical Manifestations and Diagnosis

The three most common forms of skin cancer are **basal cell carcinoma**, **squamous cell carcinoma**, and **malignant melanoma**. The most deadly form of skin cancer is malignant melanoma.

A **basal cell carcinoma** most commonly occurs on the face and other sun-exposed areas, and resembles a small nodule that is waxy in appearance with pearly, translucent borders. It can ulcerate and develop crusting. This type of cancer rarely metastasizes.

A **squamous cell carcinoma** is an invasive cancer that can develop in normal skin, as well as sun-damaged skin. These cancers are thick, scaly, and rough, and may bleed. Squamous cell cancer metastasizes through the blood and lymph systems. Both types of cancer are confirmed by biopsy.

Malignant melanoma is a dangerous form of skin cancer that is responsible for approximately 2 percent of all the deaths related to cancer. It occurs primarily in young and middle-aged adults, and is the result of sun exposure or ultraviolet rays. The most common type of melanoma is **superficial spreading melanoma** that occurs on the trunk and lower extremities, and is circular with irregular edges. The lesion may be elevated or flat, and can be a combination of colors including brown, black, bluish-black, tan, gray, and white. **Nodular melanoma** has a round, raised smooth surface that is blue-black in color.

Malignant melanoma is diagnosed through biopsy of the lesion. Prognosis is poor if the lesion is deeper and thicker than 4 mm. When melanoma metastasizes, it tends to spread to the lymph nodes, lungs, liver, bone, central nervous system, and spleen. The chance of metastasis is greater if the lesion develops on the scalp, foot, or hand. Additional diagnostic testing will be ordered to detect the presence of metastasis.

Treatment

The treatment for both basal cell carcinoma and squamous cell carcinoma consists of surgical excision and/or radiation therapy. The treatment chosen will depend upon the location, type, and extent of the tumor, as well as if metastasis has occurred. Patients are usually treated as outpatients and prognosis is excellent if metastasis has not occurred.

Medical treatment of malignant melanoma consists of surgical excision of the lesion and surrounding tissues. Lymph node dissection of regional lymph nodes will be done to rule out metastasis. Chemotherapy will be used to help treat metastasis. The effectiveness of immunotherapy is being investigated. Unfortunately, if metastasis has occurred, a cure is doubtful.

Nursing Measures

Nursing care of patients with malignant melanoma includes the goals of decreasing pain and providing psychological support. Pain control may be necessary following surgery for excision of the cancer. Providing patient support during the diagnostic workup to determine the extent of metastasis is essential. This will be a fearful time for patients, and they will have many questions. If metastasis has occurred, the nursing care will be dependent upon the body systems involved in the metastasis.

The nurse has an important role in educating individuals about prevention and early detection of skin cancer. The importance of avoiding unnecessary sun exposure and sunburn, using sunscreen lotion and lip balm, avoiding tanning booths, and wearing protective clothing should be emphasized. Individuals should be instructed to regularly inspect their skin to detect new growths or changes in moles. Individuals should be taught the " A, B, C, Ds" of mole inspection: look for **asymmetry**, **irregular borders**, **color that is variegated**, and **diameter**. Suspicious moles should be investigated promptly by a health-care professional.

Stomach Cancer

Incidence and Risk Factors

Stomach (gastric) cancer occurs primarily in people who are over the age of forty. While the incidence of stomach cancer in the United States is not particularly high, the prognosis is poor. This is due to the late detection of most stomach cancers after metastasis has already occurred to the surrounding structures. Risk factors include a diet high in smoked foods with low intake of vegetables and fruits, the presence of chronic inflammation, and heredity.

Clinical Manifestations and Diagnosis

Common signs and symptoms of stomach cancer are included in Table 22.1. Symptoms are usually not present in the early stages of the disease. Diagnosis is usually achieved through endoscopy with biopsy of the lesion. CT scans, bone scans, and liver scans will be performed to determine the extent of possible metastasis.

Treatment

Unfortunately, there is no successful treatment for stomach cancer. Surgical resection of the tumor will be done. If the tumor has remained localized, this may effect a cure. In many cases, however, the surgery is palliative, with the goal of removing as much tumor as possible to alleviate symptoms of obstruction. The surgery that is performed is frequently a **subtotal gastrectomy**, although a **total gastrectomy** may be done. Chemotherapy may also be used, but it is primarily palliative in nature.

Nursing Measures

Nursing measures for the patient with stomach cancer will be to promote comfort and reduce anxiety, optimize nutrition, and provide psychological support. Following surgery, the patient will be encouraged to eat six small meals a day. It is common for the patient to develop **dumping syndrome** after gastric surgery, and the intake of small, frequent feedings can help the patient avoid the symptoms. Dumping syndrome occurs when large boluses of food are moved rapidly out of the stomach into the jejunum, creating the presence of a hypertonic mass in the intestines, which draws extracellular fluid from the blood volume into the jejunum. The patient complains of a feeling of fullness, weakness, diaphoresis, and abdominal cramping with diarrhea. The patient may feel faint and dizzy. These symptoms usually occur within thirty minutes of a meal. By eating smaller meals that are low in carbohydrates and eliminating fluid intake with the meals, the symptoms can be decreased. The syndrome usually subsides within six months to a year following surgery.

Patients will also require parenteral vitamin B_{12} if a total gastrectomy has been performed due to the loss of the intrinsic factor. Vitamin supplements may be necessary. If the patient cannot take in enough nutrients orally, total parenteral nutrition will be necessary.

Uterine and Cervical Cancers

Incidence and Risk Factors

Uterine and cervical cancers are common cancers of the female reproductive system. With early detection, both forms of cancer are considered to be curable. Yearly pelvic examinations with a Pap smear are recommended for all women to help detect cancer. Risk factors for cervical cancer include multiple sex partners, early sexual intercourse (under age twenty) and childbearing, chronic cervical infections, and smoking. However, a recent study indicates that a new vaccine may prevent cervical cancer by blocking infection from the human papilloma virus (HPV), which is the cause of a majority of cases of cervical cancer. Common risk factors for uterine cancer are aging and obesity.

Clinical Manifestations and Diagnosis

The signs and symptoms of either type of cancer in the early stages are minimal. Vaginal discharge and bleeding are later signs. Bleeding may occur at irregular intervals and after intercourse. Diagnosis of cervical cancer is made through an abnormal Pap smear followed by a biopsy. Uterine cancer is diagnosed through a biopsy. Other diagnostic tests are performed to determine the stage of the cancer and can include D & C (dilation and curettage), CT scans, and MRI.

Treatment

Treatment of cervical cancer depends upon the stage of the disease. If there are precursor changes in the cervix, cryotherapy or loop electrocautery excision procedure (LEEP) may be used. These are outpatient procedures. The patient will be followed closely by subsequent Pap smears and examination. If it is determined that the patient has cervical cancer in situ, a hysterectomy will be performed. A cancer that is more extensively involved will require a radical hysterectomy with pelvic node dissection and radiation therapy. Chemotherapy is also used to treat advanced forms of cervical cancer.

Cancer of the uterus is also treated surgically with a total hysterectomy (removal of cervix and uterus) and bilateral salpingo-oophorectomy. Radiation and chemotherapy may also be used.

Nursing Measures

Nursing care includes postoperative care of a patient following a hysterectomy. Common nursing diagnoses may include pain related to surgery, body image disturbances related to the loss of fertility, and anxiety related to the diagnosis of cancer. Patients may need some reassurance about their ability to engage in sexual intercourse, and may express concern about altered relationships and decreased satisfaction. Common postoperative complications after a hysterectomy include hemorrhage, deep vein thrombosis, and the possibility of urinary retention.

Selected Malignancies in Children

Neoplasms are the leading cause of death by disease in children who are past infancy. The following sections discuss specific nursing care for selected pediatric neoplasms—neuroblastoma, osteogenic sarcoma, and Wilms' tumor.

Neuroblastoma

Incidence and Risk Factors

The most common malignant tumors of infants are neuroblastomas. The majority of the children who develop a neuroblastoma are under the age of two. Neuroblastomas originate from embryonic neural crest cells and typically develop in the adrenal gland. The tumors may also develop in the retroperitoneal sympathetic chain, pelvis, chest, head, or neck. The cause of neuroblastomas is unknown. Depending upon the stage of the disease, the prognosis for neuroblastomas can be poor.

Clinical Manifestations and Diagnosis

Unfortunately, the majority of neuroblastomas are not diagnosed until metastasis has already occurred. Clinical manifestations of neuroblastomas are dependent upon the involved organs. Common symptoms of neuroblastomas are identified in Table 22.1 and are caused by tumor compression of surrounding structures. Generalized symptoms include weakness, irritability, anorexia, weight loss, and pallor.

Over 90 percent of the children who have a neuroblastoma will have elevated urine catecholamines. CT scans of various organs, MRI, and bone marrow aspiration are used to identify metastatic lesions and stage the disease.

Treatment

Medical management consists of surgery to remove the tumor. If the tumor cannot be completely resected, radiation therapy will be used to further shrink the tumor. Radiation therapy is sometimes used palliatively to relieve symptoms. Chemotherapy will also be used.

Nursing Measures

Nursing care will vary based upon the surgery and treatment received by the child. The child may require abdominal, thoracic, or cranial surgery, depending upon the location of the tumor. In addition, the child will receive radiation and/or chemotherapy, and will develop side effects related to these therapies. The nurse needs to provide education about the anticipated side effects. Parents need a significant amount of support as they face this life-threatening illness of their child and try to cope with the crisis. There may be a feeling of guilt at not recognizing symptoms of the disease earlier. Anger may be a predominant feeling, often directed towards the health-care providers. Nurses need to provide opportunities for the parents to discuss their fears and express their anger.

Osteogenic Sarcoma

Incidence and Risk Factors

Osteogenic sarcoma is the most common form of bone cancer in children. It most often occurs in children and young adults between the ages of ten and twenty-five. The lower extremities, particularly the metaphysis of the femur, are the primary sites of tumor growth. Tumors may also develop in the tibia, humerus, pelvis, and jaw.

Clinical Manifestations and Diagnosis

Clinical manifestations of osteogenic sarcoma include localized pain that can vary in intensity. Flexing the involved extremity might relieve the pain. A limp may be noticed and the child may not be able to maintain the usual levels of physical activity.

Diagnosis of osteogenic sarcoma is based on CT scans, radioisotope bone scans, and bone biopsy. Chest X rays or computerized tomography will be done to detect pulmonary metastasis, as the lungs are common metastatic sites.

Treatment

Medical management of osteogenic sarcoma usually consists of a combination of surgery and chemotherapy. In the past, amputation was a standard form of treatment. Today, not all patients require an amputation. Depending upon the location and extent of the tumor, a **limb salvage procedure**, which allows for the tumor to be resected and a prosthetic replacement inserted to preserve the limb, can be performed.

Nursing Measures

Nursing care will depend upon the surgical procedure used. If an amputation is to be performed, the child will need to be given some time to think about the treatment and an opportunity to ask questions. The child is usually fitted with a temporary prosthesis following surgery and physical therapy is started immediately. The child will also need to understand that chemotherapy will be required and the side effects that are associated with the treatment. Since most of the patients are adolescents and young adults, the nurse needs to be particularly sensitive to the child's response to the appearance-altering body changes that are occurring. The loss of a limb and loss of hair from chemotherapy will necessitate a grieving process, and the child needs to be encouraged to share feelings.

Wilms' Tumor (Nephroblastoma)

Incidence and Risk Factors

Wilms' tumor is a primary malignant tumor of the kidney. Wilms' tumor most commonly occurs around the third year of life. This tumor may be genetically inherited.

Clinical Manifestations and Diagnosis

The signs and symptoms of Wilms' tumor are identified in Table 22.1. The tumor appears more frequently in the left kidney than the right. Approximately 10 percent of the time, both kidneys are involved. Wilms' tumor is diagnosed through abdominal CT scan and MRI. Chest X rays and bone scans may be done to detect metastasis. Metastasis is rare.

Treatment

Surgery is performed to remove the tumor and affected kidney. Chemotherapy follows surgery. In some cases, especially with metastasis, radiation therapy may also be used. Children with a localized tumor have a survival rate of 90 percent.

Nursing Measures

Nursing care consists of preoperative and postoperative care. Surgery will be performed as quickly as possible after diagnosis to decrease the chances of tumor metastasis, so the nurse must rapidly prepare the child and family for the surgery. The child's blood pressure will be monitored preoperatively, as hypertension does occur in some children due to increased renin production. *It is absolutely essential that the abdominal mass not be palpated, as manipulation of the tumor may promote metastasis of cancer cells.*

Following the surgery, blood pressure will be monitored for a drop in measurement and the urine output will be monitored to assess function of the remaining kidney. The nurse must also prepare the child and parents for chemotherapy and radiation. Because the child only has one remaining kidney, it is important that any signs or symptoms of urinary problems be promptly reported. The child is usually told to avoid contact sports to prevent injury to the remaining kidney.

Chapter 22 Study Questions

1.   Give three examples of how the diagnosis of cancer can affect the growth and developmental stage of the patient.

2.   The nurse is caring for a patient who has recently had a cystectomy with an ileal conduit as treatment for bladder cancer. What nursing measures are appropriate for this patient?

3.   Describe lymphedema and appropriate nursing care related to this condition.

4.   Describe the GI tract preoperative care given to a patient who is about to undergo a colon resection for cancer.

5.   The nurse is teaching the patient how to irrigate his colostomy. What instructions should the nurse include in the teaching plan?

6.   Describe the characteristics of a malignant melanoma.

7.   Describe the nursing measures that can be used to help control the dumping syndrome.

8.   Describe the clinical manifestations of acute myeloid leukemia.

9.   How is Hodgkin's disease definitively diagnosed?

10.   The nurse is caring for an infant who has just been diagnosed with Wilms' tumor. What special precautions should be taken preoperatively when caring for the child?

Answers to Chapter 22 Study Questions

1.   The diagnosis of cancer can hinder a child's growth and development due to the disease process and treatment regimen. Chronic disease such as cancer can affect the development of the child's mobility and functional ability. Cancer can affect the child's ability to separate from the family to form relationships with peers, progress academically, and participate in age-appropriate recreational activities. Self-concept and self-esteem, especially in the adolescent years, can be threatened. Children may also regress to an earlier developmental stage when they are ill. The developmental stage of adults can also be affected by a diagnosis of cancer. Leaving home, marrying, and starting a career or family are all developmental tasks of a young adult that can be delayed by cancer. Coping with a chronic, possibly life-threatening illness can also affect an adult's feelings of productivity and worthiness. Fatigue, a common side effect of cancer, can seriously challenge the patient's ability to remain independent and engage in self-care activities. Body image and self-esteem can be altered by appearance-altering treatment options. Roles and responsibilities can be significantly changed, altering family relationships. It is important that the nurse allow the patient and family members the opportunity to verbalize their feelings about the life-altering impact of cancer.

2.   Nursing measures related to the care of an ileal conduit include monitoring the urinary output, assessing the stoma, applying the ostomy appliance, and maintaining skin integrity.

3.   Lymphedema, which is the swelling of the affected arm due to inadequate lymphatic and venous drainage, is a chronic problem that can be managed by arm exercises and the use of an elastic device that provides compression and improves lymphatic and venous flow. Arm, shoulder, and hand exercises are encouraged daily to restore full range of motion following surgery. The patient should be instructed to not allow blood pressures to be taken in the arm, nor should injections or blood draws be performed on the arm. Gloves should be worn while gardening to protect the patient from a break in skin integrity that can lead to an infection. Constrictive clothing should not be worn either.

4.   Preoperative nursing care prior to colon surgery includes assessing the nutritional status of the patient. If possible, the patient should be encouraged to eat a low-residue, high-calorie, high-protein, and high-carbohydrate diet. A full liquid diet is usually prescribed twenty-four to forty-eight hours prior to surgery. If the patient is not capable of taking nutrients orally, total parenteral nutrition may be prescribed. Antibiotics are administered prior to surgery to decrease the bacteria in the bowel. Laxatives and/or enemas are used before surgery to empty the colon.

5.   The nurse will assist the patient in learning how to irrigate the ostomy. Ileostomies are not irrigated. Colostomy irrigation is a clean procedure.

Typically, the irrigation will take place with the patient seated on the toilet, although if the patient's condition does not permit activity, the procedure can be performed with the patient in the bed. The patient applies an open-ended irrigating pouch to the ostomy to allow for introduction of the irrigating tube and drainage of the returning liquid into the toilet or bedpan. The open end of the pouch is placed into the toilet or bedpan. A bag of approximately 1000 ml of lukewarm tap water is prepared and placed about twenty inches above the height of the stoma to facilitate the flow of water. The tube, which can be in the form of a catheter or cone, is lubricated with water-soluble jelly, and then gently introduced into the stoma. The tube should never be forced. After introduction of the tube, the water flow is gradually started and water is allowed to flow slowly into the colon. If cramping occurs, the patient should temporarily stop the water flow until the cramping subsides, and then resume the irrigation until all the water has flowed into the colon. The tube is slowly removed; the return of water and stool should begin, with the majority of the return occurring within ten to fifteen minutes. The patient can resume activity, but will want to leave the irrigating pouch on for about forty-five minutes, to collect the remnants of the irrigation return. Following completion of the irrigation procedure, the area is cleansed and gently dried, and a clean pouch or dressing is applied.

6. The most common type of melanoma is superficial spreading melanoma that occurs on the trunk and lower extremities, and is circular with irregular edges. The lesion may be elevated or flat and can be a combination of colors, including brown, black, bluish-black, tan, gray, and white. Nodular melanoma has a round, raised smooth surface that is blue-black in color.

7. It is common for the patient to develop dumping syndrome after gastric surgery, and the intake of small, frequent feedings can help the patient avoid the symptoms. Dumping syndrome occurs when large boluses of food are moved rapidly out of the stomach into the jejunum, creating the presence of a hypertonic mass in the intestines, which draws extracellular fluid from the blood volume into the jejunum. The patient complains of a feeling of fullness, weakness, diaphoresis, and abdominal cramping with diarrhea. The patient may feel faint and dizzy. These symptoms usually occur within thirty minutes of a meal. By eating smaller meals that are low in carbohydrates and eliminating fluid intake with the meals, the symptoms can be decreased. The syndrome usually subsides within six months to a year following surgery.

8. The clinical manifestations of AML are related to the insufficient production of blood cells. A lack of erythrocytes leads to anemia, with accompanying fatigue and weakness. The decreased production of normal WBCs (leukopenia) can lead to infection. The decrease in platelets (thrombocytopenia) causes bleeding. The patient may also experience pain from increased pressure in the spleen and bone marrow caused by proliferation of cells. The major cause of death in AML is from infection and bleeding.

9.   The hallmark of Hodgkin's disease is the Reed-Sternberg cell, which is a large immature malignant lymphoid cell. Diagnosis of Hodgkin's disease is accomplished through excisional lymph node biopsy and identification of the presence of the Reed-Sternberg cell. Through analysis of the pathology of the tumor cells, the disease can be divided into different subgroups.

10.   It is absolutely essential that the abdominal mass not be palpated, as manipulation of the tumor may promote metastasis of cancer cells.

UNIT V: CONGENITAL ANOMALIES, GENETIC DISORDERS, AND DEVELOPMENTAL PROBLEMS

Chapter 23: An Overview of Congenital and Genetic Disorders

Key Terms

Genetic counseling
Mainstreaming
Multifactorial inheritance
Normalization
Teratogens

Introduction

This unit discusses congenital anomalies, genetic disorders, and associated developmental problems. It is estimated that 2 to 3 percent of the infants born annually are affected by a significant congenital defect, genetic disorder, and/or cognitive impairment. The majority of these disorders are chronic in nature and will require lifelong management. This estimate does not include the number of children who will manifest signs of a genetic disorder as they age.

When parents have a young infant or child unexpectedly diagnosed with a chronic (and sometimes fatal) disorder, family dynamics are irreversibly altered. The nurse plays a key role in providing the necessary physical care the child may require. The nurse also assumes a leadership role in educating patients and families about the disorder, provides emotional support to the families, and helps them access resources to cope with their child's needs.

This chapter is an overview of the issues related to congenital anomalies, genetic disorders, and developmental problems. Special emphasis will be placed on the impact that the diagnosis of a chronic health problem or disability can have on the child and his or her family.

Congenital and Genetic Disorders

A **congenital disorder** or **defect** is one that is present at birth. Congenital defects can occur at any time during the prenatal stage of development. The causes of congenital defects are wide-ranging and include genetic and nongenetic causes. In some cases, the cause is a single defective gene. **Cystic fibrosis**, a genetic disorder that primarily affects the respiratory and gastrointestinal systems, is an example of a congenital disease caused by a single defective gene. In other cases, the defect is caused by a **chromosomal abnormality**—**Down syndrome** is the most common example. In a chromosomal abnormality, the chromosomes are either altered in number, or they are **translocated**, which means part of one chromosome attaches itself to another chromosome, creating an abnormal chromosome.

Other causes of defects are nongenetic in nature and are caused by some event that is related to the pregnancy or mother's health habits—congenital heart defects are examples of such disorders. Besides alcohol and illegal drug use, chemical agents such as tobacco and prescribed drugs can affect the development of the fetus. The environment, such as exposure to toxins, can also significantly impact the occurrence of birth defects. Any agents that are known to cause birth defects are referred to as **teratogens**—these can be drugs, viruses, or chemicals.

Some congenital defects are the result of **multifactorial inheritance**. This means that the conditions are caused by a combination of gene and environmental factors. **Pyloric stenosis**, **cleft palate**, and **spina bifida** are examples of some congenital disorders that are thought to be of multifactorial origin.

And finally, some congenital conditions occur without any identifiable causes—either genetic, nongenetic, or multifactorial. It will never be clearly determined what factors led to the development of a congenital disorder in the infant.

There are also some diseases that have a strong familial component and may have a genetic component. Diseases such as diabetes mellitus, some cancers, coronary artery disease, and some forms of mental illness can have a familial component predisposing offspring to the development of the disease.

Whenever there is an incidence of a congenital disorder or the parents have a known family history of a disorder that is genetic in origin, **genetic counseling** is strongly encouraged.

Genetic Counseling

Genetic counseling is recommended for individuals whenever there is the presence, or the likelihood of the presence, of a genetic disorder in the family. Nurses have a responsibility to be aware of the types of situations where individuals could benefit from genetic counseling and to know how to help them get access to such counseling in their community. Guidelines for individuals or couples who may benefit from genetic counseling include the following:

- Parents who have had a previous child with a congenital or genetic disorder
- People who have a known family history of congenital or genetic disorders
- One or both of the parents is a known carrier of a genetic disorder
- Pregnant women who are over age thirty-five or have been exposed to a teratogen

- Individuals who are predisposed to ethnic-related congenital or genetic disorders
- Couples who have experienced infertility problems, multiple miscarriages, or stillbirths

Participating in genetic counseling can help individuals and couples with decision making related to pregnancy and family planning. After assessing the individual's or couple's particular situation, the counselor can discuss the potential risks and lay out a course of action for the individual or couple to consider. The nurse can act as a resource and clarify information for the individuals as they go through the decision-making process. This process takes time and may require a number of counseling sessions. The nurse can ensure that the individual(s) have access to accurate and complete information. It is important for the nurse to provide emotional support to help the individuals involved cope with the stress and anxiety related to the situation. Nurses will often encounter feelings related to guilt and grief, as these are common responses to the diagnosis of a genetic disorder.

Genetic counseling and testing can present complex ethical situations and ethical questions. Religious beliefs may prevent couples from seeking counseling or practicing birth control. These same beliefs can prevent a pregnant woman from consenting to genetic testing. Questions revolve around when testing should occur. Will the early detection of a genetic disorder that will not manifest itself with symptoms for some years prevent an individual from getting health-care insurance or from being employed? Should a healthy child be tested for his or her status as a genetic carrier, or should such testing wait until the child is an adult and can make that decision? These are examples of situations and questions that might be faced in the area of genetic counseling. Nurses have the responsibility to be well read and to keep up-to-date with the ever-increasing information about genetic disorders and genetic counseling in their area of specialization. Due to advances in technology, this field will continue to evolve and grow in importance.

Factors That Influence the Development of Congenital and Genetic Disorders

There are several factors that can influence the development of congenital and genetic health problems. This section will review some of the most common factors that the nurse needs to be aware of. Many of these factors will be addressed again as specific disorders are discussed in the following chapters.

Gender and Age

The sex of the infant can influence the types of congenital or genetic disorders that the child will be at an increased risk for developing. Some types of illnesses occur more commonly in males than in females. For example, pyloric stenosis, an obstruction of the pyloric sphincter, more commonly occurs in male infants. Hypospadias, a genitourinary defect, is a male congenital defect. Exstrophy of the bladder, a severe bladder defect, is much more common in male infants. Duchenne muscular dystrophy (DMD) is inherited only by male offspring. However, scoliosis, a skeletal defect, is more frequent in females. Cleft lip is more common in males, while cleft palate occurs more frequently in females. Each of these disorders is discussed in more detail in the following chapters.

The age and the developmental stages of the child can also influence how the child will respond to a genetic or congenital disorder. Some of the disorders, such as cerebral palsy, may not manifest themselves until it is noticed that the infant or child is not achieving normal developmental milestones. Further evaluation of the child will reveal the presence of the disorder. Scoliosis is not likely to be noticed until the child enters puberty and experiences a growth spurt. Scoliosis will occur at a time when the adolescent is very self-conscious about body image and may rebel against wearing a brace. The symptoms of Duchenne muscular dystrophy do not typically become apparent until about the age of three, after the child has displayed a history of delayed development in the area of walking and coordination. By the time the child enters puberty, walking becomes an impossible task for many who suffer from DMS.

Age and development of the child can influence the detection and response to congenital disorders. Hydrocephalus may first be detected in an infant when a more rapid than normal enlargement of the head occurs as measured by a growth chart. Preschool children who are facing genitourinary surgery may express fear of mutilation. Children with cystic fibrosis or phenylketonuria (PKU) may become reluctant to follow prescribed dietary plans because they want to be "like everyone else." The nurse must emphasize the importance of regular "well-child" examinations to help provide early detection of genetic or congenital disorders. The nurse should also be sensitive to the child's developmental stage in order to develop a care plan that is individualized for the child's needs.

Heredity

Heredity can also influence the development of congenital or genetic disorders. For example, some conditions display racial or ethnic differences. Sickle-cell anemia is associated with the African-American population. Tay-Sachs, a neurological disorder that results in mental retardation, occurs mostly in the Ashkenazi Jewish population's descendents. Cystic fibrosis rarely occurs in the Asian population, but is commonly associated with Caucasians. These ethnic and racial differences are discussed in the following chapters under specific disorders.

Socioeconomic Factors

Socioeconomic factors can also predispose an infant to congenital disorders. Poverty, lack of education, lack of access to prenatal health care, poor maternal nutrition, and premature birth are factors related to delayed intrauterine growth and development of the fetus. Lack of immunizations can create an environment for a pregnant woman that is potentially harmful to the developing fetus if she is exposed to a teratogen. For example, exposure to rubella in the first trimester of pregnancy can result in congenital heart defects. Maternal smoking predisposes the fetus to low birth weight, premature birth, and delayed growth. The use of alcohol, drugs, or being over the age of thirty-five increases the risk for congenital anomalies.

Preexisting health problems on the part of the mother can also lead to congenital disorders. Mothers who have diabetes are at an increased risk for having a baby with a congenital disorder. Mothers with hyperthyroidism also are at an increased risk for having a baby with a congenital disorder or mental retardation.

Prenatal care and good maternal health habits can help prevent a large number of the congenital disorders that occur. Patient education is an important nursing intervention to help improve the health of the mother and ultimately the growth and development of the unborn child.

Impact of Chronic Disability on the Child and Family

Congenital and genetic disorders commonly lead to a chronic disability. It is estimated that 18 percent of the children in the United States have a chronic disability that requires ongoing health care and treatment. The impact of chronic disability on the family is wide-ranging: Financial concerns, caregiver concerns, and altered family dynamics are likely to develop. The affected child faces altered patterns of growth and development. Parents may face a lifetime of providing care to a child who will not be able to live independently. Feelings of grief, guilt, and inadequacy as a parent are also common. The strain of caring for a child with a disability can affect marital relationships. Siblings may perceive that their needs are neglected, as the parents try to meet the needs of the child with the disability. In the case of a chronic disorder that will eventually lead to the death of the child, the family must cope with anticipatory grieving. It is important that the nurse anticipate the different issues that can occur and develop a care plan that will help the child and family cope with and adjust to living with a disability.

The nurse is in an ideal position to coordinate the care that a child and family members will receive. Focus of the care will be on the child's stage of development, emphasizing his or her strengths and individual capabilities. Family-centered care is the ultimate goal. Early discharge and home care that involves normalization of the child's daily activities into the family's daily schedule are trends in today's health care for the chronically disabled. Mainstreaming the child into a regular classroom is another example of how the child with special needs is encouraged and allowed to participate as fully as possible in normal social situations.

Family Coping Strategies

Families go through various stages of adjustment with a child who has a chronic condition. The first stage is shock and denial. This stage occurs when the diagnosis first becomes evident and can continue for months. The family may refuse to believe the diagnosis, may seek out second opinions, or delay seeking treatment. Gradually, most families begin to enter the second stage, which is adjustment. In this stage, the parents acknowledge the diagnosis. A variety of emotions or feelings may become apparent. The more common feelings are anger and guilt. These feelings are all normal, and parents need to understand this. The parents may also exhibit different reactions toward the child. These feelings tend to fall into four categories:

1.   Overprotection of the child
2.   Emotional rejection of the child
3.   Denial of the disorder
4.   Gradual acceptance of the disorder with realistic expectations of the child

Obviously, overprotection, rejection, and denial of the disorder will negatively impact how the child responds to the disorder. The final phase, reintegration and acknowledgment, indicates that the family accepts the child and the child's disability and has reintegrated family life to cope with a chronic disease.

The Child's Coping Strategies

The child's actual response to the chronic disorder will depend upon several factors. First of all, what is the child's developmental level? A child who is very young or cognitively impaired may not be able to comprehend the extent of his or her illness or disability. An older child is keenly aware of looking or being different than his or her peers. Older children also have an understanding of mortality.

The child's coping mechanisms will also have an impact on how the child responds to a chronic disorder. These mechanisms are dependent upon the individual child, and to some degree, family coping styles and available social support. Some coping patterns, both positive and negative, have been identified. Some children are positive, optimistic and feel competent. Other positive coping styles include seeking support and being compliant with treatment. Poor coping mechanisms include withdrawing and expressing feelings of being different, "acting out" behaviors, and being moody or irritable.

The child will also react to his or her condition based upon how the parents and significant others react to the child. Children who are raised by parents who accept them will respond more positively. And finally, the extent of the disability will also influence how the child will respond. In some cases, it appears that children with more severe disorders cope more easily than those with less limiting disorders. Obvious physical conditions can be easier for children to accept and understand than ones that do not produce concrete limitations.

The nurse plays a major role in helping the family and the child adjust to a chronic disability. The nurse will conduct an assessment that includes identifying the family support system, coping mechanisms, and current family stressors. The nurse will also want to assess each family member's understanding of the situation and response to the child. If the child is old enough, the nurse will also assess the child's understanding of the disorder, coping mechanisms, body image, and self-esteem. The nurse can provide a means for both family members and the child to express feelings and share concerns. The nurse can facilitate communication between family members and provide referrals for professional counseling services and other community resources. By providing a nonjudgmental, attentive, empathetic presence, the nurse facilitates the adjustment and coping skills of the family and child.

Chapter 23 Study Questions

1. Define congenital disorder.

2. When should genetic counseling be recommended to an individual or couple?

3. What is the nurse's role in genetic counseling?

4.   Provide two examples of how the developmental stage of a child can influence how the child will respond to a congenital disorder.

5.   Identify socioeconomic factors that can influence the development of a congenital disorder.

6.   What are the goals of care for the child with a chronic disorder or disability?

7.	Describe the stages a family experiences as they adjust to having a child with a chronic disability.

8.	What factors influence how a child will respond to having a chronic congenital disorder?

9.	Describe important assessments for the nurse to make when helping family and child adjust to a chronic disability.

Answers to Chapter 23 Study Questions

1.   A congenital disorder or defect is present at birth. Congenital defects can occur at any time during the prenatal stage of developmental. The causes of congenital defects are wide-ranging and include genetic and nongenetic causes.

2.   Genetic counseling is recommended for individuals whenever there is the presence, or the likelihood of the presence, of a genetic disorder in the family. Guidelines for individuals or couples who may benefit from genetic counseling include the following:

   •   Parents who have had a previous child with a congenital or genetic disorder
   •   People who have a known family history of congenital or genetic disorders
   •   One or both of the parents is a known carrier of a genetic disorder
   •   Pregnant women who are over age thirty-five or who have been exposed to a teratogen
   •   Individuals who are predisposed to ethnic-related congenital or genetic disorders
   •   Couples who have experienced infertility problems, multiple miscarriages, or stillbirths

3.   The nurse should act as a resource and clarify information for the individuals as they go through the decision-making process. The nurse can ensure that the individuals have access to accurate and complete information. It is important for the nurse to also provide emotional support as the individuals involved cope with the stress and anxiety related to the situation. Nurses have the responsibility to be well read and to keep up-to-date with the ever-increasing information about genetic disorders and genetic counseling in their area of specialization.

4.   Some disorders, such as cerebral palsy, may not manifest themselves until it is noticed that the infant or child is not achieving normal developmental milestones. Scoliosis is not likely to be noticed until the child enters puberty and experiences a growth spurt. Scoliosis will occur at a time when the adolescent is very self-conscious about body image and may rebel against wearing a brace. The symptoms of Duchenne muscular dystrophy do not typically become apparent until about the age of three, after the child has displayed a history of delayed development in the area of walking and coordination. Hydrocephalus may first be detected when a more rapid than normal enlargement of the head occurs. Preschool children who are facing genitourinary surgery may express fear of mutilation. Children with cystic fibrosis or PKU may become reluctant to follow prescribed dietary plans because they want to be "like everyone else."

5.   Socioeconomic factors can predispose an infant to congenital disorders. Poverty, lack of education, lack of access to prenatal health care, poor maternal nutrition, and premature birth are factors that can cause delayed intrauterine growth and development of the fetus. Lack of immunizations can create an environment for a

pregnant woman that is potentially harmful to the developing fetus if she is exposed to a teratogen. For example, exposure to rubella in the first trimester of pregnancy can result in congenital heart defects. Maternal smoking predisposes the fetus to low birth weight, premature birth, and delayed growth. The use of alcohol, drugs, or being over the age of thirty-five increases the risk for congenital anomalies.

6. The nurse is in an ideal position to coordinate the care that a child and family members will receive. Goals of care will be based upon the child's stage of development, emphasizing his or her strengths and individual capabilities. Family-centered care is the ultimate goal. Early discharge and home care that involves normalization of the child's daily activities into the family's daily schedule are trends in today's health care for the chronically disabled. Mainstreaming the child into a regular classroom is another example of how the child with special needs is encouraged and allowed to participate as fully as possible in normal social situations.

7. Families go through various stages as they adjust to a child having a chronic condition. The first stage is one of shock and denial. This occurs when the diagnosis first becomes evident and can continue for months. The family may refuse to believe the diagnosis, may seek out second opinions, or delay seeking treatment. Gradually, most families begin to enter the second stage, which is adjustment. In this stage, the parents acknowledge the diagnosis. The final phase, reintegration and acknowledgment, indicates that the family accepts the child and the child's disability and has reintegrated family life to cope with a chronic disease.

8. The child's actual response to the chronic disorder will depend upon the developmental level, coping mechanisms, and how the parents and significant others react to the child. In addition, the extent of the disability will also influence how the child will respond.

9. The nurse assesses the family support system, coping mechanisms, and current family stressors. The nurse will also assess each family member's understanding of the situation and response to the child. If the child is old enough, the nurse will also assess the child's understanding of the disorder, coping mechanisms, body image, and self-esteem.

Chapter 24: Nursing Care for Congenital and Genetic Heart Diseases

Key Terms

Aortic stenosis (AS)
Atrial septic defect (ASD)
Clubbing
Congenital heart disease (CHD)
Hypercyanotic spells
Patent ductus arteriosus (PDA)
Pulmonic stenosis (PS)
Tetralogy of Fallot (TOF)
Ventricular septal defect (VSD)

Introduction

This chapter discusses the nursing care for patients with congenital heart disease. Three of the most common forms of congenital heart disease, patent ductus arteriosus (PDA), tetralogy of Fallot (TOF), and ventricular septal defect (VSD), are covered in detail. Congestive heart failure and hypoxemia are also discussed, as both can develop as a result of congenital heart disease.

Congenital Heart Disease

Congenital heart disease (CHD) is the term used to describe structural abnormalities that are present in the heart at birth. Because of these abnormalities, the normal blood flow of the heart is disrupted, frequently leading to the development of hypoxemia and/or congestive heart failure. With the exception of premature birth, CHD is a leading cause of death in children under the age of one.

The cause of CHD is usually unknown. However, some factors that are associated with congenital heart disease are related to the mother's health. A woman who is over the age of forty, suffers from alcoholism, has Type I diabetes mellitus, or comes in contact with rubella during the pregnancy has a higher risk of having a baby with CHD. Infants with chromosomal disorders or other congenital abnormalities also demonstrate a higher incidence of CHD.

Pathophysiology of CHD

The presence of a structural defect in the heart disrupts the heart's blood flow pattern and alters the hemodynamic characteristics of the heart. Heart defects are classified according to the hemodynamic alterations that occur as a result of the defect. Defects can cause either an increase or decrease in pulmonary blood flow, obstruction to blood flow throughout the heart, or a mixing of oxygenated and deoxygenated blood within the heart. Heart defects that cause an **increase** in pulmonary blood flow can lead to congestive heart failure. Examples of heart defects that cause increased pulmonary blood flow include atrial septal defects, ventricular septal defects, and patent ductus arteriosus. Heart defects that cause a **decrease** in pulmonary blood flow can cause cyanosis. Tetralogy of Fallot is an example of a heart defect that leads to a decrease in pulmonary blood flow.

Heart defects that obstruct blood flow out of the ventricles can lead to either congestive heart failure or cyanosis, depending upon which side of the heart experiences the obstruction. Obstructed blood flow is due to a structural narrowing, or stenosis. If the stenosis is on the left side, the patient can develop congestive heart failure. An example of a left-sided heart defect that can lead to congestive heart failure is aortic stenosis, which is a narrowing of the aortic valve. If the stenosis is on the right side of the heart, as in pulmonic stenosis, which is a narrowing of the pulmonic valve, the patient can develop cyanosis.

Heart defects leading to a mixing of oxygenated and deoxygenated blood causes both congestive heart failure and hypoxemia. The mixing of oxygenated and deoxygenated blood leads to a decreased oxygen desaturation of the systemic blood flow. Cyanosis may or may not be present. These defects are usually complex with clinical manifestations that vary depending upon the extent of oxygenated and deoxygenated blood mixing. Examples of mixed defects include transposition of great arteries and hypoplastic left heart syndrome.

We will now focus more specifically on the pathophysiology of three cardiac defects: patent ductus arteriosus (PDA), ventricular septal defect (VSD), and tetralogy of Fallot (TOF). A discussion of the clinical manifestations of CHD will follow.

Patent Ductus Arteriosus (PDA)

Patent ductus arteriosus (PDA) develops when the fetal ductus arteriosus, an artery that prior to birth connects the aorta and the pulmonary artery, fails to close as normal during the first few weeks of the newborn's life. Because the ductus arteriosus does not close, a connection remains between the aorta and pulmonary artery.

The aorta has a higher level of pressure than the pulmonary artery; this higher level of pressure causes the blood to flow through the patent ductus arteriosus from the aorta to the pulmonary artery. As the blood flows from the aorta to the pulmonary artery, there is an increase in pulmonary blood flow and pulmonary vascular congestion. The extra blood flow circulates from the lungs to the left atrium and ventricle, thus increasing the workload of the left side of the heart. Because of the increased pulmonary vascular congestion, the right side of the heart may eventually hypertrophy as well.

Figure 24.1 Patent Ductus Arteriosus

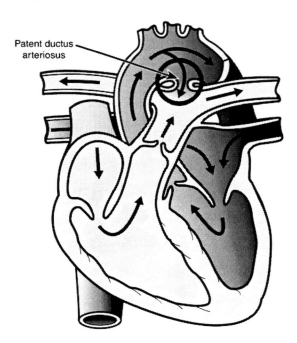

The clinical manifestations of PDA are related to this extra blood flow and depend upon the size of the ductus arteriosus. A murmur that is characteristically described as "machine-like" is present. The infant may also exhibit signs of congestive heart failure. With treatment, prognosis of the infant is good. The goal of treatment is to close the defect. Treatment of PDA may include the administration of a prostaglandin inhibitor (indomethacin) to close the PDA, insertion of coils via cardiac catheterization to occlude the PDA, or surgical intervention to close the PDA.

Ventricular Septal Defect (VSD)

Ventricular septal defect (VSD) is the presence of an abnormal opening connecting the right and left ventricles. The defect can range in size from minute to a completely missing septum, resulting in one common ventricle.

Because of the opening in the septum, blood flows from the left ventricle, which is an area of higher pressure, to the right ventricle, which is an area of lower pressure. The increased blood flow into the right ventricle leads to an increase in pulmonary artery blood flow, and eventually an increase in pulmonary resistance can develop. If pulmonary resistance develops, the workload of the right ventricle will increase, leading to right ventricular hypertrophy. The workload of the right atrium can also be increased by incomplete right ventricular emptying.

Figure 24.2 Ventricular Septal Defect

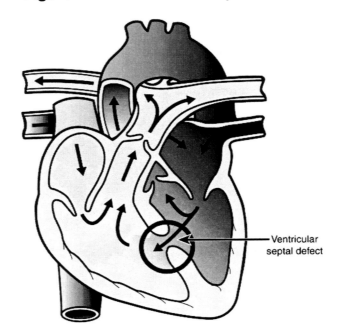

Ventricular
septal defect

The clinical manifestations of VSD are related to size of the defect and the development of congestive heart failure. A murmur may be detected. In children who have small- or medium-sized defects, the opening can close spontaneously during the first year of life. Other children require surgery to close the defect. Prognosis of the child varies depending upon the size of the defect and the extent of needed repairs. Mortality rates can range from less than 5 percent to greater than 20 percent.

Tetralogy of Fallot (TOF)

Tetralogy of Fallot (TOF) is a more complex heart defect than the two we have previously discussed. As the name implies, there are actually four defects present in TOF. The four heart defects are the following:

1. Pulmonic stenosis
2. Ventricular septal defect
3. Overriding aorta
4. Right ventricular hypertrophy

The hemodynamic alterations that develop in TOF can vary widely, depending upon the extent of the defects, especially the VSD and pulmonic stenosis.

Pulmonic stenosis restricts blood flow into the lungs, thus decreasing the amount of blood available for reoxygenation. If the pulmonic stenosis is significant, the pressure within the right ventricle will increase, causing a shunting of blood from the right to the left side of the heart. If the systemic resistance is greater than the pulmonary resistance created by the pulmonic stenosis, the shift in blood will be from the left side of the heart to the right side (as in VSD). Depending upon the extent of the aortic defect, both right and left ventricular blood flow may empty into the aorta.

Figure 24.3 Defects of Tetralogy of Fallot

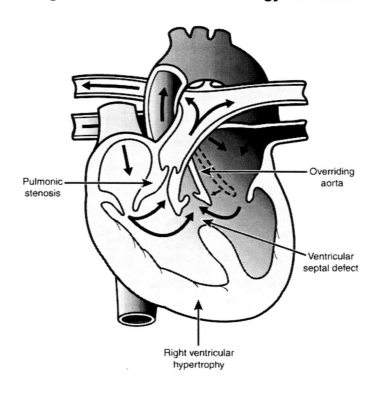

Right ventricular hypertrophy develops as a result of pulmonary resistance. The clinical manifestations of TOF include cyanosis. The cyanosis may be mild or severe, depending upon the severity of the pulmonic stenosis. As the stenosis worsens, the cyanosis can become progressively more severe. The infant may be susceptible to acute hypoxia and cyanotic episodes known as **hypercyanotic spells** ("blue" or "tet" spells). These episodes typically occur when the infant is stressed, crying, feeding, or having a bowel movement. As the child ages, clubbing of the fingers may develop, and the child demonstrates a poor growth pattern. Squatting may also be evident, as the child squats during activity in an attempt to relieve hypoxia.

Treatment of TOF is surgical repair of the defects, usually during the first year of the infant's life. The mortality rate for surgical repair is less than 5 percent.

Clinical Manifestations of CHD

The clinical manifestations of CHD are typically related to the development of two problems: **congestive heart failure** and **hypoxemia**. These problems will be discussed separately.

Congestive Heart Failure

Because the structural defects of CHD cause alterations in blood volume and pressure levels in the heart, CHD frequently leads to the development of congestive heart failure (CHF). In CHF, the heart is unable to pump an adequate amount of blood systemically to meet the oxygen demands of the body's tissues. (CHF is also discussed in chapter 12.)

Heart failure is usually described as left- or right-sided heart failure. In **left-sided heart failure**, the left ventricle is unable to effectively pump blood forward systemically throughout the body. This causes pulmonary congestion and increased pressure to develop in the left atrium and pulmonary veins. In **right-sided heart failure**, the right ventricle is unable to effectively pump blood forward into the lungs through the pulmonary artery. This ineffective pumping leads to increased pressure in the right atrium and systemic venous congestion.

In children, it is most common to see combined left- and right-sided heart failure. If the function of one side of the child's heart is impaired, the function of the other side of the heart will also likely be affected. The signs and symptoms that are observed in CHF will depend upon the severity of the heart defects and the extent of CHF that develops. The signs and symptoms of CHF result from impaired cardiac function, pulmonary congestion, and venous congestion.

The child with **impaired cardiac function** may exhibit the following signs and symptoms:

- Weakness, fatigue
- Restlessness
- Anorexia
- Tachycardia, decreased blood pressure
- Gallop rhythm
- Diminished peripheral pulses
- Cool, pale extremities
- Decreased urinary output
- Enlarged heart (cardiomegaly)

If the child develops **pulmonary congestion**, the following signs and symptoms may be observed:

- Increased respiratory rate
- Dyspnea
- Orthopnea
- Cyanosis
- Coughing, wheezing, hoarseness, crackles
- Flaring nares, retractions
- Activity intolerance

If the child develops **systemic venous congestion**, signs and symptoms may include the following:

- Peripheral edema
- Periorbital edema
- Ascites
- Hepatomegaly
- Weight gain
- Neck vein distention

Hypoxemia

Children with CHD may develop **hypoxemia** if unoxygenated blood is allowed to enter the systemic circulation without circulating through the lungs. Hypoxemia refers to a clinical state in which the arterial oxygen tension (PaO_2) is below normal. Hypoxemia leads to the development of **hypoxia**, which is the reduction of tissue oxygenation.

The hypoxemia that develops in CHD is chronic in nature, and may range from mild to severe, depending upon the extent of the defects. In response to this chronic hypoxemia the child may develop polycythemia and clubbing.

Polycythemia, which is an increased number of red blood cells, develops in response to the chronic hypoxemia. The body attempts to compensate for the decreased oxygen saturation levels by producing more red blood cells to increase the blood's oxygen-carrying capacity. Polycythemia increases the viscosity of the blood.

Clubbing of fingertips and toes also develops in chronic hypoxemia. The cause of clubbing is believed to be related to the polycythemia. In clubbing, the tips of the fingers and toes become thickened and flattened.

Other signs and symptoms related to hypoxemia include cyanosis, fatigue, increased respiratory rate, and dyspnea. The infant or child may experience difficulty eating and activity intolerance due to fatigue, and thus exhibit poor weight gain with delayed growth and development. As described earlier, squatting may be evident in toddlers and children with tetralogy of Fallot. The child will squat during periods of activity in an attempt to relieve hypoxia. Hypercyanotic spells are also seen in infants with tetralogy of Fallot. Children who have chronic cyanosis and hypoxia as a result of CHD are at a risk for developing neurological complications, such as delayed growth and development and cerebrovascular accidents (CVA).

Diagnostic Tests

An infant or child who is suspected of having a CHD undergoes a variety of diagnostic tests to confirm the diagnosis. A **chest X ray** provides information about cardiac size and blood flow patterns in the lungs. An **ECG (EKG)** is performed to determine the electrical activity of the heart. **Echocardiography** is used to provide images of heart structures. A **cardiac MRI** may be performed to evaluate the vascular anatomy around the heart.

The definitive procedure for diagnosing cardiac defects is **cardiac catheterization**. Pre- and postoperative adult nursing care for this procedure is described in chapter 9, and this care applies to infants and children as well. The nurse must take special care to explain the procedure to the family and to the child in terms that the child can understand. The child may become frightened by the darkness of the room, appearance and noise of the machine, and the "warm" feeling that is felt when the contrast medium is injected. Preoperative explanations can help the child to understand what is happening during the procedure.

The child usually receives some form of sedation prior to the procedure, but the type of sedation used varies with institutions and also depends on the condition of the child. Following the cardiac catheterization, the child is returned to the hospital room to be monitored closely for potential complications. A heart monitor will be used to monitor cardiac arrhythmias, and a pulse oximeter will be used to monitor oxygen saturation.

The catheterization site (femoral or antecubital area) is checked for hemorrhage and hematoma development. A pressure dressing is usually kept in place until the day following the procedure. The site must be kept clean and dry to avoid infection. If the child wears diapers, the area will be kept covered with a waterproof dressing.

Vital signs are taken every fifteen minutes for at least the first hour following the procedure. The apical pulse must be taken for one full minute to detect any arrhythmias. Peripheral pulses, temperature, and color of the catheterized extremity are carefully assessed at frequent intervals. Coolness and paleness of the extremity could indicate arterial occlusion. The child must keep the extremity (usually a leg) straight for approximately six to eight hours following the procedure. Parents may be encouraged to hold the child to help keep the extremity straight if the child has difficulty maintaining the correct position.

Intravenous fluids will be administered to the child, and oral fluids are encouraged to prevent dehydration and to promote removal of the contrast medium from the body. The child may resume a normal diet as soon as desired. Following the recovery period from the procedure, the child will be discharged home if his or her clinical condition is satisfactory.

Medical Management of CHD

Medical management of CHD focuses on treatment of the defect through surgical intervention and treatment of the clinical consequences that can develop as a result of CHD.

Surgical intervention is the treatment of choice for most cardiac defects if the defect is amenable to surgery and the patient's condition is stable enough for the patient to tolerate surgery. Either a **median sternotomy**, in which the sternum is split, or a **lateral**

thoracotomy, where the incision runs from the midaxillary line to the scapula, will be used to access the heart. A **ministernotomy**, which is a minimally invasive procedure that only requires an incision in the sternum's lower half, is becoming more common and will be used whenever possible, as it promotes quicker postoperative healing and recovery with less pain.

Managing CHF in the Child with CHD

The prevention and management of congestive heart failure is usually a key component of the medical management of CHD. The goals of medical management are the following:

- Increase cardiac function
- Decrease fluid volume overload
- Decrease cardiac workload and oxygen consumption
- Increase tissue oxygenation

Pharmacological therapy is used to help increase cardiac function. **Digoxin (Lanoxin)** is used to increase cardiac output. Oral preparations of digoxin are available as an elixir (0.05mg/ml). The nurse must carefully note the dosage to avoid a medicine error, especially noting the placement of decimal points. When administering digoxin to infants, be sure to remember that the dosage will be calculated in micrograms (1000 micrograms = 1 milligram). It is rare for an infant to receive more than 50 micrograms/1ml in one dose; if you calculate a dosage larger than this, it is very likely that you have made a dosage calculation error.

The dosage of digoxin will vary depending upon the age, weight, and condition of the child. The therapeutic serum digoxin levels range between 0.8–2.0 micrograms/L. For children, there is a very small safety margin between the therapeutic, toxic, and lethal doses of digoxin. Common signs and symptoms of **digitalis toxicity** in children include bradycardia (apical pulse rate below 90 in infants/young children and below 70 in older children), arrhythmias, anorexia, nausea, and vomiting.

The apical pulse should always be taken for one full minute prior to administration of digoxin. If the child exhibits any of the symptoms of digoxin toxicity, the drug should be withheld and the physician notified.

Angiotensin-converting enzyme (ACE) inhibitors are also used to treat CHF and improve cardiac function. ACE inhibitors cause vasodilation to occur, resulting in decreased pulmonary resistance, lowered blood pressure, and a reduced afterload. Captopril (Capoten) is a commonly administered ACE inhibitor, especially for infants and young children. Potassium supplements or potassium-sparing diuretics, such as spironolactone, should not be given with ACE inhibitors because hyperkalemia can develop. Also, ACE inhibitors can lead to hypotension, so the patient's blood pressure should be carefully monitored before and after each dose.

To reduce fluid volume overload, diuretics, fluid restriction, and sodium restriction may be implemented. **Diuretics** are an essential component of treatment of CHF. The most commonly administered diuretics are furosemide (Lasix), chlorothiazide (Diuril), and spironolactone (Aldactone). If potassium-losing diuretics (furosemide and chlorothiazide) are administered, potassium supplements will also be administered. The nurse can place the potassium elixir in fruit juice to entice the youngster to take the bitter-tasting medicine. Fluid restriction is used selectively, because in infants and young children, the CHF makes it difficult for them to eat and maintain adequate fluid intakes; infants, in particular, can become easily dehydrated. Fluid restriction is more likely to be used during acute periods of CHF. Sodium restriction is used sparingly in children as well, and usually consists of limiting high-sodium foods and eliminating table salt.

Decreasing cardiac workload and oxygen consumption are achieved by limiting the child's physical activity and reducing metabolic demands. A semi-Fowler's position helps decrease the work of breathing, and bed rest helps reduce metabolic demands. Body temperature is conserved by avoiding chilling. Fevers are promptly treated, as fever increases the body's metabolism, oxygen consumption, and cardiac workload. Tissue oxygenation is increased by administering supplemental oxygen.

Managing Hypoxemia in the Child with CHD

Children with chronic hypoxemia must be protected from any respiratory infections that can increase hypoxemia and further decrease the functioning of their lungs. Medical management of hypoxemia that supports lung functioning includes **chest physiotherapy**, **supplemental oxygen**, and **antibiotics** to treat infections. Fevers are treated promptly to decrease metabolic demand and the potential for dehydration. Because polycythemia can develop as a result of chronic hypoxemia, the child must be kept adequately hydrated to decrease blood viscosity. The child's lab values will be monitored closely to check for anemia, which can further decrease the oxygen-carrying capacity of the blood.

If a child experiences a hypercyanotic spell, prompt intervention is required. IV fluids will be administered and morphine will be given to decrease spasms and increase pulmonary blood flow. Oxygen will also be administered. Sedatives may be used to quiet the infant or child and help them relax. A knee-to-chest position is recommended for infants during the spell to help increase oxygenation.

Nursing Care of the Child with CHD

Nursing Process: Assessment

Nursing assessment of a child with suspected CHD includes a comprehensive nursing history. The nurse should seek information about any previous history of cardiac defects in the child's family, history of the pregnancy, and any known contact by the mother during pregnancy with factors that are associated with defects. The presence of any other congenital defects or chromosomal abnormalities should also be noted. In addition, the nurse should seek information about the child's growth and development, susceptibility to respiratory infections or breathing problems, and any noted difficulty with feeding (especially in infants), difficulty gaining weight, or activity intolerance.

The physical assessment should include a thorough investigation of all body systems. An assessment of the cardiovascular system should include an inspection of the chest for any deformities in shape or size. The child's color may also provide clues to the cardiovascular status—cyanosis indicates lack of oxygenation and is common in CHD; pallor indicates a lack of adequate tissue perfusion. Neck vein distention or pulsation should be noted, as these can be seen in CHF that is brought on by CHD. The heart sounds should be auscultated, listening for any murmurs and muffled or extra heart sounds. Palpation of the chest may reveal a thrill, which is a palpable vibration. The apical heart rate and rhythm should be noted. Peripheral pulses are also assessed bilaterally for strength, rhythm, and rate.

The child's respiratory system should also be carefully assessed. Respiratory rate and rhythm are assessed, noting any tachypnea, dyspnea, or expiratory grunting. Lung sounds should be auscultated for any adventitious breath sounds, such as crackles, that may occur as a result of excess fluid. Fingers and toes should be examined for evidence of clubbing that is caused by chronic hypoxemia.

The nutritional status of the child should also be assessed. Does the child display weight loss and a failure to thrive? Evidence of dehydration may be present if the child is not able to take in adequate amounts of fluid due to fatigue or fever. Palpation of the abdomen may reveal hepatomegaly, which can develop as a result of venous circulatory congestion, and splenomegaly, which develops as a result of polycythemia.

Nursing Process: Nursing Diagnosis and Planning

Based upon an analysis of the gathered data, the following **nursing diagnoses**, while not intended to be inclusive, may be appropriate for the patient with congenital heart disease:

- Decreased cardiac output related to impaired myocardial functioning
- Ineffective breathing pattern related to excess fluid in the lungs
- Activity intolerance related to impaired tissue oxygenation and inability to meet the energy demands of the body
- Altered nutrition, less than body requirements related to fatigue and respiratory difficulties
- Fear related to lack of knowledge about diagnosis and surgical repair of defect
- Altered family processes related to the child experiencing a life-threatening illness

Primary goals for the patient with congenital heart disease include the following:

- Improve cardiac functioning
- Improve respiratory functioning
- Increase activity tolerance
- Maintain adequate nutritional intake
- Maintain fluid and electrolyte balance
- Access community resources to help the family cope with illness

Nursing Process: Implementation

Children with CHD and their families need much support and skilled nursing care to help them cope with this stressful time in their lives. Many infants, toddlers, or children will be candidates for surgical intervention to correct the heart defect. There are some defects, however, that will not be able to be completely repaired. Prior to the surgery, the nurse focuses on supporting the patient's cardiac and respiratory functioning, maintaining adequate nutritional status, and addressing any concerns of the patient or family members.

Medications and Tests

A priority nursing action for supporting cardiac functioning is to administer prescribed cardiac drugs promptly and safely. (See also chapter 10.) This important nursing responsibility cannot be overemphasized. Since many parents will be responsible for administering the medications in the home setting, it is also important that the nurse work closely with the family to educate the primary caregivers on safe administration of the child's medications.

In addition to administering the prescribed medications, the nurse should also strive to decrease the child's cardiac demands. Infants in particular need to conserve energy for feeding. The parents should be encouraged to hold their infant or young child if this helps the child to rest more peacefully. Nursing activities should be planned and organized; rest periods and sleep should not be interrupted when at all possible. Older children may benefit from planned "quiet time" with activities that are engaging but not physically demanding. The patient's temperature should be carefully monitored, as either chilling or fever can increase energy demands on the heart.

The nurse should also take care to decrease anxiety and stress for the child, as emotional distress can increase cardiac demands. Diagnostic tests and all equipment should be explained to the child in terms that are appropriate. It may help the child to anticipate events by providing him or her with a planned calendar for each day. The parents should also be informed about tests and procedures so that they can also help reduce anxiety by answering any questions the child may have about planned activities.

In addition to supporting cardiac functioning, it is also essential to support the child's respiratory functioning. Children should be positioned with the head of the bed elevated at a 45° angle. Infants can be placed in an infant seat to achieve this position. Clothing should be nonrestrictive, and supplemental oxygen should be administered as needed. Pulse oximetry, which measures oxygen saturation, is used to measure the patient's response to oxygen therapy. It is important that the child be protected from respiratory infection as much as possible. Individuals having contact with the child should practice good hand-washing technique prior to caring for the child.

Nutritional Status

Maintaining adequate nutritional status can be a challenge. Infants and children have a greater metabolic demand because of their poor cardiac functioning and increased pulse and respiratory rates. Yet they fatigue easily when eating, and they cannot always take in enough nourishment to meet their bodies' energy needs. Scheduling feeding times more frequently (about every three hours) with smaller servings may help increase intake. Additives may also be placed in the formula to increase calorie density. Infants may benefit from the use of a nipple with an enlarged opening to make it easier to suck. They should be held in a semi-upright position to facilitate breathing while eating. The infant may need to rest periodically throughout the feeding. If the infant or child is unable to take in adequate nutrition orally, enteral feedings may be implemented.

An adequate fluid intake must be maintained, especially in children who have chronic hypoxemia. Dehydration can further increase the blood viscosity present with polycythemia and precipitate a CVA. Adequate fluid intake can be difficult to achieve if the child is fatigued. Fluids should be offered frequently. IV fluids may be administered if the child cannot tolerate oral intake. If the child is experiencing CHF, fluid restriction may be a necessity; although because of the difficulty of feeding, it is rare for infants to have fluid restrictions. Accurate intake and output records should be maintained and daily weights obtained.

Social and Emotional Support

The nurse should also focus on providing emotional support to the child and family. A diagnosis of a congenital heart defect is shocking and creates much stress and anxiety in the family. Parents grieve the loss of a "normal" child and, at the same time, must cope with the demands of caring for a chronically, seriously ill child. Financial concerns may be a significant stressor. Normal parent-infant bonding may be affected by prolonged hospitalizations of the seriously ill infant. Other family members may feel neglected because of the amount of attention the child requires. Normal growth and development of the child can be affected because of decreased cardiac functioning and fatigue.

Social interactions with other children may become limited if care is not taken to foster normal relationships with peers. It is important for parents to avoid fostering overdependency; rather, parents should encourage the child to participate in appropriate social activity as much as possible. Children will usually learn to naturally limit their activities, and parents do not need to be concerned about overexertion. The nurse can help the parents locate community resources and support groups that will help the family cope with the crisis situation that they are facing. Being an empathetic listener, responding to questions, providing education about the disorder, and reassuring the parents that their feelings and concerns are valid are all important support activities for the nurse to implement.

Preparations for Surgery

Preparing the child and parents for cardiac surgery is another important nursing action. Preoperatively, it is usually beneficial if the child and parents can visit the intensive care unit, to be familiarized with equipment and introduced to the staff that will be caring for the child postoperatively. Following surgery, the child will have numerous IV lines, an endotracheal tube, chest tubes, incisional dressing, and a urethral catheter in place. The nurse should reassure the child and family that pain medication will be available to help control postoperative pain. Questions should be encouraged. However, the nurse needs to be sensitive to providing more information at any one time than the child and parents can cope with, as this can further increase stress.

Postoperatively, vital signs will be monitored frequently to detect any early changes in the patient's condition. Arterial lines are inserted to allow for hemodynamic monitoring. Any alterations in cardiac rhythm are promptly reported to the physician. A slight elevation of temperature (about 100° F) is considered to be normal the first forty-eight hours following surgery as a response to tissue injury; after forty-eight hours, the presence of an elevated temperature can indicate an infection.

Lung sounds are auscultated hourly to note the development of diminished breath sounds that can indicate atelectasis or crackles that can indicate the development of pulmonary congestion. The endotracheal tube is usually removed in the early postoperative stage (within the first twenty-four hours). If the child requires suctioning while intubated, suctioning is maintained for only five seconds to avoid oxygen depletion. Following extubation, the child should be encouraged to cough and deep breathe hourly. The nurse should help the child splint the incision. Pain medication should be administered regularly to keep the child comfortable and encourage deep breathing and coughing.

Chest tube drainage is monitored hourly. Bright red drainage will be normal immediately after surgery, but gradually should change to serous drainage. Excessive drainage (more than 3 ml/kg/hr) should be reported promptly to the surgeon, as this could indicate hemorrhage. Drainage will subside after the first twelve to twenty-four hours, and the tubes are usually removed by the third postoperative day.

Urine output and specific gravity are measured hourly to monitor renal function. BUN and creatinine will also be monitored. Fluids will be closely monitored to avoid fluid volume overload in the early postoperative phase. Strict intake and output records are kept.

Activity will gradually be resumed beginning on the second postoperative day, as long as the patient's cardiovascular and respiratory status is stable. The child will begin by sitting on the edge of the bed, and activity can be increased as tolerated. Heart and respiratory rate, color, oxygen saturation levels, and fatigue levels should be assessed by the nurse during the activity.

Ensuring that the child is kept comfortable following surgery is a major goal of nursing care. Intravenous analgesics will most likely be the drugs of choice during the early postoperative phase. The amount of pain the child experiences will be somewhat impacted by the location of the incision—sternal incisions are usually better tolerated than thoracotomy incisions. Supporting the incision during movement will help decrease pain.

Emotional support of parents and the child is essential during the postoperative phase. It is stressful for the parents to observe their child in an intensive care unit with monitors and tubes attached. They may feel that there is little they can do to help their child. The nurse should be sure to include the parents in the child's care as much as possible, explaining everything that is being done to support the child's recovery. Children will sometimes become angry with the parents and demonstrate feelings of rejection. The nurse can support the parents during this time by reassuring them that this is normal behavior that will subside with time. The child should also be given the opportunity to express fears and other feelings during this recovery period.

Parents will need clear instructions for care of the child following discharge. If the child is old enough to participate in self-care, the nurse will need to include the child in any education sessions. The child's health-care needs following discharge can vary considerably. For some children, surgery will eventually mean a complete recovery from the CHD. For others, the recovery may only be partial and the child's prognosis remains unclear. Some children may experience residual heart damage, which means that they must be monitored for the development of CHF—even after repair of the defect has been accomplished. Continued medical care and emotional support will be necessary for these children and their families.

Nursing Process: Evaluation

The effectiveness of nursing interventions for the child with CHD can be measured by the achievement of the following expected outcomes by the patient and family:

- Demonstrates adequate cardiac output with heartbeat within normal limits
- Maintains normal tissue perfusion
- Maintains normal respiratory rate without dyspnea
- Participates in activities of daily living without fatigue
- Maintains normal fluid and electrolyte balance
- Maintains adequate nutritional intake
- Verbalizes understanding of heart condition and home self-care behaviors (parents and child)
- Verbalizes adequate emotional support (parents and child)
- Verbalizes adequate pain control postoperatively
- Avoids complications of CHD (CHF, hypoxemia, respiratory infections)

The nurse evaluates the child and family for achievement of expected outcomes and adjusts the nursing care plan accordingly. It is important to remember that realistic expectations for outcomes of care will depend upon the extent of the child's defect and whether or not it can be surgically corrected. The above outcomes will need to be adjusted depending upon the child's prognosis and what he or she can realistically be expected to accomplish.

Chapter 24 Study Questions

1.   Describe the four classifications of congenital heart disease.

2.   An infant has been diagnosed with patent ductus arteriosus (PDA). What is the underlying pathophysiology in PDA?

3.   Describe the pathophysiology of a ventricular septal defect (VSD).

4.   Describe the four cardiac defects associated with tetralogy of Fallot (TOF).

5.   An infant who has a CHD is hospitalized with CHF. What signs and symptoms might the nurse anticipate observing in this infant?

6.   A child has returned to his room following a cardiac catheterization. What are the priority nursing actions for immediately following the procedure?

7.   Identify six priority nursing diagnoses for a child with CHD.

8.   The nurse is caring for a twelve-year-old child who is receiving Lanoxin as treatment for CHF. The child complains to the nurse about feeling nauseated, and that he has no appetite for food. The nurse takes his pulse and notes an apical pulse rate of 65 beats/minute. What should be the nurse's response to these findings?

9.   The nurse is caring for a three-month-old infant with CHD. Describe the nursing interventions that would be appropriate for supporting the infant's respiratory functioning.

10.   Describe some of the factors the nurse should consider when providing emotional support to parents of a child with a CHD.

11.   A mother is frightened by the presence and appearance of her son's chest tubes following surgery to correct a heart defect. What can the nurse tell the mother about the chest tubes to decrease the mother's anxiety?

12.   Identify four out of the ten expected outcomes listed in the study guide that would be appropriate for a child following successful surgery for a CHD.

Answers to Chapter 24 Study Questions

1. Defects can cause either an increase or decrease in pulmonary blood flow, an obstruction to blood flow throughout the heart, or a mixing of oxygenated and deoxygenated blood within the heart.

2. Patent ductus arteriosus develops when the fetal ductus arteriosus, an artery that prior to birth connects the aorta and the pulmonary artery, does not close as normal during the first few weeks of the newborn's life. Because the ductus arteriosus does not close, a connection remains between the aorta and pulmonary artery. The aorta has a higher level of pressure than the pulmonary artery; this higher level of pressure causes the blood to flow through the patent ductus arteriosus from the aorta to the pulmonary artery. As the blood flows from the aorta to the pulmonary artery, there is an increase in pulmonary blood flow and pulmonary vascular congestion. The extra blood flow circulates from the lungs to the left atrium and ventricle, thus increasing the workload of the left side of the heart. Because of the increased pulmonary vascular congestion, the right side of the heart may eventually hypertrophy as well.

3. Ventricular septal defect is the presence of an abnormal opening connecting the right and left ventricles. The defect can range in size from minute to a completely missing septum with one common ventricle. Because of the opening in the septum, blood flows from the left ventricle, which is an area of higher pressure, to the right ventricle, which is an area of lower pressure. The increased blood flow into the right ventricle leads to an increase in pulmonary artery blood flow, and eventually an increase in pulmonary resistance can develop. If pulmonary resistance develops, the workload of the right ventricle will increase, leading to right ventricular hypertrophy. The workload of the right atrium can also be increased by incomplete right ventricular emptying.

4. Tetralogy of Fallot involves pulmonic stenosis, ventricular septal defect, overriding aorta, and right ventricular hypertrophy.

5. The child with impaired cardiac function from CHF may exhibit the following signs and symptoms: weakness; fatigue; restlessness; anorexia; tachycardia; decreased blood pressure; gallop rhythm; diminished peripheral pulses; cool, pale extremities; decreased urinary output; and cardiomegaly. If the child develops pulmonary congestion, the following signs and symptoms may be observed: increased respiratory rate, dyspnea, orthopnea, cyanosis, coughing, crackles, wheezing, hoarseness, flaring nares, retractions, and activity intolerance. If the child develops systemic venous congestion, signs and symptoms may include peripheral edema, periorbital edema, ascites, hepatomegaly, weight gain, and neck vein distention.

6. Vital signs are taken every fifteen minutes for at least the first hour following the procedure. The apical pulse must be taken for one full minute to detect any

arrhythmias. Peripheral pulses, temperature, and color of the catheterized extremity are carefully assessed at frequent intervals. Coolness and paleness of the extremity could indicate arterial occlusion. The child must keep the extremity (usually a leg) straight for approximately six to eight hours following the procedure. Parents may be encouraged to hold the child to help keep the extremity straight if the child has difficulty maintaining the correct position. Intravenous fluids will be administered to the child and oral fluids encouraged to prevent dehydration and to promote removal of the contrast medium from the body. The child may resume a normal diet as soon as desired.

7.   The following nursing diagnoses may be appropriate for the patient with congenital heart disease:

- Decreased cardiac output related to impaired myocardial functioning
- Ineffective breathing pattern related to excess fluid in the lungs
- Activity intolerance related to impaired tissue oxygenation and inability to meet the energy demands of the body
- Altered nutrition, less than body requirements related to fatigue and respiratory difficulties
- Fear related to lack of knowledge about diagnosis and surgical repair of defect
- Altered family processes related to the child experiencing a life-threatening illness

8.   The child's complaints could be indicative of digitalis toxicity. Common signs and symptoms of digitalis toxicity in children include bradycardia (apical pulse rate below 90 beats/min. in infants and young children and below 70 beats/min. in older children), arrhythmias, anorexia, nausea, and vomiting. If the child exhibits symptoms of digoxin toxicity, the drug should be withheld and the physician notified. The nurse should check the child's digoxin level.

9.   To support the infant's respiratory functioning, the infant should be positioned with the head elevated at a 45° angle. Infants can be placed in an infant seat to achieve this position. Clothing should be nonrestrictive, and supplemental oxygen should be administered as needed. Pulse oximetry, which measures oxygen saturation, is used to measure the patient's response to oxygen therapy. It is important that the infant be protected from respiratory infection as much as possible. Individuals having contact with the infant should practice good hand-washing technique prior to caring for the infant.

10.   The nurse should provide emotional support to the child and family. A diagnosis of a congenital heart defect creates much stress and anxiety in the family. Parents grieve the loss of a "normal" child and must cope with the demands of caring for a chronically, seriously ill child. Financial concerns may be a significant stressor. Normal parent-infant bonding may be affected by prolonged hospitalizations of the child. Other family members may feel neglected because of the amount of

attention the child requires. Normal growth and development of the child can be affected because of decreased cardiac functioning and fatigue. Social interactions with other children may become limited.

The nurse can help the parents locate community resources and support groups that will help the family cope with the crisis situation that they are facing. Being an empathetic listener, responding to questions, providing education about the disorder, and reassuring the parents that their feelings and concerns are valid, are all important support activities for the nurse to implement.

11.   The nurse can decrease the mother's anxiety by explaining what is normal and what to expect as the child recovers from surgery. The nurse should reassure the mother that the chest tube drainage will be monitored hourly and that bright red drainage is normal immediately after surgery. Gradually, the drainage will change to serous drainage. Drainage will subside after the first twelve to twenty-four hours, and the tubes are usually removed by the third postoperative day.

12.   The effectiveness of nursing interventions for the child with CHD can be measured by the achievement of the following expected outcomes by the patient and family:

- Demonstrates adequate cardiac output with heartbeat within normal limits
- Maintains normal tissue perfusion
- Maintains normal respiratory rate without dyspnea
- Participates in activities of daily living without fatigue
- Maintains normal fluid and electrolyte balance
- Maintains adequate nutritional intake
- Verbalizes understanding of heart condition and home self-care behaviors (parents and child)
- Verbalizes adequate emotional support (parents and child)
- Verbalizes adequate pain control postoperatively
- Avoids complications of CHD (CHF, hypoxemia, respiratory infections)

Chapter 25: Nursing Care for Congenital and Genetic Respiratory Disorders

Key Terms

Azotorrhea
Cystic fibrosis (CF)
Cystic fibrosis transmembrane regulator
Esophageal atresia
Steatorrhea
Tracheoesophageal fistula (TEF)

Introduction

Congenital and genetic defects can cause life-threatening chronic respiratory disorders. One of the most common genetic respiratory disorders is cystic fibrosis (CF), an incurable, progressive disease that primarily affects the respiratory and gastrointestinal systems. Tracheoesophageal fistula (TEF) is a congenital structural defect resulting in an abnormal connection between the trachea and esophagus. Patients with TEF can develop severe respiratory problems. TEF is a rare defect, but can be fatal if not diagnosed and treated promptly.

Cystic Fibrosis (CF)

Cystic fibrosis (CF) is a genetic disorder caused by an inherited autosomal recessive trait. For a child to inherit CF, both parents must be carriers of the defective gene. The defective gene and its protein product, **cystic fibrosis transmembrane regulator** (CFTR), are found on chromosome 7. The identification of this gene in 1989 was considered a major breakthrough in the treatment of CF. Research on the CF gene continues in the hope that a cause for the CF gene can be found, and that a vaccination and additional drugs that will slow the progression of lung damage will be developed. The average life expectancy of an individual with CF in 1997 was thirty-one and a half years, and maximum survival was estimated to be thirty-five to forty years.

Pathophysiology of CF

CF primarily affects the secretory glands of the gastrointestinal and respiratory systems. The major clinical symptom is the production of thick, viscous, mucous gland secretions. The thick secretions obstruct small passageways in the bronchioles, leading to respiratory problems, and in the pancreas, leading to decreased production and blockage of pancreatic enzyme secretion absorption in the small intestine. In the newborn, the thick mucus can cause a blockage of the small intestine; this is referred to as a **meconium ileus**. Clinical indications of a meconium ileus in the newborn include vomiting, no stool passage, and abdominal distention. The liver can also be affected, leading to biliary obstruction and eventual liver fibrosis.

Clinical Manifestations of CF

Pulmonary complications are very common, and respiratory failure is the cause of most deaths that are related to CF. Respiratory problems tend to be noticed when the child is about one year old. Over time, the blockage of bronchioles leads to atelectasis and then hyperinflation of the lungs. These pathophysiological changes are similar to emphysema. Respiratory functioning deteriorates. Signs and symptoms of respiratory involvement include the following:

- Nonproductive cough that eventually becomes paroxysmal
- Wheezy respirations with increasing dyspnea
- Cyanosis, barrel-shaped chest, and clubbing

Hypoxia, hypercapnia, and respiratory acidosis develop. The thick mucus is difficult for the child to expectorate, thus increasing the child's susceptibility to respiratory tract infections. Pancreatic complications include the development of pancreatic fibrosis and the subsequent blockage of pancreatic enzyme secretion. The pancreatic enzymes cannot reach the duodenum. Digestion and absorption of nutrients is adversely affected, leading to the development of **steatorrhea** (bulky, fatty stools).

Eventually with cellular destruction, pancreatic functioning can deteriorate, leading to a loss of insulin production and the development of diabetes mellitus. Because patients with CF are living longer, more diabetes mellitus is now found in this population. Specific signs and symptoms of gastrointestinal involvement include the following:

- Large, loose, very foul-smelling (**azotorrhea**) and frothy stools
- Gradual loss of appetite with weight loss; distended abdomen
- Failure to achieve normal growth pattern
- The development of anemia and deficiencies of vitamins A, D, E, and K

Diagnostic Tests

CF is diagnosed by the use of the **sweat chloride test** that demonstrates a chloride concentration that is greater than 60 mEq/L. Normal levels are less than 40 mEq/L. In addition to these findings, a positive family history of CF, demonstrated pancreatic insufficiency, and chronic pulmonary insufficiency are considered to be indicative of CF. Pulmonary function tests may show a decrease in pulmonary functioning in the small airways. Stool analysis for trypsin and fat may also be conducted.

Medical Management of CF

The goals of the medical management of CF include the following:

- Preventing pulmonary complications

- Maintaining adequate nutrition
- Helping the child and family to cope with the demands of living with a chronic illness

Preventing the development of pulmonary complications includes an aggressive program of daily chest physiotherapy to help mobilize and remove the viscous secretions. Chest physiotherapy is usually performed on the patient in the morning upon rising and again before the patient goes to bed. Aerosol bronchodilator medications are used before the chest physiotherapy exercises to increase movement of secretions. Dornase alfa (Pulmozyme) is an aerosolized form of a recombinant human enzyme deoxyribonuclease that reduces the viscosity of the secretions. It has been widely used since 1994 and has had a positive effect on maintaining pulmonary functioning. In addition to medications, the child is encouraged to remain active and exercise, especially to engage in aerobic exercise.

Respiratory infections are treated promptly. Prophylactic antibiotics may be prescribed to prevent infections. Oxygen therapy is used with caution when patients are acutely ill with respiratory complications. As in emphysema, CF patients eventually retain carbon dioxide, and hypoxia becomes their stimulus for breathing. Too much oxygen can impair this stimulus.

Replacement pancreatic enzymes are used to treat pancreatic insufficiency. These enzymes are taken with meals and snacks to help with digestion and absorption of nutrients. The child can either sprinkle the enzyme over the food or swallow the capsules whole. The dosage of the enzymes is adjusted to relieve GI symptoms and reduce the number of stools. The child is encouraged to eat a high-calorie, high-protein, high-carbohydrate diet to promote normal growth and development. Because of impaired absorption, a larger intake of calories is required to meet daily requirements. If the child cannot eat enough to meet nutritional needs, supplemental enteral feedings or total parenteral nutrition may be implemented.

Nursing Management of the Patient with CF

Nursing Process: Assessment

The nurse should focus assessment of the CF patient on three primary areas: respiratory, gastrointestinal, and psychosocial factors. The nursing history is focused on the patient's description of respiratory symptoms, such as dyspnea upon exertion, wheezing, shortness of breath, and fatigue. Physical assessment should include the following:

- Auscultation for adventitious lung sounds
- Inspection for cyanosis and clubbing
- Respiratory rate and temperature
- Presence of cough
- Color and consistency of sputum
- A review of ABGs and oxygen saturation

The nurse should also solicit information from the patient about gastrointestinal symptoms. For example, the nurse should ask the patient to describe the color, consistency, and frequency of bowel movements. The patient should be asked about appetite, dietary patterns, abdominal discomfort, and any weight loss. The nurse should note the patient's general appearance (observe for being underweight) and assess bowel sounds.

It is also important that the nurse assess how the child and family are coping with this chronic, and potentially fatal, illness. The nurse should assess their knowledge of CF and its treatment, assess financial concerns, and identify coping strategies and support structures. It is especially important to determine how CF affects the child's activities of daily living and achievement of developmental stages. The nurse should also assess the need for genetic counseling.

Nursing Process: Nursing Diagnosis and Planning

Based upon an analysis of the gathered data, the following **nursing diagnoses**, while not intended to be inclusive, may be appropriate for the patient with cystic fibrosis:

- Ineffective airway clearance related to thick, tenacious secretions
- Impaired gas exchange related to ventilation/perfusion imbalance
- Fatigue related to impaired oxygenation and poor nutrition
- Altered nutrition, less than body requirements related to malabsorption
- Altered family processes related to child experiencing a life-threatening, chronic illness

Primary goals for the patient with cystic fibrosis include the following:

- Maintain effective respiratory functioning
- Maintain adequate nutritional intake
- Increase activity tolerance
- Demonstrate effective coping techniques
- Avoid complications of respiratory infection, respiratory failure, and malabsorption

Nursing Process: Implementation

CF is an incurable, progressive disease. The child and family require skilled nursing care and strong support systems to help them effectively cope with the diagnosis. Recent treatment advancements have increased the life span of many children with CF, so the nurse is likely to see increased numbers of young adults who are coping with CF while adjusting to the age-appropriate developmental tasks of choosing a career, college, and marriage. **Genetic counseling** for the parents, and ultimately the child, is an essential part of the health care.

The nurse emphasizes nursing interventions that promote respiratory functioning. When the child is hospitalized with an acute illness, chest physiotherapy, aerosol treatments, and cautious use of oxygen will be key components of care. If the problem is caused by an infection, antibiotics will also be administered. The nurse should support the child in fully cooperating with the respiratory therapy. Treatments should not be scheduled around mealtimes. The nurse must educate the patient and parents on the importance of maintaining medication regimes, chest physiotherapy, and breathing exercises at home. Postural drainage is important to successful removal of respiratory secretions and to decreasing the likelihood of acquiring a respiratory infection. The parents should also understand the importance of having the child receive routine immunizations, as well as flu and pneumococcus vaccinations.

Another primary nursing intervention is supporting the adequate nutrition of the child. In the early stages of the disease, the child usually has an excellent, maybe even excessive, appetite. A lack of appetite gradually develops as the disease progresses, mostly due to increased respiratory distress. The nurse should work closely with the child to provide high-calorie, high-protein, and high-carbohydrate meals that are appealing to the child. The child needs to understand the importance of taking pancreatic enzymes with all meals and snacks to promote nutrient absorption. If the child is young, the enzymes can be easily mixed into foods such as applesauce. Fluids are encouraged to prevent dehydration. Dehydration causes the mucous secretions to thicken. Oral hygiene can help increase a child's appetite, as well as help prevent the occurrence of oral infections.

Providing emotional support to the child and family is probably the most challenging aspect of nursing care. The nurse should help the family locate local support groups for emotional support and community resources that can help provide financial resources, treatment supplies, and medications. The nurse should anticipate that the parents may exhibit feelings of guilt for having passed on the CF gene to their child. As the disease progresses, the parents may experience anticipatory grieving as they accept the fact that their child is terminally ill. Counseling is very beneficial and can help the family and the child prepare for making end-of-life decisions.

It is possible that the patient may display anger, and at times, rebel against the prescribed treatment. Helping the child to express his or her feelings of anger, frustration, or grief is essential. Age-appropriate activities can help the child express these feelings. As much as possible, children should be encouraged to engage in normal activities so that normal growth and development can be fostered. The goal should be to foster independence and responsibility for self-care so that the child can mature into an independent adult.

Nursing Process: Evaluation

The effectiveness of nursing interventions for the child with CF can be measured by the achievement of the following expected outcomes by the patient and family:

- Maintains adequate respiratory functioning
- Demonstrates improved gas exchange
- Maintains normal nutritional status
- Demonstrates effective coping skills

- Demonstrates appropriate self-care activities
- Avoids complications of CF (respiratory infection, respiratory failure, malabsorption)

Maintaining adequate respiratory functioning and normal nutritional status indicates that the nursing interventions are effective. The nurse evaluates the patient for achievement of the identified expected outcomes by assessing the respiratory and gastrointestinal system, assessing coping skills, and adjusting the nursing plan as necessary in collaboration with the family and patient.

Tracheoesophageal Fistula (TEF)

Tracheoesophageal fistula (TEF) is a relatively rare congenital defect of the trachea and esophagus. **Esophageal atresia** may occur in conjunction with TEF. The cause of these defects is unknown, but many infants who are born with the defect have a low birth weight. It is estimated that the defects occur in 1 in 3,000–3,500 live births. Males and females are equally affected. If not identified and treated promptly, TEF is fatal.

Pathophysiology of TEF

TEF and esophageal atresia can take the form of a number of different congenital malformations. What they all have in common is that there is an interruption in the continuity of the esophagus. In the case of TEF, the trachea is joined to the esophagus by a fistula. In the most common form of TEF, the proximal end of the esophagus ends in a blind pouch, while the distal end of the esophagus is joined to the trachea. Because of the potential for the introduction of fluids directly into the lungs, the development of **aspiration pneumonia** is a very likely occurrence.

Clinical Manifestations of TEF

TEF is manifested by what is known as the "three C's of TEF"—coughing, choking, and cyanosis. Additional signs and symptoms include excessive salivation and drooling, and apnea. After a feeding, the infant will demonstrate an increase in respiratory distress, as the feeding enters the lungs instead of the gastrointestinal tract. Abdominal distention may also present as air enters the abdomen.

Diagnostic Testing

The presence of a TEF is first suspected based upon the clinical manifestations. In addition, a chest X ray will be used to diagnose the presence of malformations. A radiopaque catheter may be inserted and advanced until it hits an obstruction.

Medical Management of TEF

Treatment of TEF consists of surgical repair of the malformation. When a TEF is first suspected, the child is placed on NPO status and IV fluids are started. Frequent oral suctioning will be required to remove secretions that the infant cannot swallow.

Aspiration pneumonia is a very real danger, so the infant will be placed in an upright position that will help prevent aspiration of secretions. Antibiotic therapy will also be implemented. The surgical repair consists of a thoracotomy, with a separation of the trachea from the esophagus, and the completion of an end-to-end anastomosis of the esophagus. Prognosis of the infant is dependent upon the extent of the defect, the infant's birth weight, how quickly the defect was diagnosed, and if the infant has additional congenital defects.

Nursing Management of the Patient with TEF

The nurse should begin assessment for TEF immediately after the birth of the infant. Any infant that has a large amount of frothy saliva, is cyanotic, or cannot swallow secretions is immediately suspected of having a TEF. The infant's first feeding is usually water that is given or supervised by the nurse so that the infant's response can be closely monitored. If the infant begins to cough and choke after swallowing the fluid or the fluid comes back up through the nose and mouth, this is an indication of TEF. The infant should be suctioned to remove the secretions.

An infant who is suspected of having TEF will be placed supine with the head elevated 30°. An indwelling catheter is placed in the blind pouch of the esophagus so that periodic suctioning can take place to remove secretions.

Postoperative care of the infant will initially be provided in the ICU. A gastrostomy tube will be inserted to provide feedings until the infant can tolerate oral feedings. After the fifth to seventh postoperative day, oral feedings of sterile water will begin and will progress to formula as tolerated. When the infant is feeding normally, the gastrostomy tube will be removed, and the infant will usually be discharged.

The most common complications following surgery originate in the respiratory system and include pneumonia, atelectasis, and pneumothorax. In addition, the nurse should observe for signs of a leaking anastomosis—elevated temperature, elevated WBC count, and purulent chest tube drainage. These signs should be reported promptly to the surgeon so that the anastomosis can be repaired.

The parents will require much support during this stressful time. Normal parent/infant bonding is disrupted, as the infant is placed in intensive care and then undergoes surgery. The nurse can help facilitate the attachment process by encouraging the parents to visit the infant and allowing them to participate in the infant's care as fully as possible. Expected outcomes of nursing care include the following:

- Maintain normal respiratory functioning as evidenced by lack of coughing, choking, or cyanosis
- Avoid respiratory complications
- Resume normal eating patterns without difficulty swallowing
- Demonstrate normal healing process of the surgical incision

Chapter 25 Study Questions

1.   Describe the pathophysiology of cystic fibrosis (CF).

2.   The nurse is caring for a child with CF. What signs and symptoms would the nurse anticipate finding related to the child's respiratory status?

3.   The nurse is assessing the functioning of the child's gastrointestinal system. What information should the nurse gather?

4.   What laboratory test is diagnostic of CF?

5.   Identify three goals for the medical management of the child with CF.

6.   What medications would the nurse anticipate administering to the child with CF?

7.   Identify five priority nursing diagnoses that would be appropriate for the child with CF.

8.   Develop a care plan for the child with CF that focuses on promoting respiratory functioning, supporting adequate nutrition, and providing emotional support.

9.   Describe three of the six identified expected outcomes for a child with CF that
       measure the effectiveness of nursing interventions.

10.   The nurse is caring for a newborn who has been diagnosed with
       tracheoesophageal fistula (TEF). The nurse knows that the infant is at high risk
       for developing what potentially fatal complication?

11.   What are the clinical manifestations of TEF in an infant?

12.   Describe the assessment and nursing care the nurse can anticipate providing to an
       infant with TEF.

Answers to Chapter 25 Study Questions

1. Cystic fibrosis (CF) is a genetic disorder caused by an inherited autosomal recessive trait. The defective gene and its protein product, cystic fibrosis transmembrane regulator (CFTR) is found on chromosome 7. CF primarily affects the gastrointestinal and respiratory systems. The major clinical symptom is the production of thick, viscous, mucous gland secretions. The thick secretions obstruct small passageways in the bronchioles, leading to respiratory problems, and in the pancreas, leading to decreased production and blockage of pancreatic enzyme secretion absorption in the small intestine.

2. Signs and symptoms of respiratory involvement include nonproductive cough; wheezy respirations with increasing dyspnea; cyanosis; barrel-shaped chest; and clubbing. Hypoxia, hypercapnia, and respiratory acidosis develop. The thick mucus is difficult for the child to expectorate, and the child becomes susceptible to respiratory tract infections.

3. The nurse should ask the patient/parents to describe the color, consistency, and frequency of bowel movements. The patient should be asked about appetite, dietary patterns, abdominal discomfort, and any weight loss. The nurse should note the patient's general appearance (observe for being underweight) and assess bowel sounds.

4. CF is diagnosed by the use of the sweat chloride test that demonstrates a chloride concentration that is greater than 60 mEq/L. Normal levels are less than 40 mEq/L.

5. The goals of the medical management of CF include preventing pulmonary complications, maintaining adequate nutrition, and helping the child and family to cope with the demands of living with a chronic illness.

6. The nurse should anticipate administering bronchodilator medications (used to increase movement of secretions); dornase alfa (Pulmozyme), an aerosolized form of a recombinant human enzyme deoxyribonuclease that reduces the viscosity of the secretions; prophylactic antibiotics (to prevent infections); oxygen therapy; and replacement pancreatic enzymes (used to treat pancreatic insufficiency).

7. Based upon an analysis of the gathered data, the following nursing diagnoses may be appropriate for the patient with cystic fibrosis:

   - Ineffective airway clearance related to thick, tenacious secretions
   - Impaired gas exchange related to ventilation/perfusion imbalance
   - Fatigue related to impaired oxygenation and poor nutrition
   - Altered nutrition, less than body requirements related to malabsorption
   - Altered family processes related to child experiencing a life-threatening, chronic illness

8.   The nurse emphasizes nursing interventions that promote respiratory functioning. Chest physiotherapy, aerosol treatments, and cautious use of oxygen will be key components of care. The nurse should support the child in fully cooperating with the respiratory therapy. Treatments should not be scheduled around mealtimes. The nurse teaches the patient and parents about maintaining medication regimes, chest physiotherapy, and breathing exercises at home. The child is encouraged to participate in aerobic exercise. The parents should also understand the importance of having the child receive routine immunizations and flu and pneumococcus vaccinations. Another primary nursing intervention is supporting the adequate nutrition of the child. High-calorie, high-protein, and high-carbohydrate meals that are appealing to the child are provided. The child and the family need to understand the importance of using pancreatic enzymes with all meals and snacks. Fluids are encouraged to prevent dehydration. Oral hygiene can help increase a child's appetite, as well as help prevent the occurrence of oral infections. Providing emotional support to the child and family is another primary nursing intervention. The nurse should help the family locate local support groups for emotional support and community resources that can help provide financial help, treatment supplies, and medications. The nurse should anticipate that the parents may exhibit feelings of guilt. The parents may experience anticipatory grieving as they accept the fact that their child is terminally ill. Counseling is very beneficial. The nurse helps the child to express his or her feelings of anger, frustration, or grief. Age-appropriate activities can help the child express these feelings. Children should be encouraged to engage in normal activities so that normal growth and development can be fostered.

9.   The effectiveness of nursing interventions for the child with CF can be measured by the achievement of the following expected outcomes by the patient and family:

    •   Maintains adequate respiratory functioning
    •   Demonstrates improved gas exchange
    •   Maintains normal nutritional status
    •   Demonstrates effective coping skills
    •   Demonstrates appropriate self-care activities
    •   Avoids complications of CF (respiratory infection, respiratory failure, malabsorption)

10.   Because of the potential for the introduction of fluids directly into the lungs, the development of aspiration pneumonia is likely.

11.   TEF is manifested by what is known as the "three C's of TEF"—coughing, choking, and cyanosis. Additional signs and symptoms include excessive salivation, drooling, and apnea. After a feeding, the infant will demonstrate an increase in respiratory distress, as the feeding enters the lungs instead of the gastrointestinal tract. Abdominal distention may also present as air enters the abdomen.

12.   The nurse should begin assessment for TEF immediately after the birth of the
        infant. Any infant that has a large amount of frothy saliva, is cyanotic, or cannot
        swallow secretions is immediately suspected of having a TEF. The infant's first
        feeding is usually water that is given or supervised by the nurse so that the
        infant's response can be closely monitored. If the infant begins to cough and
        choke after swallowing the fluid or the fluid comes back up through the nose and
        mouth, this can be an indication of TEF. The infant should be suctioned to
        remove the secretions. When a TEF is first suspected, the child is placed on NPO
        status and IV fluids are started. Frequent oral suctioning will be required to
        remove secretions that the infant cannot swallow. The infant will be placed in a
        supine, upright position with the head elevated 30° to prevent aspiration of
        secretions. Antibiotic therapy will also be implemented.

Chapter 26: Nursing Care for Congenital and Genetic Neurological Disorders

Key Terms

Down syndrome
Guthrie blood test
Hydrocephalus
Inborn error of metabolism
Phenylketonuria (PKU)
Trisomy 21
Ventriculoperitoneal (VP) shunt

Introduction

This chapter will discuss some commonly occurring neurological disorders that are congenital and/or genetic in origin. Down syndrome, hydrocephalus, and phenylketonuria (PKU) are the neurological disorders that require long-term management to prevent further disability. Each of these disorders can cause cognitive impairment.

Down Syndrome

Down syndrome is the most common syndrome associated with an abnormality of the chromosomes. Another term associated with Down syndrome is **trisomy 21** because there is an extra chromosome 21 in 95 percent of the children born with the syndrome. The cause is unknown. While approximately 80 percent of the children born with Down syndrome are born to mothers who are less than thirty-five years of age, there is a statistically significant increased risk for Down syndrome in children born to women over age thirty-five.

Pathophysiology

Down syndrome results from a chromosomal abnormality and is associated with various physical problems and reduced cognitive function. Some of the most common physical problems these children will face include congenital heart defects, respiratory tract infections, congenital hypothyroidism, and an increased rate of leukemia. A common cause of death, especially before the age of one, is respiratory tract infection combined with a congenital heart defect.

Clinical Manifestations

Numerous clinical manifestations are associated with Down syndrome. The following are the most common characteristics associated with the disorder:

- Upward and outward slanted eyes
- Small nose, with depressed bridge
- Flattened occiput
- Narrow, high arched palate
- Tongue protrudes
- Neck short, broad with excess skin
- Low-set ears
- Mental retardation
- Brushfield spots (white spots on iris)
- Hypotonic muscles
- Muscle weakness
- Hyperflexible joints
- Big toe and second toe widely spaced with plantar crease
- Impaired skin integrity

Diagnostic Tests

The practitioner will make a preliminary diagnosis based upon the observation of the clinical findings associated with Down syndrome. A **chromosomal analysis** will be conducted to confirm the diagnosis. The infant will likely undergo additional studies to determine the presence of any other congenital defects, especially cardiac septal defects.

Prenatal diagnosis may also be possible in some cases. The nurse can help ensure that the parents seek out genetic counseling in cases where the mother is older or if there is a previous family history of Down syndrome. Down syndrome can be identified prenatally through the use of amniocentesis and chorionic villus sampling. A low maternal serum alpha-fetoprotein level, low unconjugated estriol level, and high chorionic gonadotropin level may indicate the presence of Down syndrome in the fetus; an amniocentesis would be used to confirm it.

Medical Management

Medical management focuses on preventing complications related to the physical problems associated with Down syndrome. Surgery may be required to correct congenital defects, especially cardiac. There is no cure for Down syndrome, but with regular health care, the life expectancy improves to at least the third decade. Over 80 percent of the individuals with Down syndrome live past the age of thirty.

Nursing Care of the Child with Down Syndrome

Nursing Process: Assessment

It is important for the nurse to assess the parents' coping skills at the time of the infant's diagnosis. Diagnosis is frequently made at birth based upon the presence of clinical manifestations. This is a time of crisis for the parents, and they will require a significant amount of support from the nurse and other members of the health-care team. The parents will be grieving the loss of their "perfect" child, and at the same time, they are faced with multiple decisions.

In addition, the nurse will assess the infant's cardiovascular and respiratory status, noting any abnormal findings that may indicate the presence of a congenital heart defect. Muscle tone will be hypotonic and the infant's extremities may be flaccid and limp. The nurse will also assess the infant's ability to nurse. Breathing difficulties related to the depressed nasal bridge and excess nasal mucus will likely affect the infant's ability to suck for any prolonged periods. As the infant grows, the degree of cognitive impairment will determine the infant's potential for achieving normal developmental tasks and the degree of independence the individual will be able to experience with the activities of daily living. The nurse will carefully assess the infant's growth and development at the appropriate stages. Children with Down syndrome do experience a slower growth rate than other children.

Nursing Process: Nursing Diagnoses and Planning

Based upon an analysis of the gathered data, the following **nursing diagnoses**, while not intended to be inclusive, may be appropriate for the child with Down syndrome and the family:

- Decreased cardiac output related to impaired myocardial functioning
- Ineffective breathing pattern related to decreased respiratory expansion and inadequate drainage of nasal mucus
- Altered nutrition, less than body requirements related to excess nasal mucus, protruding tongue, and difficulty sucking and feeding
- Potential for impaired skin integrity related to the excessive skin roughness and dryness characteristic of Down syndrome
- Altered growth and development related to physical problems and impaired cognitive functioning
- Fear related to lack of knowledge about diagnosis and future welfare of child
- Altered family processes related to having a child with a diagnosis of Down syndrome with accompanying mental retardation

Primary goals for the child with Down syndrome and family include the following:

- Improve or maintain cardiac functioning
- Improve or maintain respiratory functioning
- Maintain adequate nutritional intake
- Maintain skin integrity

- Achieve optimum growth, development, and socialization potential
- Verbalize concerns, fears, and questions
- Demonstrate acceptance of infant
- Access community resources and support groups to help cope with diagnosis of Down syndrome
- Avoid complications of Down syndrome (related to congenital heart defects, respiratory tract infections)

Nursing Process: Implementation

Support of the family is a priority nursing intervention for the birth of an infant with Down syndrome. The nurse should be sensitive to the parent's emotional needs and provide a nonjudgmental, empathetic, listening presence as the parents express their feelings. Helping to secure additional information about Down syndrome and providing the parents with referrals to support groups or professional counseling are essential nursing activities. Parents may be uncertain about their ability or willingness to care for the infant at home; these are decisions that the parents will need to make. Parents are likely to have questions about the degree of the child's mental retardation and developmental potential. The nurse must carefully answer these questions or assist the parents in finding out the answers to their questions. Some parents may opt to place their child up for adoption or place the child in foster care if they decide that they will be unable to cope with and meet the needs of the child.

In addition to helping the family cope with the emotional crises they are facing, the nurse must also help them learn to physically provide care to the infant in preparation for discharge. An infant with Down syndrome has flaccid muscles and hyperextensible joints. This can make it difficult to hold and position the infant. The nurse can teach the parents how to securely hold the infant by bundling the infant in a blanket to support the extremities and provide the infant with a sense of security.

The same lack of muscle tone that makes it difficult to hold the infant also affects the infant's respiratory status by decreasing expansion of the respiratory muscles. Flatness of the nasal bridge also impedes the flow of mucus, and the infant must breathe by mouth. Mouth breathing eventually produces dryness of the oropharyngeal tissues and predisposes the infant to respiratory infections. The nurse will teach the parents how to cleanse the nasal secretions out with a bulb syringe and to rinse the mouth out with water following feedings to prevent infection and minimize dryness. Cool mist vaporizers can also minimize dryness and liquefy nasal secretions. Additional patient education instructions will include the importance of good hand washing prior to handling the infant and the importance of changing the infant's position frequently to promote nasal drainage. Chest physiotherapy may also be used to promote drainage.

To encourage adequate feeding, the nurse will teach the parents to remove secretions from the nose prior to feeding the infant. The infant will need frequent rest periods while feeding to allow the infant to breathe through the mouth. Small, frequent feedings are usually best tolerated. When the infant advances to solid food for feeding, the parents will be most successful if they place the food toward the side or back of the mouth to avoid it being pushed back out by the tongue. The nurse must emphasize the importance of patience during feeding times and help the parents to understand that the tongue pushing is an involuntary reflex, and not a deliberate attempt to refuse the feeding.

As the child with Down syndrome ages, the skin characteristically roughens and cracks, and is predisposed to infection. To minimize the potential for skin breakdown, lotion is frequently applied to the skin. Drying soaps are avoided. Parents need to be instructed on the importance of protecting the skin from extremes of hot and cold.

Another important nursing intervention is helping the family understand the importance of allowing the child to develop acceptable socialization and behavioral skills. The ultimate goal is for the child to achieve the optimum level of growth and development of which he or she is capable. Realistic goals must be set and the child provided opportunities to meet these goals. The nurse can be a major catalyst in helping identify the child's readiness to learn, assessing developmental progress, and developing the child's self-care skills. Children with Down syndrome have the same need for discipline and limit-setting as do other children, and they also have the same need for social interaction with peers. Eventually, the family will need to investigate special day care programs and schools for the child. Vocational training is another option. The nurse can help the family locate community resources that will help them make appropriate choices for their child.

Nursing Process: Evaluation

The effectiveness of nursing interventions for the child with Down syndrome can be measured by the achievement of the following expected outcomes by the child and family:

- Demonstrates adequate cardiac output with heartbeat within normal limits
- Maintains normal respiratory functioning without respiratory tract infections
- Maintains adequate nutritional intake
- Maintains skin integrity
- Participates in activities of daily living with appropriate independence and with optimum use of capabilities
- Participates in peer social experiences and displays appropriate behavior
- Demonstrates acceptance of child (parents and family)
- Verbalizes understanding of Down syndrome and home care (parents)
- Verbalizes adequate emotional support (parents)
- Utilizes community resources for information about support groups and appropriate educational/training opportunities
- Avoids complications of physical problems associated with Down syndrome

Because of advances in the treatment of congenital heart defects, improved antibiotic therapy, and a greater understanding of the growth and development needs of individuals with Down syndrome, many infants born with Down syndrome live long and productive lives, even into their fifties and sixties. Access to regular health care, comprehensive education programs and support groups for parents and families, and opportunities for the child to have appropriate socialization and educational experiences are key components that ensure the child will have a long and productive life. The nurse plays a major role in providing the quality of care necessary to achieve these goals.

Hydrocephalus

Hydrocephalus is caused by accumulated cerebrospinal fluid (CSF) in the ventricular system. As the CSF accumulates, it causes dilation of the ventricles and increased **intracranial pressure (ICP)**. Hydrocephalus is the result of a pathophysiological disorder; the causes are numerous, but can be categorized in two ways—either congenital or acquired. This discussion will focus on the congenital form of hydrocephalus and its treatment in the newborn.

Pathophysiology

Hydrocephalus is the end result of an underlying disorder of the brain that causes either an obstruction of CSF flow in the ventricles or inadequate CSF absorption in the subarachnoid space. Normally, CSF circulates through the ventricular system and then is reabsorbed into the subarachnoid space. When this normal process of circulation and reabsorption is disrupted, the CSF accumulates in the ventricles, eventually causing the ventricles to dilate and intracranial pressure to increase. As the ventricles begin to dilate, pressure is applied to the surrounding brain tissue. When this occurs in infants whose cranial sutures have not yet fused, the skull enlarges, producing a prominent forehead.

The majority of congenital cases of hydrocephalus are caused by developmental malformations that lead to obstruction within the CSF circulatory pathway. A very common obstructive cause of hydrocephalus in newborns is spina bifida (myelomeningocele). Other causes of hydrocephalus in newborns are meningoencephalitis, perinatal hemorrhage, and infection acquired in utero.

Clinical Manifestations

The most obvious indication of hydrocephalus in infants is an enlarged forehead. In addition, the infant's head growth may be abnormally rapid, fontanels may bulge or be tense to touch, and the sutures will be separated. Inspection of the scalp may reveal enlarged scalp veins.

As the forehead begins to enlarge, the eyes will appear depressed and the sclera will be visible above the iris (sundown sign). Pupils may be sluggish, and there may be an unequal pupillary reaction to light. The infant may be irritable, difficult to feed, and lethargic. As the pressure increases, vomiting may also occur.

Diagnostic Tests

A diagnosis of hydrocephalus is made based upon the finding that the infant's head circumference is increasing at an abnormally rapid rate. Neurological signs, such as papillary changes and changes in level of consciousness, that are indicative of increased

ICP will also be noted. A MRI and/or CT are used to confirm the diagnosis of hydrocephalus. The infant will be sedated for these tests so that the infant lies completely still.

Medical Management

Hydrocephalus is treated surgically. The goal of surgery is to relieve ventricular pressure by promoting drainage of the CSF. During surgery, a ventriculoperitoneal (VP) shunt, which consists of a catheter that is threaded under the skin, is inserted to promote CSF drainage from the ventricles to the peritoneal cavity. Complications related to the placement of the shunt include the risk of infection, obstruction, and kinking or separation of the tubing. The shunt will require revision from time to time as the child grows or to correct obstruction of the shunt.

Nursing Care of the Child with Hydrocephalus

The nurse carefully assesses the newborn's head circumference as a baseline so that abnormally rapid head growth can be detected early. In infants who have a myelomeningocele or an intracranial infection, head circumference is measured daily as both conditions can predispose the infant to hydrocephalus. In addition, the nurse closely observes the infant for signs of increased intracranial pressure, including irritability, changes in level of consciousness, difficulty feeding, and sluggish, unequal pupil response to light. The nurse also carefully palpates and assesses the infant's fontanels, as another indication of increased ICP is bulging, tense fontanels.

The infant should also be observed for seizure activity. In the event of a seizure the nurse should ensure that the area where the infant is lying is free of any hard objects and that the infant is safe from falling. The nurse should time the seizure, remain calm, and reassure family members. The infant should not be restrained and the head should be protected. Restrictive clothing should be loosened. **Do not** give the infant anything to drink or place anything in the infant's mouth. Observe closely for vomiting and keep the infant side lying to prevent aspiration. Supply oxygen if the infant becomes cyanotic. Following the seizure, assess the infant for breathing and check the position of the tongue and the head. Keep the infant lying on his or her side and remain at the bedside until the infant begins to respond.

When the nurse is moving or feeding an infant with an enlarged head circumference, the nurse must carefully support the head of the infant to avoid strain on the neck. Immobility can become a problem if the head circumference continues to increase. The infant should be repositioned at frequent intervals to prevent the development of pressure areas.

After the infant has surgery for placement of the VP shunt, the nurse will be responsible for providing postoperative care. The nurse will position the infant on the unoperated side to prevent pressure on the shunt. The infant may be placed flat to prevent too rapid removal of CSF, or if increased ICP is present, the infant may be positioned with head elevated. Activity levels may be restricted immediately following surgery. The surgeon prescribes the desired position and activity level. Pain control will be achieved with the use of analgesics.

Following surgery, the nurse will continue to assess the infant's neurological status. Changes in neurological status can indicate that the shunt is not functioning as it should, most likely due to obstruction or kinking. Another complication the nurse will assess the infant for is peritonitis or a paralytic ileus. Abdominal distention is an indication of these complications. Feeding is resumed when bowel sounds return.

Infection is the most likely complication, and the nurse must carefully monitor the infant's condition to detect early signs of infection. The incision lines and shunt tract are assessed regularly for signs of inflammation or CSF leakage. Diapers should not be placed on or near the suture line to prevent contaminating the incision. Antibiotics are usually given intravenously to treat infection.

Another important nursing intervention is to provide support to the parents during the time that the infant is diagnosed with hydrocephalus and undergoes treatment. The diagnosis can be very frightening to parents, as it is indicative of another underlying condition that is likely to be chronic or even life threatening. The nurse needs to carefully answer the parent's questions, explain the infant's condition, and describe how the placement of the shunt, while not correcting the underlying problem, will treat the symptom of hydrocephalus and decrease the pressure on the brain. Discharge teaching for the family will include shunt care, how to detect shunt malfunction and changes in neurological status, and signs of infection. Parents should be told to observe the child for elevated temperature, changes in behavior (especially lethargy), difficulty feeding, vomiting, or seizure activity.

Parents should also be instructed in how to safely care for the child if a seizure occurs. In addition to the seizure care already identified, parents should be instructed to call emergency medical services (EMS) if the child stops breathing, has a seizure that lasts longer than five minutes or suffers reoccurring seizures, is unresponsive to pain after the seizure ends, vomits frequently, or experiences an injury.

Management of hydrocephalus and the shunt is a lifelong concern, and the child's condition will need to be followed carefully by health-care professionals. Parents need to be encouraged to not be overprotective of the child, as it is important to have the child live as normal and independent a life as possible. Activities are usually not limited by the presence of the shunt, with the exception that the child should be advised not to participate in contact sports. If the child has experienced some cognitive impairment, special education programs may be indicated. The nurse can recommend community resource programs and support groups that the parents can contact for additional information and to help develop their coping skills. The National Hydrocephalus Foundation is one potential source of information for families.

Phenylketonuria (PKU)

Phenylketonuria (PKU) is an inherited genetic disease (autosomal-recessive trait) that occurs in about 1 in 10,000 births. It is most common in Caucasians. It is very rare for PKU to affect individuals with Japanese, Jewish, or African heritage.

Pathophysiology

PKU is a disorder that is classified as an **inborn error of metabolism**. This means that it is an inherited disease in which a substance that is essential to cellular metabolism is missing. In PKU, the substance that is missing is the enzyme phenylalanine hydroxylase, which is necessary to metabolize the amino acid phenylalanine.

Phenylalanine hydroxylase is a hepatic enzyme that helps convert phenylalanine to tyrosine. Because the enzyme is lacking, phenylalanine cannot be converted to tyrosine. Phenylalanine accumulates in the bloodstream and eventually the metabolites of phenylalanine are excreted in the urine. The high levels of phenyl acids present in the urine produce a distinctive musty odor.

The absence of tyrosine inhibits the formation of melanin, epinephrine, and thyroxine. Because of the lack of melanin, children with PKU are likely to be blond and blue-eyed with skin that is fair and susceptible to dermatological problems. In addition, because of the lack of tyrosine, there are decreased levels of dopamine and tryptophan. The lack of these neurotransmitters affects the development of the central nervous system and brain, resulting in mental retardation. Mental retardation develops before phenyl acids are detected in the urine, so early detection of PKU is essential.

Clinical Manifestations

The clinical manifestations of PKU include behavioral problems. Children with PKU display erratic, hyperactive behavior. They are irritable and can engage in head banging, arm biting, and other bizarre behaviors. Failure to thrive and vomiting are other clinical manifestations.

Diagnostic Tests

PKU must be diagnosed early to prevent the development of mental retardation. All newborns are screened by a blood test, the **Guthrie blood test**, which detects the abnormally high levels of phenylalanine in the blood. Normal levels of phenylalanine are 1.6 mg/dl. Prenatal detection of PKU is also possible.

Medical Management

PKU is managed by diet to control the phenylalanine levels in the blood. The child's diet will be limited to 20–30 mg of phenylalanine per kilogram of body weight. The goal is to keep phenylalanine levels between 2–8 mg/dl. Danger levels of greater than 10 mg/dl can lead to significant brain damage. Since phenylalanine is necessary for tissue growth, it is necessary to adjust phenylalanine to promote normal growth and development of the child. The level of phenylalanine must be kept above 2 mg/dl to support normal growth patterns.

Infants with PKU can be breast-fed without difficulty, or they can be fed special formulas that have decreased phenylalanine amounts. As the child ages, a diet of solid food low in phenylalanine will be introduced. This diet must be followed through the child's adolescence.

Nursing Care of the Child with PKU

The nurse must emphasize the importance of PKU screening to all parents. If infants have been screened for PKU before they are twenty-four hours old, they must be rescreened within two weeks. Many infants are discharged early from the hospital and follow-up repeat screening is not obtained. These infants are at risk for having PKU that is not diagnosed until mental retardation has occurred.

Once PKU is diagnosed, the nurse's primary intervention is instructing the family about the infant's dietary restrictions. The amount of phenylalanine in the diet must be measured so that the blood levels are maintained within the recommended guidelines. High-protein foods are restricted or eliminated from the diet. Aspartame, an artificial sweetener, is eliminated from the diet as well, because it contains phenylalanine. As the child ages, control of the diet becomes more problematic. Toddlers can sometimes refuse to eat, thus decreasing the intake of phenylalanine to unsatisfactory levels. On the other hand, adolescents may succumb to peer pressure and eat pizza, hamburgers, and other high-protein food increasing the phenylalanine to dangerously high levels. The nurse should help the family contact a registered nutritionist for dietary guidance. The nutritionist will help design a meal plan based on an exchange list and provide nutritional education.

Even with adequate control of the disorder, many children with PKU experience some cognitive disability. Problems can include difficulty with language acquisition, hyperactivity, poor concentration, and learning and behavior problems.

Additional nursing interventions include providing genetic counseling for the parents. The parents must decide whether or not to have future children. As the affected child enters adulthood, genetic counseling is also important for him or her when making a decision to have children. Another concern is pregnant women who have PKU: They must be counseled to resume a low-phenylalanine diet before they become pregnant in order to avoid affecting the normal growth and development of the unborn child and causing mental retardation.

Chapter 26 Study Questions

1.   A child with Down syndrome is likely to have what other additional health problems?

2.   Describe important nursing assessments for a newborn infant who has been diagnosed with Down syndrome.

3.   What nursing diagnoses would likely be appropriate for a child with Down syndrome?

4.   Develop a nursing care plan for an infant who has been born with Down syndrome.

5.   Describe the pathophysiology associated with hydrocephalus.

6.   An infant with hydrocephalus has a ventriculoperitoneal shunt inserted. For what complications should the nurse closely assess the infant?

7.   The nurse is providing instructions to the parents of an infant who has been diagnosed with PKU. What dietary instruction should the nurse include in this instruction?

Answers to Chapter 26 Study Questions

1. Down syndrome is associated with various physical and cognitive problems. Some of the most common physical problems these children will face include congenital heart defects, respiratory tract infections, congenital hypothyroidism, and an increased rate of leukemia. A common cause of death, especially before the age of one, is respiratory tract infection combined with a congenital heart defect.

2. It is important for the nurse to assess the parent's coping skills at the time of the infant's diagnosis of Down syndrome. The parents will be grieving the loss of their "perfect" child. In addition, the nurse will assess the infant's cardiovascular and respiratory status, noting any abnormal findings that may indicate the presence of a congenital heart defect. Muscle tone will be hypotonic and the infant's extremities may be flaccid and limp. The nurse will also assess the infant's ability to nurse.

3. The following nursing diagnoses may be appropriate for the child with Down syndrome:

    *   Decreased cardiac output related to impaired myocardial functioning
    *   Ineffective breathing pattern related to decreased respiratory expansion and inadequate drainage of nasal mucus
    *   Altered nutrition, less than body requirements related to excess nasal mucus, protruding tongue, and difficulty sucking and feeding
    *   Potential for impaired skin integrity related to the excessive skin roughness and dryness characteristic of Down syndrome
    *   Altered growth and development related to physical problems and impaired cognitive functioning

4. Support of the family is a priority nursing intervention upon the birth of an infant with Down syndrome. The nurse should be sensitive to the parent's emotional needs and provide a nonjudgmental, empathetic, listening presence as the parents express their feelings. Helping to secure additional information about Down syndrome and providing the parents with referrals to support groups or professional counseling are essential nursing activities.

    The nurse must also help the parents to learn to physically provide care to the infant. The nurse can teach the parents how to securely hold the infant by bundling the infant in a blanket to support the extremities and provide the infant with a sense of security.

    The nurse will teach the parents how to cleanse the nasal secretions out with a bulb syringe and to rinse the mouth out with water following feedings to prevent infection and minimize dryness. Cool mist vaporizers also minimize dryness and liquefy nasal secretions. Additional patient education instructions include the importance of good hand washing prior to handling the infant and the importance of changing the infant's position frequently to promote nasal drainage. Chest physiotherapy may also be used to promote drainage.

To encourage adequate feeding the nurse will teach the parents to remove secretions from the nose prior to feeding the infant. The infant needs frequent rest periods while feeding to allow for mouth breathing. Small, frequent feedings are usually best tolerated. When the infant advances to solid food for feeding, the parents will be most successful if they place the food toward the side or back of the mouth to avoid it being pushed back out by the tongue. The nurse must emphasize the importance of patience during feeding times.

To minimize the potential for skin breakdown, lotion is frequently applied to the skin. Drying soaps are avoided. Parents need to be instructed on the importance of protecting the skin from extremes of hot and cold.

Another important nursing intervention is helping the family understand the importance of allowing the child to develop acceptable socialization and behavioral skills. Realistic goals must be set and the child provided opportunities to meet these goals. The nurse can help the family locate community resources that will help them make an appropriate choice for their child.

5. Hydrocephalus is the end result of an underlying disorder of the brain that causes either an obstruction to CSF flow in the ventricles or inadequate CSF absorption in the subarachnoid space. Normally, CSF circulates through the ventricular system and then is reabsorbed into the subarachnoid space. When this normal process of circulation and reabsorption is disrupted, the CSF accumulates in the ventricles, eventually causing the ventricles to dilate and intracranial pressure to increase. As the ventricles begin to dilate, pressure is applied to the surrounding brain tissue. When this occurs in infants whose cranial sutures have not yet fused, the skull enlarges, producing a prominent forehead.

6. Following surgery, the nurse will continue to assess the infant's neurological status. Changes in neurological status can indicate that the shunt is not functioning as it should, most likely due to obstruction or kinking. Another complication the nurse will assess the infant for is peritonitis or a paralytic ileus. Abdominal distention is an indication of these complications. Infection is the most likely complication, and the nurse must carefully monitor the infant's condition to detect early signs of infection. The incision lines and shunt tract are assessed regularly for signs of inflammation or CSF leakage.

7. The amount of phenylalanine in the diet must be measured so that the blood levels are maintained within the recommended guidelines. High-protein foods are restricted or eliminated from the diet. Aspartame, an artificial sweetener, is eliminated from the diet as well, because it contains phenylalanine. The nurse should help the family contact a registered nutritionist for dietary guidance.

Chapter 27: Nursing Care for Congenital and Genetic Musculoskeletal and Neuromuscular Disorders

Key Terms

Abduction splint
Arthrodesis
Cerebral palsy
Clubfoot
Developmental dysplasia of the hip (DDH)
Dislocation
Duchenne muscular dystrophy
Hip spica cast
Muscular dystrophy
Myelomeningocele
Orthotics
Pavlik harness
Scoliosis
Spina bifida
Subluxation
Talipes equinovarus

Introduction

Congenital and genetic musculoskeletal and neuromuscular disorders are some of the most common chronic childhood disorders leading to physical disabilities. These disorders typically require multidisciplinary health-care teams to meet the needs of the patients and their families. The nurse is most likely to be the team member with the ultimate responsibility of coordinating the efforts of the entire team. The primary goals of care in most of the disorders is to preserve function and to prevent or delay the onset of complications so that the child can live a full and independent life as much as possible. This chapter will discuss the musculoskeletal disorders of hip dysplasia, clubfoot, and scoliosis, and the neuromuscular disorders of cerebral palsy, spina bifida (myelomeningocele), and muscular dystrophy.

Congenital and Genetic Musculoskeletal Disorders

Congenital musculoskeletal defects appear in a variety of forms. Skeletal defects are relatively common. Many are diagnosed immediately after birth, although some defects, such as scoliosis, may not manifest until the child reaches pre-adolescence. Treatment of congenital musculoskeletal disorders can take several months to correct with bracing or casting. Surgical intervention is sometimes required as well. This section will discuss three common congenital musculoskeletal disorders: developmental dysplasia of the hip (DDH), clubfoot, and scoliosis.

Developmental Dysplasia of the Hip (DDH)

Developmental dysplasia of the hip (DDH) is a term that refers to a variety of disorders caused by abnormal congenital hip development. Typically, the abnormalities that occur in DDH include a shallow acetabulum, subluxation, or dislocation.

Girls are affected by DDH more often than boys. DDH has a tendency to occur more frequently in the left hip. Causes of DDH include intrauterine positioning of the infant, maternal hormone secretion (estrogen), twins, and large-sized infants.

Pathophysiology

There are three degrees of DDH:

1. In the first degree of DDH is **acetabular dysplasia**, the femoral head is still in the acetabulum, but the acetabulum is shallow.
2. The second degree of DDH is **subluxation**, which is a partial dislocation of the hip. Subluxation is the most common form of DDH.
3. The third degree of DDH is **dislocation** where the head of the femur is displaced from the acetabulum.

Clinical Manifestations

Clinical indications of DDH in the infant include asymmetrical gluteal and thigh folds, shortened femur appearance, and limited abduction of the hip. An Ortolani click can also be elicited in the hip as the joint is externally rotated. In the older child, a positive Trendelenburg sign may be evident: The child's pelvis will tilt downward on the unaffected side when the child stands on one foot bearing weight on the affected hip.

Diagnostic Testing

DDH is diagnosed by observing the clinical manifestations noted above. When the infant is over four months of age, X rays of the hip confirm the diagnosis. Prior to that time, an ultrasound of the hip is a more reliable test, as bones are difficult to visualize on X rays in early infancy.

Medical Management

DDH will be treated as soon as the diagnosis is confirmed. The earlier treatment is implemented, the more satisfactory the clinical outcomes. By the age of four, it is very difficult to treat DDH satisfactorily; after the age of six, it is almost impossible to correct the deformity.

In newborn infants and prior to six months of age, the **Pavlik harness** (or a similar type of soft splint) will be used to maintain the hip in a state of flexion. By keeping the hip flexed, the femoral head maintains contact with the acetabulum and will eventually become stable. If the infant has an adduction contracture, it will be necessary to keep the hip in a state of abduction. When it is difficult to achieve abduction with a brace, this will be achieved by using a **spica hip cast**. As the infant grows, the cast will be periodically changed to maintain a correct fit, eventually being replaced with an **abduction splint** as the hip stabilizes in position.

If the child is older than six months, **skin traction** will be initially applied to reduce hip adductor and flexor muscle contractures, followed by casting to immobilize the hip. When the hip is stabilized, the cast will be removed. If reduction (return to normal placement) of the hip cannot be achieved with traction and casts, surgery may be required. An **open reduction** of the hip will be performed and a spica cast will be applied, followed by an **abduction splint**.

Nursing Care for the Child with DDH

The nurse should carefully assess the infant's legs and hips for any shortening or asymmetry of the gluteal and thigh skin fold. An ideal time to assess the infant is during bathing and diapering activities. In youngsters who are beginning to walk, any unusual gait should be further evaluated.

When caring for an infant who is being treated for DDH, a primary nursing goal is to maintain correct alignment of the hip through the proper application of the reduction device. The nurse will be responsible for teaching the parents how to apply the harness or splint. Skin care is very important regardless of the type of device used. The parents should be taught to inspect the skin daily for any irritation or breakdown. Powders and skin lotions are avoided because they will tend to cake under the device. T-shirts and long socks are placed under the device to prevent skin friction.

If the child has a cast, the nurse will instruct the parents on how to provide cast care. The following points on cast care will be emphasized:

- Wet casts should be supported by pillows and handled by the palms of the hands to prevent misshaping the cast.
- Neurovascular checks will be conducted frequently after any cast application to detect early signs of compromised circulation and nerve impairment. Signs to be immediately reported include pain, swelling, decreased sensation, inability to move toes and feet, lack of pulses, presence of pallor or cyanosis, and coolness to touch.
- Note any drainage on the cast or any odor coming from the cast—drainage, if not excessive, is considered to be normal following surgery; however, odor is indicative of a possible infection and should be reported.
- Do not let casted extremities hang down; they should be kept slightly elevated to avoid swelling.
- Do not place anything down inside the cast. Inspect skin around the cast edges for irritation daily.
- Avoid moisture on the cast—waterproof and protect the cast's perineal opening with plastic wraps for elimination. Protect the cast with plastic wrap during bathing/showering.

Even when the child is immobilized with a splint, brace, or cast, an effort should be made to keep the child engaged in family and other social activities. The parents should be encouraged to keep the child involved in age-appropriate activities as much as possible to support normal growth and development.

Clubfoot

The term "clubfoot" is used to describe a variety of foot and ankle deformities that prevent the foot from assuming a normal position. The foot may be inverted (bent inward) or everted (bent outward). The foot may also be in a position of plantar flexion (toes pointed down) or a position of dorsiflexion (toes pointed up). The most common clubfoot deformity is **talipes equinovarus** (TEV) where the toes are pointed down and the foot is inverted.

The deformity may be unilateral or bilateral. Boys are affected more frequently than girls. The cause is unknown, but it is thought to be due to improper positioning in the uterus or arrested embryonic development.

Pathophysiology

There are three categories of clubfoot. Clubfoot may be **mild**. In mild cases, exercise and casting may be sufficient to correct the problem. Sometimes the deformity corrects itself. Another form of clubfoot is **tetralogic clubfoot**, where the deformity occurs in association with other congenital deformities. Tetralogic clubfoot requires surgical intervention to be corrected. The third form of clubfoot is **congenital idiopathic clubfoot**, which also requires surgical intervention to be corrected because of bone abnormalities.

Clinical Manifestations

The clubfoot deformity is easily identified at birth. The deformity is fixed in position, which helps differentiate it from positional deformities.

Diagnostic Testing

Clubfoot is diagnosed by observation of the foot. Frequently, it is even detected through ultrasound before the infant's birth.

Medical Management

Treatment includes correcting the deformity, maintaining the correction, and providing follow-up care. A common form of treatment is the use of serial casting to correct the deformity. In serial casting, the casts are changed regularly (weekly) to keep up with the infant's rapid growth rate. The casts help attain proper foot alignment by progressively stretching the skin and structures located on the medial side of the foot. It may take as long as three months to achieve the appropriate amount of correction. Following correction by serial casting, X rays are taken to evaluate bony alignment. If the bones are not correctly aligned, surgical intervention will be used to achieve alignment. Surgery is most successful if performed before the infant reaches one year of age.

Nursing Care for the Child with Clubfoot

Nursing care involves teaching the parents how to care for a child with a cast. Pertinent nursing assessments include skin inspection to prevent irritation from the cast and frequent neurovascular checks to detect any circulatory or neurological impairment. The parents should be encouraged to interact with the child and keep the child active to promote the achievement of normal infant development. The nurse should also reinforce the importance of follow-up care and keeping appointments to promote a satisfactory outcome.

Scoliosis

Scoliosis is a spinal deformity that typically becomes apparent during early adolescence when the child enters a growth spurt. The deformities that occur in scoliosis include lateral curvature of the spine, spinal rotation with rib asymmetry, and hypokyphosis in the thoracic region of the spine.

Idiopathic scoliosis is most common in girls. While scoliosis is most frequently first diagnosed during the early adolescent phase, scoliosis can also be congenital or develop during early childhood.

Pathophysiology

There are three major categories of scoliosis. **Idiopathic scoliosis** is the most common. It has no known cause, but it is believed to have some genetic factors. **Neuromuscular scoliosis** is caused by other neuromuscular diseases, such as cerebral palsy or muscular dystrophy, which lead to the development of spinal deformities. **Congenital scoliosis** is present at birth as a result of fetal malformations of the spine.

The first pathophysiological changes occur in the muscles and ligaments. The muscles and ligaments shorten on the concave side of the curve, leading to deformities of the vertebrae and ribs. The curve may be "C" or "S" shaped. As the child grows, the deformity begins to increase and the curve increases by degrees.

Clinical Manifestations

Clinical manifestations will vary depending upon the severity of the defect. For example, in mild or early stages, the child may initially notice that clothing does not fit correctly or hang evenly. The shoulders may be uneven. As the deformity progresses, hip height is asymmetrical, and the scapula and ribs develop prominence. Unilateral, posterior rib humps become noticeable when the child bends forward. Severe cases may lead to pulmonary, cardiac, and digestive impairment.

Diagnostic Tests

Scoliosis is diagnosed through observation and X rays. The child will be asked to undress and the spine will be inspected while the child is standing. Any asymmetry of hips, shoulders, and scapula will be noted. The child will then be asked to bend forward at the waist and let the arms hang down. Rib asymmetry (rib hump) may then be noticeable. X rays are used to measure the degree of the spinal curvature.

Medical Management

Scoliosis is treated with **orthotics** (braces), exercise, and surgical intervention. The type of treatment used depends upon the severity of the deformity, age of the child, and any other accompanying diseases.

Braces are frequently used for the adolescent. The use of the brace prevents the curvature from increasing in degrees during the child's growth period. A common brace is a form of custom molded plastic that is fit to the child's body and shaped to help correct the deformity. This type of brace is called a **TLSO**, thoracolumbosacral orthotic.

If the defect is severe, surgical intervention may be required. The surgery involves realigning and straightening the spine with internal fixation using rods and wires. A bony fusion (arthrodesis) of the spine is also performed. Following the surgery, the child will be log-rolled to prevent movement of the spine and a molded plastic brace will be used to provide support and spinal stability while the fusion heals.

Nursing Care for the Child with Scoliosis

Treatment of scoliosis occurs during the time of an adolescent's life when appearance and being "one of the crowd" is very important developmentally. The visible presence of a deformity and the need to wear a brace may create a negative body image in the adolescent. The nurse must be empathetic towards the child's feelings and provide support and encouragement. The child should be encouraged to participate in social functions and other peer activities as much as possible. Positive reinforcement from health care providers and parents is very important at this time.

The child and parents should receive a thorough explanation about treatment, the importance of consistently wearing the brace, and the importance of performing any prescribed exercises. The nurse can provide guidance about selecting clothing that will be comfortable and attractive.

If surgical intervention is required, the nurse will provide preoperative teaching to the child and parents. Preoperative care will include obtaining autologous blood donations from the child to use as blood replacement following surgery. The child will also be familiarized with the intensive care unit and equipment to ease anxiety about the hospital environment. The child should also be encouraged to practice **log-rolling** prior to surgery, so when asked to do so after surgery, the child will have a better understanding of what is expected. Log-rolling involves turning the patient as a "unit," hips and shoulders kept in alignment, so that the spine maintains a straight, aligned position and is not twisted while the patient is being turned.

Postoperative nursing assessments will include frequent neurovascular checks of the patient's lower extremities. These neurovascular checks will include assessment of circulation, sensation, and movement. The patient may have a nasogastric tube in place due to the likelihood of a paralytic ileus developing to some degree, and an indwelling catheter is frequently inserted to treat the urinary retention that is common in the immediate postoperative phase. Skin care is important to prevent skin breakdown.

It is important that nursing interventions focus on pain control during the first few days following surgery. It is common for the child to experience considerable pain during this time period. Opioids will be necessary for pain control; they are usually administered either epidurally or intravenously. If the child is old enough, patient-controlled analgesia will provide the child with a maximum amount of control over achieving pain relief. The nurse will want to encourage the child to take pain medication as needed, and reassure the parents that the pain medication will be effective without causing dependency on the drugs.

Physiotherapy, range-of-motion, and independence with the activities of daily living will be encouraged as soon as the patient is able to tolerate the activity. Encouraging movement will decrease the likelihood of respiratory complications and skin breakdown. The child will be discharged home with a brace or cast on to provide continued stability to the spine until recovery is complete.

Congenital and Genetic Neuromuscular Disorders

Congenital and genetic neuromuscular disorders are among some of the most common causes of permanent disabilities in children. These disorders have a major impact on the family structure and almost always require long-term, multidisciplinary health care. We will discuss three chronic neuromuscular disorders that are either congenital or genetic in nature—cerebral palsy, spina bifida (myelomeningocele), and muscular dystrophy.

Cerebral Palsy

Cerebral palsy is characterized by delayed motor development, altered muscle tone, altered reflexes, abnormal motor performance, and abnormal posture. Other associated disabilities can include impaired intellectual ability, sensory impairment, and language deficits.

Cerebral palsy (CP) is the most common cause of permanent disability among children. There are thought to be multiple causes of CP. Causes include prenatal brain abnormalities. **Premature birth** is the most important risk factor.

Pathophysiology

There is no single pathophysiological pattern associated with CP. **Anoxia**, caused secondarily by multiple factors, is the most common pathophysiological feature associated with brain damage. CP can be classified in three ways:

1. **Spastic** is characterized by hypertonicity and scissor gait.
2. **Dyskinetic** is characterized by involuntary abnormal movements.
3. **Ataxic** is characterized by a wide gait.

There is also a **mixed type** of CP that is a combination of the spastic and dyskinetic types.

Clinical Manifestations

The clinical manifestations of CP are primarily related to impaired movement and posture. These problems may be noted early if the infant exhibits poor sucking, feeding problems, and persistent tongue thrust. The infant may be stiff or rigid when being held, or in contrast, limp. However, it is not uncommon for CP to be diagnosed after the infant ages and does not begin to achieve expected motor developmental tasks. The following signs and symptoms are considered to be warning signs of CP, and health-care professionals should carefully evaluate an infant exhibiting any of them:

- Lack of head control after three months of age
- Limp posture
- Rigid extremities
- Arching back
- Unable to sit without support by eight months
- Difficulty with feeding
- Unilateral use of hand
- Excessive crying, irritability, lack of smiling by three months

Diagnostic Tests

CP is suspected when an infant begins to display signs of delayed motor development and abnormal movement and posture. A thorough neurological examination will help confirm the diagnosis. No diagnostic tests exist to specifically diagnose CP. However, diagnostic tests may be ordered to rule out other neurological disorders that can produce similar signs and symptoms, such as a brain tumor.

Medical Management

The goal of medical management is to prevent complications of CP. There is no cure for the disorder and the disabilities are permanent. Treatment is symptomatic and centered upon promoting the functional ability of the child, especially in the areas of mobility, communication, and achievement of self-care activities. Developing socialization skills and providing appropriate educational opportunities will also be emphasized. A multidisciplinary health-care team is required to help meet the needs of the child and parents.

To promote mobility, many children will require assistive devices such as braces, walkers, and crutches. To improve mobility some children may require surgery to release and correct contractures and spastic deformities. A more conservative approach to treatment is the use of pharmacologic agents. Skeletal muscle relaxants and antianxiety agents may be used to help relieve spasticity. Dantrolene (Dantrium) is one example of a skeletal muscle relaxant that is prescribed for older children. Diazepam (Valium) is also used to decrease spasticity in older children. Lioresal (Baclofen) is also infused intrathecally via a pump to help control spasticity without side effects.

Some children with CP are subject to seizures. Antiepileptic medications, such as phenobarbital and phenytoin (Dilantin), are administered to control seizure activity.

Physical therapy and occupational therapy are very useful in helping to develop the functional ability of children with CP. Physical therapists can help design an exercise program to preserve joint function and mobility, and decrease the development of contractures. Occupational therapists can help the child adapt to living with disabilities and learn to use devices to perform activities of daily living. Since many children with CP live into adulthood, promoting self-care activities will help them lead independent, productive lives as adults.

Nursing Care of the Patient with CP

Nursing Process: Assessment

The nurse begins the assessment for CP when caring for the newborn. It is frequently the nurse who first notices abnormal movements or posturing in the infant. The nurse inspects the infant for the early warning signs associated with CP, especially for delayed achievement of developmental activities as the infant ages. The nurse should be especially alert to assessing the infant for motor, feeding, and behavioral problems whenever the infant is brought in for "well-baby" checkups.

Nursing Process: Nursing Diagnosis and Planning

Based upon an analysis of the gathered data, the following **nursing diagnoses**, while not intended to be inclusive, may be appropriate for the patient with CP:

- Impaired physical mobility related to abnormal muscle tone, motor performance, and posture
- Activities of daily living self-care deficit related to impaired physical ability and possible perceptual and cognitive impairment
- Impaired verbal communication related to abnormal muscle tone and motor performance (dysarthria)
- Risk for injury related to physical impairment and possible perceptual and cognitive impairment
- Body image disturbance related to physical impairment
- Altered family processes related to having a child with a permanent disability

Primary goals for the child with CP include the following:

- Maintain optimum mobility
- Perform activities of daily living within limits of capability
- Develop verbal and nonverbal communication skills using assistive devices as necessary
- Avoid injury
- Develop a positive body image
- Demonstrate positive coping skills related to having a child with a permanent disability

Nursing Process: Implementation

The child with CP is usually not hospitalized unless they require corrective surgery or have some other medical problem. The nurse will most frequently interact with the child and family in an outpatient setting. Nursing interventions will be focused on helping the child develop the skills needed to perform activities of daily living, as well as helping the child learn to feed and communicate. The nurse's role is frequently as coordinator of a multidisciplinary health-care team, and the nursing care plan will reflect this coordination and the incorporation of the various supporting therapies. Providing family support is another important nursing intervention.

The nurse should help the parents understand the importance of participating in physical therapy, occupational therapy, and speech therapy to help the child achieve and maintain function within his or her capabilities. The child should be encouraged to achieve motor functions such as sitting, crawling, and walking at the age-appropriate times. Toys and play therapy can be used to help the child perform exercises and improve hand coordination and motor function.

Feeding may be a particular challenge due to a lack of coordinated jaw control. The nurse can help the parents learn how to position the child in a normal position for eating while providing hand support to the child's jaw to promote stability of the head, neck, and jaw. Speech therapy can be very useful in helping the child develop proper feeding techniques, as well as a method of communication.

A care plan for the child's educational experiences and social/recreational activities will be implemented according to the developmental and cognitive level of the child. Some children will be able to participate in regular classes, while others will require special educational arrangements. The child should be allowed to function to the optimum level of his or her capabilities and not sheltered from other children or social situations.

Providing support to the family is likely to be the most important nursing intervention of all. The parents will require significant support while adjusting and learning to cope with their child's diagnosis of CP. Siblings may resent the attention the child with CP receives, feel neglected or ignored, and engage in disruptive behavior as a result. Parent support groups can be very helpful, as can contact with national organizations such as the United Cerebral Palsy Association. Counseling may also be of benefit. The nurse can be a source of consistent support and encouragement to the family, as the family interacts with multiple care providers.

Nursing Process: Evaluation

The effectiveness of nursing interventions for the child with CP can be measured by the achievement of the following expected outcomes by the patient and family:

- Maintains optimum mobility and motor function with use of assistive devices as necessary
- Avoids injury

- Communicates effectively using assistive devices, as necessary
- Demonstrates self-care at the optimum level of ability as related to activities of daily living
- Displays evidence of a positive body image
- Verbalizes ability to cope with demands of having a child with a permanent physical disability
- Identifies community resources to help provide care for the child with CP

The nurse can evaluate the expected outcomes by observing the child's movements and activities, and communicating with the child. Talking with the parents and observing the parent's interactions with the child can also provide data to help evaluate outcomes and modify the care plan, if necessary.

Spina Bifida

Spina bifida, or **myelomeningocele**, is a congenital disorder that is caused by an abnormality in the development of the embryonic neural tube. The result is a spinal defect that involves the external protrusion of a sac that contains meninges, spinal fluid, and nerves.

Pathophysiology

Usually, a sheath of bones and meninges protectively surrounds the spinal cord. In spina bifida, the neural tube fails to close, and this protective sheath is not formed. A sac containing the meninges, spinal fluid, and nerves protrudes through the opening and external to the body. The etiology of the disorder is unknown, but it could be due to an increase in cerebrospinal fluid during the early trimester of the pregnancy. Most myelomeningoceles occur at the **lumbar** and **sacral** level. **Hydrocephalus**, caused by excess cerebrospinal fluid, is present in 90 to 95 percent of the infants who have a myelomeningocele.

Clinical Manifestations

The clinical manifestations of spina bifida will be neurological in nature and dependent upon the level of the deformity. If the defect is located below the level of the second lumbar vertebra, the clinical manifestations will include partial paralysis of the lower extremities, sensory deficits, lack of bowel control, and overflow incontinence (neurogenic bladder).

If the defect is located below the level of the third sacral vertebra, there is no motor impairment of the lower extremities, only bladder and bowel dysfunction.

Children with spina bifida sometimes have joint deformities as well. These deformities can include hip dislocation, scoliosis, kyphosis, and inverted (talipes varus) or everted (talipes valgus) foot contractures.

Diagnostic Testing

The diagnosis of spina bifida is made upon examination of the external meningeal sac. Additional tests may be conducted to evaluate the brain and spinal cord. These tests can include magnetic resonance imaging (MRI), myelogram, CT of the brain, and ultrasound.

Sometimes neural tube defects can be detected in utero. An elevated level of alpha-fetoprotein (AFP) in the amniotic fluid can be indicative of a myelomeningocele. Prenatal ultrasounds can also detect the presence of a myelomeningocele.

Medical Management

A child with spina bifida will require specialized medical care to treat the health problems associated with spina bifida: lower extremity paralysis, potential joint deformity, genitourinary and bowel dysfunction, and hydrocephalus.

A primary goal of care for the newborn is the prevention of infection. The external meningeal sac is a potential site for infection that can lead to meningitis. For this reason, the myelomeningocele is usually surgically closed during the first twenty-four hours following the birth of the infant. This early closure decreases the likelihood of infection developing, or damage occurring to the tissues and nerves in the sac that could cause further motor dysfunction. A shunt may also be inserted to relieve any hydrocephalus.

The child with spina bifida is also prone to developing urinary tract and respiratory tract infections. Antibiotic therapy will be used to treat any infections.

Maintaining and supporting motor function is another important goal of care. Treatment may include various forms of orthopedic surgery to release contractures, as well as the use of braces and other walking devices to help the child remain mobile. Genitourinary dysfunction is another source of concern. Children with spina bifida have a neurogenic bladder that leads to urinary incontinence. The degree of urinary dysfunction will depend upon the level of the myelomeningocele. The goal of medical care will be to prevent urinary tract infection, preserve renal function, and achieve some level of urinary continence. These goals are usually achieved through a combination of clean intermittent catheterization and medications that will increase bladder continence. Loss of bowel control is another concern. To achieve bowel continence, a program of bowel training will be implemented that will include diet modifications and a regular schedule for toileting. Bowel elimination may be aided by suppositories, enemas, or laxatives.

The prognosis for children with spina bifida has improved in recent years. Early and aggressive intervention, including prompt closure of the defect, antibiotic therapy to prevent and treat infections, treatment of hydrocephalus, and prevention of urinary complications, is essential to increasing the survival rate of these children.

Nursing Care of the Child with Spina Bifida

Prevention of spina bifida must be emphasized. Nurses have an important role in educating women how to decrease the incidence of spina bifida. Women who are pregnant or planning to become pregnant can help decrease the occurrence of spina bifida by increasing their folic acid intake. The Centers for Disease Control and Prevention has estimated that women can decrease the incidence of neural tube defects by 50 to 70 percent simply by taking 0.4 mg of folic acid daily. Nurses can help educate women of childbearing age about the importance of taking folic acid supplements and adding folic-rich foods to their diet. These foods would include fortified breads, cereals, rice and pastas, as well as leafy green vegetables and citrus fruits.

When caring for a newborn with spina bifida, the nurse will focus assessments upon the neurological status of the infant, including movement of extremities, urinary output, bladder distention, presence of anal reflex upon stimulation, and head circumference. The fontanels will also be assessed for bulging, which indicates the presence of hydrocephalus.

Nursing interventions for newborns with spina bifida will be focused on the following:

- Preventing infection
- Preventing trauma to the sac
- Providing postoperative care after closure of the sac
- Providing support to the parents

It is essential that the myelomeningocele sac be protected from trauma until surgically closed. The nurse will cover the sac with a sterile dressing moistened with normal saline. This dressing will be changed frequently and the sac is inspected for leaks, trauma, or any indication of infection. It is important that the sac not be contaminated by urine or stool to help prevent infection. Early signs of an infection include irritability, lethargy, and elevated temperature.

Prior to surgery, the infant is usually placed in a prone position with hips slightly flexed and legs in a position of abduction to decrease tension on the sac and the potential for trauma. Following surgery, the infant can be held as long as there is no pressure placed on the surgical site. The infant will continue to be placed in a prone position when not being held; a side-lying position may also be used. It is important that the incision be kept clean and dry, and that the nurse inspects the site carefully for the leakage of cerebrospinal fluid.

Additional postoperative care includes monitoring of vital signs, controlling pain, assessing for signs of infection, monitoring intake and output, and resuming feedings. Diapering may be contraindicated in order to avoid trauma to the new incision.

The nurse will provide education and support to the parents. As the infant recovers from surgery, the parents must be prepared to care for the infant at home. The parents will need to be instructed on how to perform clean intermittent catheterization to help achieve bladder continence. A bowel-training program will be implemented. Skin care and position changes are important to preventing skin breakdown in paralyzed extremities. Parents need to understand the importance of inspecting the skin daily for irritation and breakdown. Range-of-motion will be performed daily to prevent or decrease the incidence of contractures. An additional source of concern is the potential for developing an allergy to latex. Children with spina bifida are prone to latex allergies, so creating an environment that decreases their contact with latex products is important. The nurse can provide the parents with guidelines that can be implemented in the home setting to minimize contact with latex.

Parent support groups can be a good source of information for the parents. The Spina Bifida Association of America can provide resources and services to families. The nurse can help the parents connect with these community resources. The child with spina bifida has a life expectancy that is about average, so long-term planning of care to help the child reach maximum potential as an adult is essential.

Muscular Dystrophy

Muscular dystrophy (MD) is a broad term used to refer to a group of genetic muscle diseases that result in progressive, symmetrical muscle weakness and wasting. The most common form of MD is **Duchenne muscular dystrophy**, also known as **pseudohypertrophic muscular dystrophy**. Because it is an X-linked inheritance disorder, Duchenne MD occurs only in males. The cause of Duchenne MD is unknown, but is thought to be related to a metabolic disorder.

Pathophysiology

In Duchenne MD the muscle fibers begin to degenerate, eventually leading to muscle weakness, wasting, deformity, and disability. The onset of muscle weakness is subtle, beginning around the age of three. Symmetrical muscle groups are affected. The child may initially display weakness during physical activities, such as riding a bike or running. Gait will be affected as the disorder progresses.

The muscles become infiltrated with fat, which cause the calf muscles to appear enlarged (pseudohypertrophy). Contractures develop in the joints, causing deformities, and impeding ambulation. By the time the child begins to reach puberty, unassisted ambulation is usually no longer feasible. As the child enters the terminal stage of the disorder, the respiratory muscle groups become involved and the heart enlarges. The child with Duchenne MD most commonly dies of heart failure or respiratory failure by the age of thirty.

Clinical Manifestations

Clinical manifestations include frequent falls and a waddling gait. The child may display the Gower sign, where the child attempts to get into an upright position by turning onto the side or abdomen, kneeling, and then using the hands to "walk" up the legs to assume a standing position. Pseudohypertrophy develops in calf muscles, thighs, and upper arms. The muscles will feel firm upon palpation. As the disease progresses the muscles atrophy. Joint contractures develop in the ankles, knees, and hips, further compounding the child's difficulty with ambulating. The muscle weakness and muscle atrophy is slowly progressive until the child's death. Children affected by MD frequently display a mild mental deficit.

Diagnostic Testing

A child who displays clinical manifestations that could be indicative of MD will undergo laboratory blood tests to confirm the diagnosis. **Serum creatine phosphokinase** levels are elevated in individuals who have MD. **Serum glutamic-oxaloacetic transaminase (SGOT) levels**, also known as **aspartate aminotransferase (AST)**, are also elevated. As the disease progresses and muscles deteriorate, these enzyme levels will drop. A **muscle biopsy** will show muscle fiber atrophy as well as fatty tissue. An **EMG** (electromyography) will demonstrate a decrease in duration of muscle action potential.

Medical Management

There is no cure for MD and no known effective medical treatment. A goal of medical management is to preserve function for as long as possible. Physical therapy, use of orthoses (braces), and range-of-motion exercises are used to help preserve function and independence as long as possible. Weight gain leading to obesity can become a problem further affecting mobility. The use of a wheelchair will be delayed as long as possible, as immobility will hasten muscle deterioration. Surgery may be needed to help release contractures. Respiratory exercises are also used to help preserve respiratory functioning and decrease likelihood of respiratory infection developing.

Nursing Care of the Child with Duchenne Muscular Dystrophy

Nursing care of the individual with Duchenne MD will be supportive. The nurse will coordinate a multidisciplinary team to provide care to the patient. Primary goals of care will be to preserve function, encourage independence in activities of daily living within the limits of the patient, and prevent complications.

The parents of the child with Duchenne MD will require emotional support as they come to terms with the terminal nature of the disease. Parents will also require genetic counseling. Community support groups can help parents deal with their possible feelings of guilt and grief. Mothers, in particular, can feel guilty because of the nature of the genetic transmission of the disease from mother to son. As the child's disease progresses, he will eventually require skilled nursing care. Placement in a nursing home or other skilled care facility may become necessary. The parents need to be helped to understand that placing the child or adolescent in a long-term care facility may be the best course of action. The nurse can help the family investigate the options available to them and support them in their difficult decision making. The community branch of the Muscular Dystrophy Association of America can also provide information and assistance to families.

Chapter 27 Study Questions

1.   The nurse is caring for a three-month-old infant who has developmental dysplasia of the hip. In what position should the infant's affected hip be maintained?

2.   The nurse is preparing to teach parents of an infant with developmental dysplasia of the hip how to apply a Pavlik harness. What should the nurse include in the teaching plan about care of the skin under the harness?

3.   A lower extremity cast has just been applied as treatment to correct a clubfoot deformity. The nurse is assessing the neurovascular status of the affected extremity. What signs and symptoms would indicate that there is neurovascular impairment to the foot?

4.   A fourteen-year-old girl has been diagnosed with scoliosis. What deformities would the nurse most likely note in an assessment of this patient's spine?

5.   The school nurse is conducting a screening program for detection of scoliosis. What signs and symptoms would indicate that a child should undergo further evaluation?

6.   Identify nursing interventions that would be appropriate for an adolescent who is reluctant to wear the orthosis prescribed to treat her scoliosis?

7.   A nurse who works in an ambulatory clinic is responsible for conducting well-baby checkups and assessing for normal growth and development patterns. What are the warning signs of cerebral palsy that the nurse should keep in mind when performing these assessments?

8.   Identify six potential nursing diagnoses that would be appropriate for a child with cerebral palsy.

9.   The nurse is caring for a child with cerebral palsy. What are some expected outcomes of care that can be used to measure the effectiveness of the nurse's interventions?

10.   Describe the clinical manifestations associated with spina bifida.

11.   The nurse works in a clinic providing care to women who are pregnant. What instructions should the nurse include in the prenatal teaching to help prevent the development of neural tube defects such as spina bifida?

12.   Describe the preoperative nursing interventions essential to the care of an infant with spina bifida.

13.   Develop a care plan focusing on immediate postoperative care for an infant with spina bifida.

14.   When developing a nursing care plan for a child with Duchenne muscular dystrophy, what primary goals of nursing care should the nurse keep in mind?

Answers to Chapter 27 Study Questions

1. In newborn infants and prior to six months of age, the Pavlik harness (or a similar type of soft splint) will be used to maintain the hip in a state of flexion.

2. Skin care is very important regardless of the type of device used. The parents are taught to inspect the skin daily for any irritation or breakdown. Powders and skin lotions are avoided because they will tend to cake under the device. T-shirts and long socks are placed under the device to prevent skin friction.

3. Neurovascular checks will be conducted frequently after any cast application to detect early signs of compromised circulation and nerve impairment. Signs to be immediately reported include pain, swelling, decreased sensation, inability to move toes and feet, lack of pulses, presence of pallor or cyanosis, and coolness to touch.

4. The deformities that occur in scoliosis include lateral curvature of the spine, spinal rotation with rib asymmetry, and hypokyphosis in the thoracic region of the spine.

5. The child's clothing may not fit correctly or hang evenly. The shoulders may be uneven. Hip height may be asymmetrical. Unilateral, posterior rib humps may become noticeable when the child bends forward. Any of these signs are an indication that additional evaluation is needed.

6. Treatment of scoliosis occurs during the time of an adolescent's life when appearance and being "one of the crowd" is very important. The visible presence of a deformity and the need to wear a brace may create a negative body image in the adolescent. The nurse must be empathetic towards the child's feelings and provide support and encouragement. The child should be encouraged to participate in social functions and other peer activities as much as possible. Positive reinforcement from health-care providers and parents is very important at this time. The child should be instructed about treatment, the importance of consistently wearing the brace, and of performing any prescribed exercises—these activities will facilitate treatment. The nurse can provide guidance about selecting clothing that will be comfortable and attractive.

7. The following signs and symptoms are considered to be warning signs of CP, and health-care professionals should carefully evaluate an infant exhibiting any of them: lack of head control after three months of age; limp posture; rigid extremities; arching back; unable to sit without support by eight months; difficulty with feeding; unilateral use of hand; excessive crying; irritability; or lack of smiling by three months.

8.   Potential nursing diagnoses for a child with cerebral palsy include the following:

- Impaired physical mobility related to abnormal muscle tone, motor performance, and posture
- Activities of daily living self-care deficit related to impaired physical ability and possible perceptual and cognitive impairment
- Impaired verbal communication related to abnormal muscle tone and motor performance (dysarthria)
- Risk for injury related to physical impairment and possible perceptual and cognitive impairment.
- Body image disturbance related to physical impairment
- Altered family processes related to having a child with a permanent disability

9.   The effectiveness of nursing interventions for the child with CP can be measured by the achievement of the following expected outcomes by the patient and family:

- Maintains optimum mobility and motor function with use of assistive devices as necessary
- Avoids injury
- Communicates effectively using assistive devices as necessary
- Demonstrates self-care at the optimum level of ability as related to activities of daily living
- Displays evidence of a positive body image
- Verbalizes ability to cope with demands of having a child with a permanent physical disability
- Identifies community resources to help provide care for the child with CP

The nurse can evaluate the expected outcomes by observing the child's movements and activities and communicating with the child. Talking with the parents and observing the parent's interactions with the child can also provide data to help evaluate outcomes and modify the care plan, if necessary.

10.   The clinical manifestations of spina bifida will be neurological in nature and dependent upon the level of the deformity. If the defect is located below the level of the second lumbar vertebra, the clinical manifestations will include partial paralysis of the lower extremities, sensory deficits, lack of bowel control, and overflow incontinence (neurogenic bladder). If the defect is located below the level of the third sacral vertebra, there will be no motor impairment of the lower extremities, but there will be bladder and bowel dysfunction. Children with spina bifida sometimes have joint deformities, which can include hip dislocation, scoliosis, kyphosis, and inverted (talipes varus) or everted (talipes valgus) foot contractures.

11.   Nurses have an important role in educating women how to decrease the incidence of spina bifida. Women who are pregnant or planning to become pregnant can

help decrease the occurrence of spina bifida by increasing their folic acid intake. Nurses can help educate women of childbearing age about the importance of taking folic acid supplements and adding folic-rich foods to their diet. These foods would include fortified breads, cereals, rices and pastas, as well as leafy green vegetables and citrus fruits.

12.   Preoperative nursing interventions for newborns with spina bifida are directed toward preventing infection, preventing trauma to the sac, and providing support to the parents. The myelomeningocele sac must be protected from trauma until surgically closed and is covered with a sterile dressing moistened with normal saline. This dressing is changed frequently and the sac is inspected for leaks, trauma, or any indication of infection. The sac must not be contaminated by urine or stool. The infant will be assessed for early signs of an infection including irritability, lethargy, and elevated temperature. Prior to surgery, the infant is placed in a prone position with hips slightly flexed and legs in a position of abduction.

13.   Postoperative care includes proper positioning of the infant. The infant can be held as long as no pressure is placed on the surgical site. The infant will be placed in a prone position when not being held; a side-lying position may also be used. The incision must be kept clean and dry. The nurse frequently inspects the site carefully for leakage of cerebrospinal fluid. Additional postoperative care in the nursing care plan includes monitoring of vital signs, controlling pain, assessing for signs of infection, monitoring intake and output, and resuming feedings. Diapering may be contraindicated in order to avoid trauma to the new incision.

14.   Nursing care of the individual with MD will be supportive. The nurse will coordinate a multidisciplinary team to provide care to the patient. Primary goals of care will be to preserve function, encourage independence in activities of daily living within the limits of the patient, and prevent complications.

Chapter 28: Nursing Care for Congenital Gastrointestinal Disorders

Key Terms

Biliary atresia
Cholestasis
Cleft lip
Cleft palate
Hirschsprung's disease
Imperforate anus

Introduction

Congenital defects of the gastrointestinal tract can affect any portion of the alimentary canal extending from the mouth to the rectum. Congenital defects include structural defects, such as cleft lip and cleft palate, which affect food intake. Other defects affect gastric motility leading to intestinal obstruction. An example of a congenital defect that decreases gastric motility is Hirschsprung's disease. Other congenital defects cause obstruction or lack of structural continuity within the gastrointestinal system. Biliary atresia and imperforate anus are examples of these types of defects. Resulting problems related to congenital defects include impaired nutritional intake, decreased gastric motility and absorption, and delayed growth and development.

Cleft Lip and Cleft Palate

Cleft lip and **cleft palate** are congenital facial defects that can occur separately, but most commonly occur together. Cleft lip and cleft palate occur more frequently in some Native Americans tribes and in Asian populations. Cleft lip occurs in approximately 1 out of every 800 live births. Cleft palate occurs in approximately 1 out of every 2,000 live births. Cleft lip and cleft palate may be caused by environmental factors or teratogens. Individuals who have chromosomal abnormalities have a higher incidence of cleft lip and cleft palate. First trimester maternal smoking is also associated with cleft lip and cleft palate.

Pathophysiology

A **cleft lip** occurs when the medial and maxillary nasal processes do not fuse together during embryo development. Typically the fusion is complete during the seventh and eighth gestational weeks. The extent of the cleft lip defect can vary from a minor malformation of the lips to an extensive defect that extends into the nose. A cleft lip can either be unilateral or bilateral.

A **cleft palate** develops as a midline fissure when the two sides of the palate do not fuse together in utero, as should occur between the seventh and twelfth weeks of gestation. It can affect both the soft and hard palates, and it may involve only the midline of the palate or the fissure can extend into the sides of the palate.

Figure 28.1 Illustration of Cleft Lip and Cleft Palate

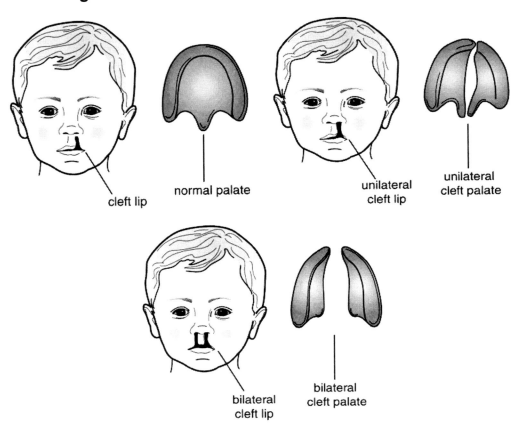

Diagnostic Tests
================

A diagnosis of cleft lip is made on the basis of the infant's appearance, as the defect is readily apparent. A diagnosis of cleft palate is made by examining the infant's palate with a gloved finger or visually inspecting the palate when the infant is crying.

Medical Management
==================

The medical management of cleft lip and cleft palate consists of surgical intervention. Surgical closure of the cleft lip is usually accomplished when the infant is between six to twelve weeks old. Following surgery, a protective device is taped to the infant's cheeks to help protect the suture line. The infant's arms are also gently restrained at the elbows to prevent touching of the incision. Healing is usually accompanied with minimal scar formation, as long as trauma and infection are avoided. Cleft palate repair is usually delayed until the child is twelve to eighteen months old, after the palate has undergone further changes that are part of normal growth and development.

In addition to the surgical intervention, there are some additional concerns that need to be addressed. One concern is that of improper dental alignment; many children will require some form of orthodontia to correct dental problems. Most children also require some speech therapy to help correct speech impairments. Also, children with cleft palate may experience inefficient functioning of the eustachian tubes, which leads to frequent episodes of otitis media and resulting hearing impairment.

Nursing Care of the Child with Cleft Lip/Cleft Palate

Nursing Process: Assessment

Assessment of the cleft lip and cleft palate is accomplished by inspection of the child's facial features and palate. A cleft palate can be palpated with a gloved finger to determine the extent of the defect.

The nursing assessment is also focused on the emotional response of the parents to the child's defect. Cleft lip and cleft palate can be very distressing to parents because of the cosmetic nature of the disability, as well as the functional impact. The nurse will want to closely assess how well the parents are accepting the infant and coping with the presence of the defect.

The nutritional intake of the infant can also be affected by the presence of a cleft lip or cleft palate. Because of the defect, infants will have difficulty creating enough pressure to successfully suck and take in enough nourishment. The nurse will assess the amount of difficulty the infant has sucking and the amount of intake the infant is able to ingest. Does the infant cough or choke when attempting to feed? Is formula escaping out the nose during feedings? How comfortable are the parents when attempting to feed the infant?

Nursing Process: Nursing Diagnosis and Planning

Based upon analysis of the data, the following may be priority **nursing diagnoses** for the infant and family with a diagnosis of cleft lip and cleft palate:

- Altered nutrition, less than body requirements related to structural defects of the lip and/or palate
- Risk for altered parenting related to presence of facial deformity
- Pain related to surgical repair of defect

Primary goals for the infant with cleft lip and/or cleft palate and the parents include the following:

- Maintain adequate nutrition
- Demonstrate accepting behaviors toward infant
- Minimize pain and discomfort following surgical repair of defects
- Avoid complications related to defect and surgical repair (aspiration of feeding and infection)

Nursing Process: Implementation

Nursing care is primarily focused on successfully feeding the infant, providing emotional support to the parents, and avoiding postoperative complications.

Prior to surgery, it can be challenging to feed an infant with cleft lip or cleft palate. The degree of difficulty will depend upon the extent of the defect. Because of the defects the infant will have a difficult time sucking. This is true for bottle-fed and breast-fed babies. Sometimes the formula or breast milk will return through the infant's nose instead of being swallowed. Choking can also be a concern. Holding the infant in an upright position helps to facilitate feeding and decreases the risk of choking. Special nipples are also required—the most successfully used nipples are those that are large, soft, and have larger holes. If the infant is breast-feeding, the nipple should be placed well toward the back of the oral cavity. If the infant cannot suck on a nipple, various feeding devices, such as an Asepto syringe or medicine dropper, can be used in place of the nipple. The mother should be encouraged to practice feeding the baby as much as possible in the hospital prior to discharge so that the mother is comfortable with the feeding process. These infants can swallow excess amounts of air, so frequent burping is advised.

Providing emotional support to the parents is another important nursing intervention. The parents can be devastated about the appearance of their newborn. The nurse should be available to listen while the parents express their feelings. It is important for the nurse to carefully create an accepting environment for the infant's appearance: How the nurse responds to and treats the infant can serve as a model for the parents. Showing the parents pictures of successful surgical repairs can help encourage hope.

After surgical repair, the nurse will implement actions that will help prevent suture line trauma and infection. Analgesics are administered to promote comfort and decrease agitation. Soft restraints are applied to the infant's arms at the elbow to keep the infant from disrupting the incision. These restraints should be removed at frequent intervals to permit range-of-motion and exercise, to provide the infant with some relief from the constant feeling of restriction, and to inspect the skin for signs of friction. After each feeding the suture line is cleansed with saline to help prevent infection. It is important to keep the suture line intact and clean and dry, as this will minimize infection and scarring.

The infant will resume feedings as soon as possible following recovery from the anesthetic. Clear liquids will be given initially, and the diet will be advanced as tolerated by the infant. If the child has had cleft palate repair, the use of spoons, straws, tongue blades, or any hard foods should be avoided until otherwise notified by the surgeon to avoid damage to the repaired palate. The infant can resume formula feedings as normal, but the older child may be placed on a soft or blended-food diet.

Long-term care considerations may include the need for dental care, speech therapy, and additional plastic surgery for cosmetic reasons. Parents can be faced with financial concerns; however, parents also need to understand the reasons for follow-up care that will help facilitate the child's normal growth, development, and self-esteem. There are support groups for parents that can provide services and resources. The nurse can help the parents initiate contact with these groups, which include the March of Dimes Birth Defect Foundation, Cleft Palate Foundation, and American Cleft Palate Association.

Nursing Process: Evaluation

The effectiveness of nursing interventions for the child with cleft lip and cleft palate can be measured by the achievement of the following expected outcomes by the patient and family:

- Maintains adequate nutrition
- Verbalizes feelings related to infant's defect
- Demonstrates attitude of acceptance towards infant
- Expresses or displays behavior that indicates satisfactory pain control following surgery
- Avoids development of complications following surgery (suture line infection, aspiration, or skin irritation)
- Expresses understanding of the importance of follow-up care related to dental care, speech therapy, and plastic surgery
- Contacts community resources as appropriate for information and support

Biliary Atresia

Biliary atresia, also known as **extrahepatic biliary atresia** (EHBA), is a congenital disorder that results from a progressive inflammatory process. The inflammation causes intrahepatic and extrahepatic bile duct fibrosis, eventually ending in obstruction of the ducts. Biliary atresia is thought to begin in the late gestational or perinatal stage. While the cause is unknown, the disease may be associated with a virus or immune mechanism. It is not genetic disorder, nor is it associated with any particular racial or ethnic group. It occurs more commonly in females. The disease is usually fatal by the age of two if not treated. Cause of death is cirrhosis and hepatic failure.

Pathophysiology

In biliary atresia, progressive inflammation causes obstruction of the intra- and extrahepatic bile ducts. The obstruction eventually results in fibrosis. Bile drainage is impaired (**cholestasis**) causing retention of bile and toxins. Pruritus develops from the accumulated bile toxins. Liver damage results. Surgery must be performed within the first two to three months of life to enhance bile drainage and decrease liver damage.

Clinical Manifestations

The earliest indication of biliary atresia is jaundice. The infant may be born jaundiced or may develop it over the first two to three weeks of life. The sclera are affected first. Other clinical manifestations include dark yellow urine that stains the diapers and light-colored stools. The infant will be irritable and demonstrate poor weight gain and a failure to thrive. Pruritus causes the infant to be fussy. Eventually, abdominal distention, hepatomegaly, and splenomegaly develop.

Diagnostic Tests

A definitive diagnosis for biliary atresia is achieved through an exploratory laparotomy with an intra-operative cholangiogram that demonstrates bile duct obstruction. Liver biopsy will demonstrate liver tissue damage. Other tests that may be used to evaluate the hepatic system include hepatobiliary scintigraphy and abdominal ultrasound. Liver enzymes (AST and ALT) and bilirubin blood tests are also be performed. Results would be elevated, indicating bile retention and liver damage.

Medical Management

Treatment of biliary atresia is the surgical anastomosis of a segment of the intestine to the porta hepatis, thus restoring bile drainage. This procedure is called a **hepatic portoenterostomy**, or **Kasai procedure**. The surgery must be performed within the first two to three months of life to decrease the likelihood of progressive hepatic damage. Even if the surgery is successfully performed, approximately 80 to 90 percent of the children will still require a liver transplant at some time because of progressive cirrhosis. The shortage of donor livers is a major issue, leading to the deaths of young children whose lives could otherwise be saved.

In addition to the surgery, the children often require nutritional supplementation including multivitamins, fat-soluble vitamins, and minerals. The formula will have essential fatty acids and medium-chain triglycerides added to it. If the infant is suffering from failure to thrive, total parenteral nutrition or enteral feedings will also be considered. Drug therapy may also be prescribed to help treat pruritus.

Nursing Care of the Child with Biliary Atresia

The major nursing interventions associated with the care of patients with biliary atresia include providing family education and support. Families need to be educated about the long-term treatment the infant needs. The nurse will need to instruct the parents about administering tube feedings and parenteral nutrition if ordered. Skin care is important to help relieve the pruritus. The infant's fingernails are kept trimmed to avoid scratching the skin.

The stress associated with biliary atresia is considerable. It is very difficult to cope with the uncertainty of the outcome of the illness. The child may be placed on a waiting list for a transplant, but there is no guarantee that a donor liver will become available in time to prevent the child's death. Financial concerns, because of the need for long-term nutritional supplements and medications, can be considerable. The Children's Liver Disease Foundation can be an important resource for families. Counseling and support groups can provide outlets through which the parents can express their concerns and fears.

Hirschsprung's Disease

Hirschsprung's disease, or **congenital aganglionic megacolon**, is characterized by decreased motility of the intestine. The decreased motility leads to mechanical obstruction of the intestine. More common in males, the disease is usually diagnosed in neonates, infancy, or early childhood. The symptoms of early childhood cases are more chronic in nature. Children who have Down syndrome have a higher incidence of Hirschsprung's disease. There may also be a familial pattern in some instances. The disease may be acute or chronic. Acute forms of the disease can be life threatening. The cause is unknown.

Pathophysiology

The pathophysiology of Hirschsprung's disease is related to the absence of ganglion cells in portions of the colon. The rectum is almost always involved, as well as proximal segments of the large intestine. This lack of enervation results in a decrease or absence of peristalsis and mechanical obstruction. Because of the mechanical obstruction, intestinal contents accumulate, and the bowel located proximally to the obstruction becomes distended. This distention is referred to as megacolon. In addition to the lack of peristalsis, the internal anal sphincter is unable to relax, which further leads to accumulation of intestinal contents. In acute cases, abdominal distention leads to ischemia of the intestinal wall. Enterocolitis, which is inflammation of the intestines, can develop. With enterocolitis the child becomes acutely ill and can die.

Clinical Manifestations

The clinical manifestations of Hirschsprung's disease will vary depending upon the acuity of the condition and the age of the child. In the newborn, the symptoms are acute. There is a lack of meconium during the first twenty-four to forty-eight hours after birth, abdominal distention, bile emesis, and difficulty taking fluids. In the infant, signs and symptoms include the following: constipation, abdominal distention, and periods of vomiting and diarrhea. The infant has a failure to thrive. There are three manifestations that are considered to be extremely serious: fever, watery diarrhea that is explosive, and severe prostration. These signs indicate the likely onset of enterocolitis and must be immediately treated before the bowel perforates, and peritonitis and shock develop.

If the disease is diagnosed in childhood, the symptoms are more chronic in nature. The signs and symptoms include constipation, ribbon-like stools, and abdominal distention. Peristalsis may be visible. The child may also be malnourished.

Diagnostic Testing

Abdominal X rays and barium enemas are used to help rule out other diagnoses. The diagnosis of Hirschsprung's disease is confirmed by a rectal biopsy that demonstrates a lack of ganglion cells in the tissue.

Medical Management

Medical management usually includes surgery to remove the aganglionic segments of the bowel. Eliminating these bowel segments restores peristaltic action and eliminates the bowel obstruction. The surgery is usually completed in two phases. The first step is to create a temporary colostomy. The establishment of a temporary colostomy relieves the obstruction and allows the bowel to decompress and return to normal size. After the child recovers, improves in nutritional status, and gains weight, the second surgery will be performed to reverse the colostomy and re-anastomose (reconnect) the ends of the bowel.

If the child is acutely ill with enterocolitis, his or her condition must be stabilized before surgery can be performed. Fluid and electrolytes must be monitored and replaced as necessary. Emergency surgery will be performed to prevent bowel perforation, peritonitis, and shock.

Nursing Care of the Child with Hirschsprung's Disease

The nursing care of the patient with Hirschsprung's disease depends upon the age of the child and the acuity of the child's condition.

Preoperative nursing care will include ensuring that the child is in an optimal nutritional state in preparation for surgery. A low-fiber, high-calorie, and high-protein diet is recommended. If the child is severely malnourished, total parenteral nutrition may also be administered. Enemas may be also be used occasionally for treating constipation. Psychological preparation is also necessary to prepare the family and the child for the temporary colostomy. If the child is old enough to understand the implications of the surgery, he or she should be fully informed about the impending surgery; visual aids can be used to help clarify instructions. Physical preparation for the surgery will include cleansing saline enemas to empty the bowel, enemas with antibiotic solutions to decrease bacteria in the bowel, as well as oral and/or intravenous antibiotics.

If the child is acutely ill with enterocolitis, the nurse must closely monitor the child's vital signs for indications of septic shock. The status of the child's fluid and electrolytes must also be monitored closely. Diarrhea, fever, vomiting, and lack of fluid intake can lead to dehydration. Indications of dehydration in the young child includes weight loss, increased pulse, decreased blood pressure, irritable behavior, dry mucous membranes, decreased tears, and sunken fontanel (infant). Intravenous fluids and electrolyte replacements will be administered to restore balance.

The nurse will also closely monitor the child for bowel perforation. Increasing abdominal distention is a serious clinical sign. The nurse will measure the abdominal circumference frequently, usually when taking the child's vital signs. The abdomen is measured with a paper tape measure at the same location on the abdomen each time, most commonly at the level of the umbilicus. The measuring point on the abdomen can be marked with an ink pen to ensure the same location is used for each measurement. Besides increasing abdominal distention, other clinical signs of bowel perforation include fever, vomiting, irritability, increasing abdominal tenderness, and dyspnea. The nurse will prepare the child for emergency surgery in the event that bowel perforation occurs.

Postoperatively, the nurse will teach the parents and child (if old enough) how to perform colostomy care. Colostomy care in the child is similar to that of adult colostomy care. (Nursing care associated with colostomies is covered in chapter 22 under the discussion on colon cancer.) Dolls can be used in teaching situations to help the child understand the ostomy and allow them to practice with equipment. Infants and toddlers may be challenging to control during pouch changes; distracting them with toys may work. Clothing that limits the youngster's access to the pouch can also help keep the child from pulling the pouch off. While the ostomy is almost always temporary, it can still be distressing to parents and the child. Enterostomal therapists can be a very useful source of information and support. Home health nurses can help with continuity of care and community support groups may also be helpful to the family. Following reversal of the ostomy, bowel retraining and dilation of anal strictures may be necessary. Otherwise, the child should be able to lead a normal lifestyle.

Imperforate Anus

Imperforate anus is a congenital anorectal malformation. Imperforate anus can present as several different malformation configurations. The one common characteristic of the different malformations is that there is no identifiable anal opening. Imperforate anus malformations are fairly common occurring in 1 in every 2,000 births.

Pathophysiology

It is common for anorectal malformations, such as an imperforate anus, to consist of a fistula that connects the distal rectum to the genitourinary system or the peritoneum. Some anorectal malformations are severe, rare anomalies that expose the bladder and bowel through the abdominal wall. Genitalia may be indistinguishable and the sex of the infant difficult to determine without chromosome studies. The presence of an imperforate anus necessitates further examination of the infant to determine if additional genitourinary and pelvic anomalies exist, and in what combination.

Clinical Manifestations

An imperforate anus is clinically evident by the absence of a normal rectal opening upon inspection of the perineum. Lack of meconium passage may be noted. However, the passage of meconium cannot be taken as an assurance that the anus is intact. If a rectovaginal fistula exists, meconium can be passed through the vagina. Rectourinary fistulas can also occur and would be suspected if meconium is found in the urine.

Diagnostic Testing

All newborn assessments include an inspection of the anus and rectum to check for a normal anal opening. The infant is also observed for rectal passage of meconium. If an imperforate anus is suspected, an abdominal ultrasound is performed to further establish the extent of the anomalies. An IVP and a voiding cystourethrogram may be conducted to determine the extent of involvement of the urinary tract.

Medical Management

An imperforate anus is surgically corrected. The membrane is cut and daily anal dilations are performed to correct any anal stenosis. The anus may also need to be surgically reconstructed in the correct position (anorectoplasty). Some reconstructive surgery is extensive, depending upon the types of anomalies present. The child's prognosis is related to the extent of the defect, and stool continence is dependent upon whether or not the interior anal sphincter is functioning. Most children do well, but some children may require a bowel program to promote bowel continence. While rare, some forms of anorectal malformations necessitate the creation of a colostomy to allow for bowel evacuation.

Nursing Care of the Child with an Imperforate Anus

The nurse will carefully assess the newborn for a patent rectum and anus. The nurse also observes the infant closely for the passage of meconium from the rectum. If a defect is diagnosed, the nurse will prepare the infant for surgery. Preoperatively, the infant will be placed on NPO status, receive IV fluids, and a nasogastric tube is inserted to decompress the gastrointestinal tract.

Postoperatively, the goal of nursing care is to prevent infection and promote healing. The rectal area is kept clean with frequent perineal care. If the infant is frequently experiencing loose stools, a protective skin ointment, such as zinc oxide, is applied to prevent skin irritation. The child will also need to be positioned in a side-lying prone position to keep pressure off of the perineal incision.

Initially following surgery, the infant may require a nasogastric tube until peristalsis returns. IV fluids will be administered until feedings are resumed. The nurse will need to educate the parents about home management of the infant's care. The mother will be encouraged to breast-feed to help prevent constipation. As the infant ages, bowel training and diet modification to include fiber is important. Stool softeners and occasional laxatives may be prescribed. The nurse should emphasize the importance of keeping track of the infant's bowel movements, including the size and shape of the stool. Ribbon-like stools indicate the development of anal strictures. Anal dilation may be required. The nurse should also help the parents understand that long-term follow-up throughout childhood may be necessary to establish normal bowel habits.

Chapter 28 Study Questions

1.   The nurse is caring for a newborn with a cleft lip. What nursing assessments are appropriate for this infant?

2.   Identify three priority nursing diagnoses for the infant with a cleft lip or cleft palate.

3.   The nurse is teaching the mother of an infant with a cleft lip how to feed the infant. What instructions should the nurse include in the teaching plan?

4.   Develop a nursing care plan outlining the postoperative care for an infant who has had a cleft lip repaired.

5.   Describe three of the seven identified expected outcomes for an infant with a cleft lip repair that indicate the nursing interventions have been effective.

6.   An infant is suspected of having biliary atresia. What clinical manifestations might the nurse expect to observe in the infant? What is the potential clinical outcome of biliary atresia?

7.   Describe a potentially fatal complication of Hirschsprung's disease. What clinical
        manifestations might indicate to the nurse that the infant is developing this
        complication of Hirschsprung's disease?

8.   Describe the nursing care plan of an infant who is postoperative the repair of an
        imperforate anus.

Answers to Chapter 28 Study Questions

1. Assessment of the cleft lip is accomplished by inspection of the child's facial features and palate. The nursing assessment is also focused on the emotional response of the parents to the child's defect. The nurse assesses the parents' acceptance of the infant and how they cope with the presence of the defect. The nutritional intake of the infant is affected by the presence of a cleft lip or cleft palate. Infants have difficulty creating enough pressure to successfully suck and take in enough nourishment. The nurse assesses the infant's ability to suck and the intake. Does the infant cough or choke when attempting to feed? Is formula escaping out the nose during feedings? How comfortable are the parents when attempting to feed the infant?

2. Three primary nursing diagnoses are as follows: altered nutrition, less than body requirements related to structural defects of the lip and/or palate; risk for altered parenting related to presence of facial deformity; pain related to surgical repair of defect.

3. The nurse should advise the mother that the infant will have a difficult time sucking, whether bottle-fed or breast-fed. Sometimes the formula or breast milk will return through the infant's nose instead of being swallowed, and choking can occur. Teach the mother to hold the infant in an upright position to facilitate feeding and decrease risk of choking. Special nipples are also available; the most successfully used nipples are those that are large, soft, and have larger holes. If the infant is breast-feeding, place the nipple well towards the back of the oral cavity. If the infant cannot suck on a nipple, various feeding devices, such as an Asepto syringe or medicine dropper, can be used, and the nurse should teach the mother how to use these devices. The infant should rest periodically throughout the feeding time. The mother should practice feeding the baby prior to discharge so that the mother is comfortable with the feeding process. These infants can swallow excess amounts of air so frequent burping is advised.

4. The nurse implements actions to prevent suture line trauma and infection following repair of the cleft lip. Soft restraints are applied to the infant's arms at the elbow to keep the infant from disrupting the incision. These restraints are removed at frequent intervals to permit range-of-motion and exercise, provide the infant with relief from the restriction, and to inspect the skin for signs of friction. The infant will resume feedings as soon as possible following recovery from the anesthetic. Clear liquids will be given initially, and the diet will be advanced as tolerated by the infant. After each feeding the suture line is cleansed with saline to prevent infection. It is important to keep the suture line intact, clean, and dry, to minimize infection and scarring. Analgesics are administered to promote comfort and decrease agitation.

5.   The effectiveness of nursing interventions for the child with cleft lip can be measured by the achievement of the following expected outcomes by the patient and family:

- Maintains adequate nutrition
- Verbalizes feelings related to infant's defect
- Demonstrates attitude of acceptance towards infant
- Expresses or displays behavior that indicates satisfactory pain control following surgery
- Avoids development of complications following surgery (suture line infection, aspiration, or skin irritation)
- Expresses understanding of the importance of follow-up care related to dental care, speech therapy, and plastic surgery
- Contacts community resources as appropriate for information and support

6.   The earliest indication of biliary atresia is jaundice. The infant may be born jaundiced or may develop it over the first two to three weeks of life. The sclera are affected first. Other clinical manifestations include dark yellow urine that stains the diapers and light-colored stools. The infant will be irritable and demonstrate poor weight gain and a failure to thrive. Pruritus causes the infant to be fussy. Eventually, abdominal distention, hepatomegaly, and splenomegaly will develop. Biliary atresia is usually fatal by the age of two if not treated. The cause of death is cirrhosis and hepatic failure. Even with surgical treatment, approximately 80 to 90 percent of the children require a liver transplant because of progressive cirrhosis.

7.   Enterocolitis is a potentially fatal complication of Hirschsprung's disease. There are three clinical manifestations that are extremely serious and likely indicate the onset of enterocolitis: fever, watery diarrhea that is explosive, and severe prostration. These signs must be immediately treated before the bowel perforates and peritonitis and shock develop.

8.   Postoperatively, the nurse prevents infection and promotes healing. The rectal area is kept clean with frequent perineal care. If the infant is frequently experiencing loose stools, a protective skin ointment, such as zinc oxide, is applied to prevent skin irritation. The child is positioned in a side-lying or prone position to keep pressure off of the perineal incision.

Immediately following surgery, the infant may require a nasogastric tube until peristalsis returns, and IV fluids are administered until feedings are resumed. The nurse educates the parents about home management of the infant's care. The mother is encouraged to breast-feed to prevent constipation. Long-term care considerations as the infant ages includes bowel training and diet modification to include fiber. Stool softeners and occasional laxatives may be prescribed. The nurse emphasizes the importance of monitoring the infant's bowel movements, including the size and shape of the stool. The nurse helps the parents understand that long-term care throughout childhood may be necessary to establish normal bowel habits.

Chapter 29: Nursing Care for Congenital and Genetic Genitourinary Disorders

Key Terms

Epispadias
Exstrophy of the bladder
Hydrocele
Hypospadias
Polycystic kidney disease

Introduction

It is estimated that congenital disorders cause structural abnormalities of the genitourinary system that affect about 10 to 15 percent of the population. Some of these conditions are relatively mild, while others can be life threatening. This chapter will focus on nursing care related to the following congenital genitourinary disorders: polycystic kidney disease, hydrocele, hypospadias and epispadias, and exstrophy of the bladder.

Polycystic Kidney Disease

Polycystic kidney disease is a form of renal cystic disorder in which multiple cysts develop within the kidney. It is the most common renal cystic disorder, affecting about 200,000–400,000 individuals in the United States. It is a genetic disorder with an **autosomal dominant trait**. Polycystic kidney disease may be diagnosed prenatally, at birth, or it can remain undiagnosed until sometime in adulthood. Males and females are equally affected by the disorder. The cause is unknown.

Pathophysiology

Polycystic kidney disease most commonly affects both kidneys. Fluid-filled cysts grow in the renal tissue, eventually applying pressure to surrounding tissue and causing ischemia. The renal tubules become obstructed by the growing cysts. The disease is progressive and leads to the development of hypertension, repeated urinary tract infections, and eventually end-stage chronic renal failure. Renal failure typically develops when patients reach their forties or fifties. Patients may experience cysts in other organs as well, including the liver, pancreas, and spleen. Patients may also have cerebral or abdominal aortic aneurysms.

Clinical Manifestations

As the kidneys grow progressively larger, the patient begins to experience abdominal or lumbar pain. The pain may be dull or sharp. Palpable renal masses may be present.

Hematuria may also develop as a result of rupturing cysts that bleed into the renal pelvis. The cysts can become infected leading to kidney infections and urinary tract infections. Hypertension develops and can be difficult to control.

Diagnostic Tests

Polycystic kidney disease is diagnosed with the use of intravenous pyelography or CT scan. Additional laboratory tests will include urine analysis, BUN, serum creatinine, and creatinine clearance tests to determine renal functioning.

Medical Management

There is no cure or specific treatment for polycystic kidney disease. The goal of treatment is to preserve renal function as long as possible and to relieve discomfort. Important aspects of medical management include aggressive treatment of hypertension and prevention or early treatment of infections.

Nursing Care of the Patient with Polycystic Kidney Disease

Nursing care is primarily supportive and focused on patient education. The patient is instructed to be alert for signs of hemorrhage and infection, and to promptly report both. While physical activity does not need to be hampered until end-stage renal disease occurs, patients are cautioned to avoid contact sports or jobs that may predispose them to renal trauma. These precautions decrease the chances of cystic rupture and hemorrhage. Even seat belts can cause rupture and should be carefully positioned so that the belts are not too tight across the abdomen.

The nurse must also reinforce the necessity of being compliant with taking prescribed antihypertensive drugs to control hypertension. If hypertension is not controlled, it can exacerbate the rate of renal destruction. The nurse must also instruct the patient on the potential complications related to the disorder and the likely outcome. **Dialysis** will be implemented when renal failure becomes severe enough.

Another important nursing intervention is encouraging the patient to seek genetic counseling. An individual with polycystic kidney disease has a 50/50 chance of having children who will inherit the gene. While genetic counseling is important, it is also true that many individuals with polycystic kidney disease have already had children before they are diagnosed with the disorder. Then the question is whether or not the young person should be screened for the disease. There is no effective treatment to stop the disease progression; early diagnosis of disorder may impact the individual's ability to acquire health insurance or employment, while not making any difference in the ultimate outcome of the disease. These factors must be carefully considered. The nurse can help the family to consider the implications of the disease and make appropriate decisions for their specific situation.

External Structural Abnormalities of the Genitourinary System

There are a variety of congenital external structural abnormalities that can occur in the genitourinary system. While some of the conditions are minor and do not require treatment, others can be life threatening and may require extensive surgery.

Hydroceles, Hypospadias, and Epispadias

Hydroceles, hypospadias, and epispadias are examples of structural abnormalities that affect the male's genitalia. A **hydrocele** is a collection of fluid in the scrotum that can affect a male of any age. It can be diagnosed by its quality of transillumination—a light shined on the scrotum will be transmitted through the fluid. If the condition is mild with no discomfort, treatment is not required. Surgery is usually not performed on infants until the infant is over one year of age, as some hydroceles can resolve spontaneously. If the hydrocele is large, causes discomfort, or compromises the circulation to the testicles, surgery can be performed to resect the hydrocele. Recovery is rapid following surgery. The patient may be given an athletic supporter to provide support and comfort as healing occurs.

Hypospadias and epispadias are two forms of congenital defects where the urethral opening is not located at the tip of the penis. Instead, in **hypospadias** the urethral opening is located on the ventral, or underside, of the penis. With **epispadias**, the urethral opening is located on the dorsal surface of the penis. In both conditions, surgery will be performed while the child is very young to correct the disorder. The type of surgery used will vary depending upon the extent of the structural defect; in addition to relocating the urethral opening, surgery may be necessary to improve the appearance of the genitalia, dilate and/or lengthen the urethra, or reconstruct the bladder neck.

Exstrophy of the Bladder

Exstrophy of the bladder is a rare congenital condition where the bladder is everted (turned inside out) and exposed through the outer abdominal wall. It occurs more commonly in males. Correction of exstrophy involves a series of staged reconstructions where the bladder is surgically corrected and the abdominal wall is closed. The urethra and genitalia require reconstructive work as well to improve bladder function, appearance, and sexual functioning. As the child ages and the bladder grows in size, surgery will be performed to ensure urinary continence. The surgery performed will be individualized to each child, based upon the extent of the defect.

When caring for a child who needs corrective genitourinary surgery, the nurse needs to be particularly concerned about the psychological implications related to the surgery. Surgery involving the genitalia can be very frightening to children, especially in the three- to six-year-old age group. This age group, as a normal developmental task, displays a strong interest in the genital area and sexual differences. They are easily frightened by anything that may threaten the functioning of this area. Children may fear castration or feel they are being punished for bad behavior or bad thoughts. Body mutilation is another common fear. The child's body image is threatened.

The earlier in life the defects are corrected, the more likely the child is to develop a positive body image. Most reconstructive surgery will be performed as early as possible (between six and eighteen months) to minimize the psychological fears and concerns. However, some staged reconstructive surgeries may require a period of years to complete, or the surgeon may need to wait for the bladder or other structures to grow in size before attempting corrective surgery.

It is very important for all care providers to be sensitive to these potential fears and to address them with the child and the parents. The child should be reassured that he or she has done nothing "bad" to cause the need for the surgery. The nurse plays an important role in educating the parents and others who interact with the child on how to respond to the child's concerns and how to foster a positive body image.

Most reconstructive surgery is quite successful. For the more extensive defects, such as exstrophy of the bladder, there are support groups that the parents and child can be referred to for further information. Professional counseling may also be indicated for the parents and the child.

Chapter 29 Study Questions

1.   A patient has been diagnosed with polycystic kidney disease. What clinical manifestations would the patient most likely exhibit?

2.   Describe the priority nursing interventions the nurse would implement for a patient with polycystic kidney disease.

3.   The nurse is caring for a four-year-old boy who is scheduled to have reconstructive genitourinary surgery. What is the nurse's primary concern for the patient at this time?

Answers to Chapter 29 Study Questions

1.   As the kidneys grow progressively larger in polycystic kidney disease, the patient begins to experience abdominal or lumbar pain. The pain may be dull or sharp. Palpable renal masses may be present. Hematuria may also develop. The patient can also have kidney infections and urinary tract infections. Hypertension develops and later in the disease, renal failure occurs.

2.   Nursing care for the patient with polycystic kidney disease is supportive and focused on patient education. The patient is instructed to be alert for, and report, signs of hemorrhage and infection. Patients are cautioned to avoid activities that predispose the patient to renal trauma. The nurse must also reinforce the need to take prescribed antihypertensive drugs. The nurse instructs the patient on potential complications related to the disorder and likely outcome. Dialysis is implemented when renal failure progresses. Another important nursing intervention is encouraging the patient to seek genetic counseling.

3.   When caring for a child who needs corrective genitourinary surgery, the nurse is particularly concerned about the psychological implications related to the surgery. Surgery involving the genitalia can be very frightening to four-year-olds. Children may fear castration or feel they are being punished for bad behavior or bad thoughts. Body mutilation is another common fear.

REFERENCES

Black, J. M. and Matassarin-Jacobs, E. 1997. *Medical-surgical nursing: Clinical management for continuity of care.* 5th ed. Philadelphia: W.B. Saunders Company.

Carpenito, L. J. 1995. *Nursing care plans and documentation: Using diagnoses and collaborative problems.* 2nd ed. Philadelphia: Lippincott

Dudek, S. G. 1997. *Nutrition handbook for nursing practice.* 3rd ed. Philadelphia: Lippincott.

Eisenhauer, L. A., L. W. Nichols, R. T. Spencer, and F. W. Bergan. 1998. *Clinical pharmacology and nursing management.* 5th ed. Philadelphia: Lippincott.

Fischbach, F. 1996. *A manual of laboratory and diagnostic tests.* 5th ed. Philadelphia: Lippincott.

Lewis, S., M. Heitkemper, and S. Dirksen. 2000. *Medical-surgical nursing: Assessment and management of clinical problems.* 5th ed. St. Louis: Mosby.

Lippincott's Nursing Drug Guide. 2000. Philadelphia: Lippincott.

McKenry, L. M. and E. Salerno. 1995. *Mosby's pharmacology in nursing.* 19th ed. St.Louis: Mosby.

Monahan, F. D. and Neighbors, M. 1998. *Medical-surgical nursing: Foundations for clinical practice.* 2nd ed. Philadelphia: W.B. Saunders Company.

Olds, S. B., M. L. London, and P. A. Ladewig. 2000. *Maternal newborn nursing: A family and community-based approach.* 6th ed. New Jersey: Prentice Hall Health.

Phipps, W. J., J. K. Sands, and J. F. Marek. 1999. *Medical-surgical nursing: Concepts and clinical practice.* 6th ed. St. Louis: Mosby.

Smeltzer, S. C. and B. G. Bare. 2000. *Textbook of medical-surgical nursing.* 9th ed. Philadelphia: Lippincott.

Wong, D. L., M. Hockenberry-Eaton, D. Wilson, M. L. Winkelstein, and P. Schwartz. 2001. *Wong's essentials of pediatric nursing.* 6th ed. St. Louis: Mosby.

PRACTICE EXAMINATION

Located at the end of this exam, you will find two sets of answer sheets to use for the Practice Examination. Use these sheets to take the Practice Examination. Then compare your answers to the Practice Examination Answer Key.

1. Which of the following activities represents the most significant lifestyle change individuals can make to reduce their risk of cancer?

    a. Decrease fat in diet
    b. Avoid cigarette smoking
    c. Increase intake of vitamin E
    d. Avoid sun exposure

2. Which of the following diets has been associated with an increased risk of colon cancer?

    a. High-protein diet
    b. High-fiber diet
    c. High alcohol intake
    d. High-fat diet

3. Which of the following sexual practices places a woman at a higher risk for developing cancer of the cervix?

    a. Using birth control pills
    b. Douching after sexual intercourse
    c. Engaging in sexual intercourse at age sixteen
    d. Having sexual intercourse with an uncircumcised male

4. The nurse is caring for a patient who has been diagnosed with Hodgkin's disease. A diagnosis of Hodgkin's disease is based upon

    a. reoccurring episodes of night sweats, fatigue, and weakness.
    b. lymphadenopathy and thrombocytopenia.
    c. history of exposure to environmental toxins.
    d. detection of Reed-Sternberg cells in lymph node tissue.

5. Which of the following cancers is the leading cause of death in women?

    a. Lung
    b. Breast
    c. Colon
    d. Liver

6.   Which of the following is a characteristic of benign neoplasms?

    a.   They proliferate rapidly.
    b.   They are poorly differentiated.
    c.   They frequently reoccur after removal.
    d.   They grow by expansion.

7.   Which of the following signs and symptoms is a systemic clinical manifestation of a malignant neoplasm?

    a.   Cachexia
    b.   Slurred speech
    c.   Hemoptysis
    d.   Intestinal obstruction

8.   The most common site for metastatic cancer to develop is in the

    a.   colon.
    b.   liver.
    c.   brain.
    d.   bone.

9.   A ten-year-old boy has been diagnosed with osteogenic sarcoma. The body organ that is the primary site of metastasis for osteogenic sarcoma is the

    a.   liver.
    b.   brain.
    c.   lung.
    d.   colon.

10.   Which of the following statements indicates the patient has understood the nurse's instructions about breast self-examination?

    a.   "I will examine my breasts each month after my menstrual period."
    b.   "While I am taking birth control pills, it is not necessary for me to examine my breasts."
    c.   "I should begin doing monthly self-examinations after I reach my fortieth birthday."
    d.   "Breast self-examination is only effective for women with small breasts."

11.   Which of the following signs or symptoms may be an early warning sign of cancer?

       a.   Pain
       b.   Weight loss
       c.   Unusual discharge
       d.   Cachexia

12.   Which of the following surgical procedures would be an example of a palliative surgery for a patient with cancer?

       a.   A surgical biopsy of a breast tumor
       b.   An insertion of a gastrostomy tube in a patient with esophageal cancer
       c.   A resection of a rectal tumor with the creation of a colostomy
       d.   An exploratory laparotomy with removal of lymph nodes

13.   Which of the following factors would be most important for the nurse to assess prior to surgery for the removal of a malignant tumor?

       a.   Bowel pattern
       b.   Spiritual beliefs
       c.   Activity level
       d.   Nutritional status

14.   A young girl with leukemia is being closely monitored by the nurse for evidence of bleeding. Which of the following laboratory findings would indicate that she is at risk for bleeding?

       a.   Thrombocytopenia
       b.   Leukopenia
       c.   Decreased hematocrit
       d.   Hypercalcemia

15.   An infant has been admitted to the hospital with a history of vomiting related to pyloric stenosis. Which electrolyte imbalance would the nurse anticipate the infant developing as a result of the vomiting?

       a.   Hypernatremia
       b.   Hypokalemia
       c.   Hypocalcemia
       d.   Hypermagnesemia

16.   Which acid-base imbalance is the infant with pyloric stenosis susceptible to developing due to persistent vomiting?

    a.   Respiratory acidosis
    b.   Respiratory alkalosis
    c.   Metabolic acidosis
    d.   Metabolic alkalosis

17.   A patient who is suspected of having lung cancer has a bronchoscopy. Which of the following nursing interventions would be most appropriate after the bronchoscopy?

    a.   Maintain the patient in a supine position.
    b.   Place the patient on NPO status until the gag reflex returns.
    c.   Administer an intermittent positive pressure breathing (IPPB) treatment.
    d.   Provide an analgesic for chest discomfort.

18.   What is the most common sign or symptom associated with cancer of the bladder?

    a.   Dysuria
    b.   Recurrent urinary tract infections
    c.   Painless hematuria
    d.   Urinary retention

19.   Which of the following is a risk factor for the development of breast cancer?

    a.   Not having children
    b.   Delayed onset of menstruation
    c.   Early onset of menopause
    d.   Ingestion of caffeine

20.   Which of the following is an important principle to managing pain related to cancer? The nurse should

    a.   individualize the pain medication therapy as guided by the patient's goals.
    b.   choose medications that will not lead to drug addiction.
    c.   administer pain medication as soon as the patient requests it.
    d.   alter pain medications occasionally to prevent the development of drug tolerance.

21. Which of the following is most likely to be a chief complaint of a patient with anemia?

    a. Fatigue
    b. Vertigo
    c. Sore gums
    d. Pale, dry skin

22. A patient with anemia is taking an iron supplement. Which of the following instructions about taking iron is correct?

    a. "Take the iron supplement before you go to bed."
    b. "Take the iron supplement with milk to decrease gastric irritation."
    c. "Iron supplements should be taken with food."
    d. "Iron supplements are best absorbed when taken with orange juice."

23. A patient is scheduled for an autologous bone marrow transplant. The nurse understands that in an autologous transplant, the bone marrow comes from

    a. an organ donor.
    b. a member of the patient's family.
    c. the patient.
    d. the growth of stem cells.

24. Which of the following signs or symptoms is indicative of thrombocytopenia in a patient receiving chemotherapy?

    a. Fatigue
    b. Elevated temperature
    c. Dyspnea
    d. Bleeding gums

25. Which of the following signs or symptoms would most likely be exhibited by a patient with Hodgkin's disease?

    a. Tachypnea
    b. Night sweats
    c. Chest pain
    d. Painful lymphadenopathy

26. A significant adverse side effect of chemotherapy is

    a. alopecia.
    b. bone marrow suppression.
    c. stomatitis.
    d. nausea and vomiting.

27.   When caring for a patient with a radiation implant, the nurse should implement which of the following activities to reduce self-exposure to the radiation?

    a.   Limit patient contact to twenty minutes per day.
    b.   Wear a lead shield apron when providing care.
    c.   Remain eight feet away from the patient.
    d.   Avoid direct contact with the patient's skin.

28.   What is the primary purpose of biotherapy?

    a.   Decrease side effects related to chemotherapy
    b.   Inhibit the development of immunosuppression
    c.   Manipulate the immune system's response to malignant cells
    d.   Prevent metastasis of malignant cells

29.   The nurse should instruct the patient who is undergoing radiation therapy to anticipate which one of the following side effects?

    a.   Headaches
    b.   Low-grade fever
    c.   Persistent diarrhea
    d.   Fatigue

30.   A patient who is receiving radiation therapy asks the nurse how to care for the skin area that is receiving radiation. Which of the following instructions would be appropriate for the nurse to give the patient?

    a.   Apply petroleum ointment to the affected skin area.
    b.   Keep the area dry.
    c.   Use antibacterial soap to cleanse the area.
    d.   Apply a heating pad if inflammation occurs.

31.   Which of the following signs or symptoms is an early indication of hypoxia?

    a.   Cyanosis
    b.   Restlessness
    c.   Shortness of breath
    d.   Circumoral pallor

32.   Which of the following diagnostic studies would most likely be used to diagnose a pulmonary embolism?

    a.   Thoracentesis
    b.   Bronchoscopy
    c.   Pulmonary function tests
    d.   Lung scan

33.   Which of the following signs or symptoms is the most common early indication of laryngeal cancer?

    a.   Sore throat
    b.   Difficulty swallowing
    c.   Hoarseness
    d.   Persistent cough

34.   Which of the following nursing interventions would be most appropriate in the immediate postoperative period following a laryngectomy?

    a.   Place the patient in a semi-Fowler's position.
    b.   Administer oxygen per nasal cannula.
    c.   Encourage intake of clear liquids.
    d.   Change pressure dressing as needed.

35.   Which of the following clinical manifestations would the nurse most likely expect to find in a patient with iron-deficiency anemia?

    a.   Jaundice
    b.   Beefy red tongue
    c.   Nausea
    d.   Bruising tendencies

36.   Which of the following would be a potential complication of polycythemia vera?

    a.   Respiratory failure
    b.   Coronary artery disease
    c.   Pernicious anemia
    d.   Thrombosis

37.   Which of the following would be a priority goal for the nursing care of a patient who has developed sickle cell crisis?

    a.   Encourage activity.
    b.   Restrict fluid intake.
    c.   Control pain.
    d.   Administer iron supplements.

38.   How should the nurse position the patient who is about to have a thoracentesis?

    a.   Sitting with elbows and head supported on bedside table
    b.   Prone position with arms extended over head
    c.   Lateral position with knees flexed
    d.   Semi-Fowler's position with legs extended

39.   Which of the following assessments would the nurse expect to find in a patient
        with emphysema?

        a.   Tracheal deviation
        b.   Pleural friction rub
        c.   Asymmetrical chest expansion
        d.   Enlarged anteroposterior chest diameter

40.   The nurse auscultates the patient's lungs and hears high-pitched sounds during
        inspiration. How would the nurse best describe this finding?

        a.   Rhonchi
        b.   Crackles
        c.   Inspiratory wheezes
        d.   Pleural friction rub

41.   Which of the following actions would demonstrate the correct technique for the
        nurse to use when suctioning a patient who has a tracheostomy?

        a.   Instruct patient to cough after suctioning.
        b.   Perform the procedure with clean technique.
        c.   Apply suction for no longer than ten seconds.
        d.   Apply suction while inserting catheter into stoma.

42.   A patient has been diagnosed with laryngeal cancer and is undergoing radiation
        therapy. Which of the following nursing interventions should be incorporated
        into the patient's care plan to minimize side effects?

        a.   Eliminate milk products from the patient's diet.
        b.   Provide frequent oral hygiene.
        c.   Tell the patient to avoid eating two hours before the radiation treatment.
        d.   Gargle with warm saltwater daily.

43.   When caring for a patient with bacterial pneumonia, the nurse notes that the
        patient's lips are cyanotic. The nurse understands that cyanosis is due to

        a.   hyperventilation.
        b.   hypoxia.
        c.   atelectasis.
        d.   hypercapnia.

44.   A patient with pneumonia is complaining of chest pain when she coughs. Which of the following nursing measures would most likely decrease the chest pain?

    a.   Increase fluid intake to 3 liters/day.
    b.   Encourage deep breathing every two hours.
    c.   Administer antitussive cough medication PRN.
    d.   Assist the patient to splint her chest with a blanket.

45.   Which of the following would be an appropriate expected outcome for a patient recovering from pneumonia?

    a.   Arterial blood gas values are normal
    b.   Mild dyspnea when ambulating
    c.   A fluid intake of 1000 cc/24 hrs
    d.   Expectoration of small amounts of yellow sputum

46.   A patient with emphysema states he feels too tired to eat. He has lost five pounds since his last visit. Which of the following nursing diagnoses would be most appropriate for this patient?

    a.   Activity intolerance related to hypoxemia
    b.   Altered nutrition, less than body requirements related to fatigue
    c.   Ineffective breathing pattern related to fatigue
    d.   Ineffective therapeutic management related to lack of knowledge about disease

47.   Which of the following expected outcomes would be appropriate for the client with emphysema who is being discharged from the hospital? The patient

    a.   maintains fluid intake of 1000 cc/day.
    b.   has a normal chest X ray.
    c.   resumes activities as tolerated.
    d.   expresses relief from chest pain.

48.   Pursed-lip breathing is encouraged in patients with COPD primarily because it helps to

    a.   prolong inspiratory phase of respiratory cycle.
    b.   prevent the collapse of alveoli.
    c.   decrease loss of carbon dioxide.
    d.   prevent the development of respiratory infections.

49. Which of the following goals is a priority for a patient with emphysema?

    a. Decreasing amount of sputum
    b. Eliminating need for supplemental oxygen
    c. Seeking genetic counseling
    d. Conserving energy

50. The pulmonary function tests of a patient with emphysema are most likely to demonstrate a/an

    a. increased forced expiratory volume.
    b. decreased total lung capacity.
    c. decreased residual volume.
    d. increased total lung capacity.

51. A patient is taking furosemide (Lasix) for treatment of congestive heart failure. Which of these symptoms would indicate the patient is developing drug toxicity?

    a. Shortness of breath
    b. Tachycardia
    c. Difficulty hearing
    d. Headache

52. The nurse is developing a teaching plan for a patient who has been placed on captopril (Capoten). Which of the following instructions should the nurse include in the teaching plan?

    a. Increase dietary intake of potassium.
    b. Limit fluid intake to 1500 ml/day.
    c. Take pulse before each dose.
    d. Take the first dose at bedtime.

53. A patient has been admitted to the hospital with a diagnosis of right-sided heart failure. Which of the following signs and symptoms would the nurse expect to find as a result of this diagnosis?

    a. Hemoptysis
    b. Dependent edema
    c. Cough
    d. Bradycardia

54.   The nurse is caring for a patient who has COPD. The patient's arterial blood gas report has values of pH 7.30; $PaCO_2$ 55; HCO_3 26. These values indicate the patient has which of the following acid-base imbalances?

     a.   Respiratory acidosis
     b.   Respiratory alkalosis
     c.   Metabolic acidosis
     d.   Metabolic alkalosis

55.   A patient with diabetes mellitus is experiencing Kussmaul's respirations. Arterial blood gas values for this patient are pH 7.27; $PaCO_2$ 32; HCO_3 12. These assessment findings indicate the patient has which of the following acid-base imbalances?

     a.   Respiratory acidosis
     b.   Respiratory alkalosis
     c.   Metabolic acidosis
     d.   Metabolic alkalosis

56.   The nurse is caring for a patient who is in the immediate post-op period following a transurethral resection of the prostate (TURP). The patient's urethral catheter is draining bright red urine with numerous clots. Based upon this finding, the nurse should implement which of the following actions?

     a.   Reassess the bleeding in one hour.
     b.   Irrigate the catheter with sterile normal saline.
     c.   Take vital signs and notify the physician.
     d.   Increase the patient's IV flow rate.

57.   A patient is recovering from an abdominal hysterectomy for the treatment of cancer of the uterus. She is complaining of pain in her left calf. Which of the following additional assessments should the nurse perform at this time?

     a.   Flex the patient's foot to elicit calf pain.
     b.   Inspect the calf for redness.
     c.   Assess for internal rotation of the leg.
     d.   Have patient dangle legs to assess pedal pulses.

58.   A patient has been diagnosed with deep vein thrombosis. The nurse notes the patient is restless and anxious with an increased respiratory rate. How should the nurse respond to these findings?

     a.   Notify the physician.
     b.   Reassure the patient.
     c.   Administer a mild analgesic.
     d.   Assess reaction of pupils to light.

59.   Which of the following diets would be most appropriate for a patient with emphysema?

    a.   Low-fat, low-cholesterol diet
    b.   Bland, soft diet
    c.   Full liquid diet
    d.   High-carbohydrate, high-protein diet

60.   Which of the following effects would the nurse evaluate the patient for when administering theophylline to a patient with asthma?

    a.   Decrease in patient's fever
    b.   Increase in respiratory rate
    c.   Relaxation of bronchial airways
    d.   Thinning of tenacious secretions

61.   When teaching a patient with emphysema how to cough effectively, which of the following instructions should be included?

    a.   Lie supine, splint ribcage, breathe deeply, and cough.
    b.   Inhale slowly through the nose, then exhale while coughing with short repeated coughs.
    c.   Take three deep breaths and then cough forcefully.
    d.   Sit in Fowler's position, lean forward with arms extended, and cough.

62.   The nurse is assessing a patient who is experiencing an exacerbation of his asthma, and notes nasal flaring, use of accessory muscles, and greatly diminished lung sounds. What action would be most appropriate for the nurse to take?

    a.   Obtain pulse oximetry reading.
    b.   Administer oxygen at 2 liters/nasal cannula.
    c.   Initiate immediate intervention to provide respiratory support.
    d.   Draw blood for arterial blood gas values.

63.   Which of the following arterial blood gas results would the nurse anticipate in a patient who is having a prolonged severe asthma attack?

    a.   Increased $PaCO_2$, decreased PaO_2, and decreased pH
    b.   Decreased $PaCO_2$, decreased PaO_2, and decreased pH
    c.   Increased $PaCO_2$, increased PaO_2, and decreased pH
    d.   Decreased $PaCO_2$, increased PaO_2, and increased pH

64.   The nurse is caring for an elderly patient who is in a nursing home with a fractured hip. Which of the following signs or symptoms may indicate that the patient has developed pneumonia?

     a.   Bradypnea
     b.   Productive cough
     c.   Confusion
     d.   Chest pain

65.   The nurse is assessing a patient who has been diagnosed with pneumonia. Which of the following clinical findings would the nurse anticipate finding during the assessment?

     a.   Nasal flaring
     b.   Inspiratory wheezing
     c.   Diminished breath sounds
     d.   Hyperresonance upon percussion

66.   A patient who has chronic bronchitis is admitted to the hospital. Which one of the following sign and symptoms would be associated with his bronchitis?

     a.   Frequent coughing
     b.   Loss of weight
     c.   Vesicular breath sounds
     d.   Minimal sputum production

67.   A patient with emphysema is scheduled to have pulmonary function studies conducted. The nurse would anticipate which of the following reports from the studies?

     a.   Decreased vital capacity, decreased forced expiratory volume, decreased total lung capacity
     b.   Increased vital capacity, increased forced expiratory volume, increased total lung capacity
     c.   Increased vital capacity, decreased forced expiratory volume, decreased total lung capacity
     d.   Decreased vital capacity, decreased forced expiratory volume, increased total lung capacity

68.   The nurse is teaching pursed-lip breathing to a patient with emphysema. The patient asks why it is important for him to use pursed-lip breathing. What is the nurse's best response?

    a.   "You will require less oxygen if you breathe this way."
    b.   "Pursed-lip breathing helps to prolong your exhalation."
    c.   "This type of breathing helps to decrease sputum production."
    d.   "You will have less shortness of breath if you purse your lips."

69.   The nurse is developing a teaching plan for a patient who has been newly diagnosed with hypertension. Which of the following recommended lifestyle changes would be most appropriate for the nurse to include in the teaching plan?

    a.   Monitor the blood pressure twice a day.
    b.   Set a goal to lose thirty pounds in six months.
    c.   Incorporate aerobic exercise into daily routine.
    d.   Eliminate sodium from the diet.

70.   The nurse is listening to the lung sounds of a patient who has lung cancer and detects wheezing over the lung fields of one lung. The most likely cause of this assessment finding is that the

    a.   tumor is obstructing the airway of one lung.
    b.   patient's position is compromising respiratory function in that lung.
    c.   patient also has emphysema.
    d.   airways of the lung have filled with secretions.

71.   A patient who is receiving radiation therapy develops stomatitis. Which of the following interventions should the nurse include in the patient's care plan?

    a.   Rinse mouth with half-strength hydrogen peroxide every four hours.
    b.   Encourage the patient to drink hot liquids to soothe the tissues.
    c.   Floss the teeth after every meal.
    d.   Implement prophylactic antibiotic therapy.

72.   The patient is receiving radiation therapy to the thoracic area for treatment of lung cancer. How should the patient be instructed to care for the skin that is receiving radiation?

    a.   Apply ice packs to decrease discomfort from skin irritation.
    b.   Gently cleanse skin with lukewarm water.
    c.   Apply talcum powder after each treatment.
    d.   Keep skin covered with moist compresses between treatments.

73.   A patient with breast cancer is concerned about the side effects of chemotherapy and tells the nurse she is thinking about not taking the chemotherapy because she "doesn't want to get as sick as my friend did." How should the nurse best respond to the patient's concerns?

     a.   "You shouldn't worry about the side effects. It is more important that you concentrate on curing your cancer."
     b.   "Chemotherapy is the only sure way of treating breast cancer. You need to reconsider your decision and discuss your options with your physician."
     c.   "I understand how you feel. I am sure that I would have the same concerns that you do. Have you discussed your decision with your physician?"
     d.   "People respond differently to chemotherapy. We will monitor you closely and can give you medication to decrease your side effects."

74.   A patient is experiencing pain from metastatic bone cancer. What principles of pain management should the nurse consider when developing a care plan to manage the patient's pain?

     a.   The medication regimen should be individualized to the patient.
     b.   The nurse should select medications that will not cause addiction.
     c.   The medication regimen should keep the patient pain free.
     d.   The patient should not receive intravenous pain medication unless terminally ill.

75.   A patient who has been receiving radiation therapy is complaining of fatigue. The nurse's response to the patient's complaints is guided by the nurse's understanding that the fatigue is

     a.   a temporary problem that will resolve itself independent of nursing action.
     b.   an indication that the radiation therapy is not effectively treating the patient's cancer.
     c.   best treated by encouraging activity balanced with rest.
     d.   probably caused by an underlying health problem that requires treatment.

76.   The nurse is caring for a patient who has pernicious anemia. Which of the following statements about pernicious anemia is true? Pernicious anemia

     a.   is treated by increasing the dietary intake of foods high in vitamin B_{12}.
     b.   requires lifelong vitamin B_{12} injections to control the disorder.
     c.   is a genetic disorder for which there is no successful treatment.
     d.   is most common in women of childbearing age.

77.   The nurse is developing a community program for cancer prevention screening
       activities. Which of the following screening activities for detecting colon cancer
       should be recommended annually for low-risk individuals?

       a.   Fecal occult blood tests after age thirty
       b.   Digital rectal exams after age forty
       c.   Sigmoidoscopy after age fifty
       d.   CEA testing after age forty

78.   The nurse is caring for a patient whose skin has become dry and irritated
       following radiation therapy. How should the nurse instruct the patient to care for
       her skin?

       a.   Apply cortisone ointment to the irritated skin.
       b.   Use a hot water bottle to provide comfort.
       c.   Cleanse the skin gently with half-strength hydrogen peroxide.
       d.   Apply nonperfumed moisturizing lotion.

79.   The nurse is auscultating the lung sounds of a patient who has emphysema. The
       nurse would anticipate hearing which of the following adventitious breath
       sounds?

       a.   Rhonchi
       b.   Rales
       c.   Diminished breath sounds
       d.   Bronchovesicular

80.   A patient has a bronchoscopy with biopsy for the potential diagnosis of lung
       cancer. Nursing care following the procedure should include

       a.   monitoring the patient for signs of a pneumothorax.
       b.   encouraging the patient to use warm saltwater gargles.
       c.   administering anti-emetics as necessary.
       d.   administering oxygen at 3 liters/min per nasal cannula.

81.   Which of the following symptoms is the patient with benign prostatic hypertrophy
       most likely to report?

       a.   Sexual dysfunction
       b.   Urinary frequency
       c.   Back pain
       d.   Oliguria

82.   A patient who has had a transurethral resection of the prostate has a continuous bladder irrigation infusing. The purpose of the continuous bladder irrigation is to

   a.   prevent clots from obstructing the urethral catheter.
   b.   decrease the likelihood of postoperative hemorrhage.
   c.   prevent a bladder infection from developing.
   d.   maintain adequate fluid intake for the patient.

83.   A patient who is recovering from a TURP is complaining about dribbling urine ever since his Foley catheter was removed. The nurse notes the client has had 250 cc of urine output in the last eight hours with a 1000 mL intake. Which of the following actions would be appropriate for the nurse to take at this time?

   a.   Reinsert the Foley catheter.
   b.   Assess for bladder distention.
   c.   Obtain a urinalysis.
   d.   Encourage fluid intake to 2000 mL/day.

84.   Following a cystectomy with a creation of a urinary diversion, the patient is at risk for developing a urinary tract infection. Which of the following nursing interventions should be implemented to prevent a UTI?

   a.   Attach the urinary appliance to a leg bag at night.
   b.   Change the urinary appliance every day.
   c.   Encourage a daily fluid intake of 2500 mL to 3000 mL.
   d.   Change urinary appliance using sterile technique.

85.   A patient has been diagnosed with colon cancer and is scheduled to have an abdominal perineal resection with a colostomy. The patient's preoperative care would include which one of the following interventions?

   a.   Initiation of total parenteral nutrition
   b.   Insertion of a nasogastric tube
   c.   Measurement of the patient's abdominal girth
   d.   Administration of antibiotics

86.   Which of the following expected outcomes would be appropriate for a patient who is recovering from an abdominal perineal resection with a colostomy? The patient will

   a.   demonstrate how to change the colostomy pouch.
   b.   verbalize an understanding of the need to limit physical activity.
   c.   follow a low-residue, bland diet.
   d.   establish a colostomy irrigation schedule of every other day.

87.   The nurse is irrigating the patient's colostomy when he begins complaining of abdominal cramping. What should the nurse do in response to the patient's complaint?

    a.   Tell the patient to take deep breaths and continue to infuse the water.
    b.   Temporarily stop the flow of water until the cramping subsides.
    c.   Stop the irrigation and help the patient to the toilet.
    d.   Place the patient in a supine position and continue the irrigation.

88.   A patient has been admitted to the hospital with a deep vein thrombosis in her left leg. Which of the following nursing actions would be most appropriate for this patient's care?

    a.   Assist the patient with passive range of motion exercises in the lower extremities every shift.
    b.   Ambulate the patient to a bedside chair three times a day.
    c.   Keep the patient on bed rest with the left leg elevated.
    d.   Dangle the patient at the bedside hourly during waking hours.

89.   A patient has been diagnosed with peripheral vascular disease related to arterial insufficiency. Which of the following nursing interventions would be appropriate for achieving the goal of promoting peripheral circulation?

    a.   Position the lower extremities in a position of slight dependency.
    b.   Place a heating pad on low setting and apply to calves.
    c.   Encourage patient to sit with legs elevated on a stool.
    d.   Apply anti-embolic stockings.

90.   The nurse has instructed a patient who has been diagnosed with iron-deficiency anemia to eat foods high in iron. Which of the following foods should be included in this patient's diet?

    a.   Oranges
    b.   Cottage cheese
    c.   Chicken
    d.   Spinach

91.   A patient with iron-deficiency anemia is taking liquid iron supplements. Which of the following statements would indicate to the nurse that the patient understands how to take this drug correctly?

    a.   "If I develop diarrhea, I should stop taking the iron supplement."
    b.   "Iron can stain my teeth, so I should dilute it and drink it with a straw."
    c.   "Taking the iron with a glass of milk will increase its absorption."
    d.   "I should take the iron after my meals."

92.   The nurse is conducting an assessment of a patient's respiratory status. When evaluating the patient's lung sounds, which of the following breath sounds would the nurse expect to find over the patient's lung fields?

     a.   Bronchial
     b.   Tracheal
     c.   Vesicular
     d.   Bronchovesicular

93.   The nurse is caring for a patient who has pneumonia and impaired gas exchange. What is the most effective means of determining the patient's need for oxygen therapy?

     a.   Assessing the patient's level of dyspnea
     b.   Asking the patient if he feels comfortable
     c.   Evaluating the color of the patient's oral mucous membranes
     d.   Obtaining pulse oximeter readings to determine oxygen saturation

94.   A patient who has congestive heart failure is very restless and dyspneic. Which of the following medications would the nurse choose to administer to decrease the heart's workload and oxygen consumption, as well as decrease the patient's restlessness?

     a.   Morphine sulfate
     b.   Demerol (Meperidine)
     c.   Aminophylline
     d.   Diazepam (Valium)

95.   A patient with congestive heart failure has developed edema in both extremities. Based upon this finding, which of the following nursing diagnoses would be appropriate for this patient?

     a.   Inadequate tissue perfusion related to decreased cardiac output
     b.   Potential for impaired tissue integrity related to edema
     c.   Fluid volume excess related to decreased peripheral circulation
     d.   Ineffective management of treatment regimen related to inadequate pharmacological therapy

96.   Spironolactone (Aldactone) has been prescribed for a patient who has hypertension. Which of the following instructions should the nurse teach the patient about taking this drug?

     a.   Limit fluid intake to 1000 mL/day.
     b.   Restrict sodium intake to 2 gm/day.
     c.   Eliminate cheese from the diet.
     d.   Do not eat potassium-rich foods.

97.   A patient has been given a prescription for nitroglycerin to be taken during episodes of angina. What is an expected side effect of nitroglycerin?

   a.   Hypertension
   b.   Dyspnea
   c.   Diarrhea
   d.   Headache

98.   Which of the following methods indicates that the nurse is using the appropriate technique to apply nitroglycerin topical ointment? The nurse

   a.   wears clean gloves while applying the ointment.
   b.   applies the ointment directly from the tube to the patient's skin.
   c.   applies the new application on top of the previous application of ointment.
   d.   takes the patient's apical heart rate prior to application of the ointment.

99.   A patient is taking beclomethasone (Vanceril) inhalant for treatment of her asthma. The nurse should teach the patient that a potential side effect of this drug is

   a.   hirsutism.
   b.   gingival hyperplasia.
   c.   oral thrush.
   d.   aplastic anemia.

100.   Which of the following is an appropriate nursing action before administering digoxin (Lanoxin)?

   a.   Take the patient's blood pressure.
   b.   Assess apical heart rate for one minute.
   c.   Check the patient's prothrombin time.
   d.   Assess for the presence of chest pain.

101.   The nurse should monitor which one of the following laboratory tests when caring for a patient who is receiving heparin therapy?

   a.   Activated partial thromboplastin time (APTT)
   b.   Complete blood count (CBC)
   c.   Prothrombin time (PT)
   d.   Platelet count

102. The nurse is teaching a patient about the potential side effects of verapamil
      (Calan). Which of the following instructions would be correct?

      a.   "Take verapamil with your meals to prevent heartburn."
      b.   "To prevent constipation, you should eat a low-fiber diet."
      c.   "Take your pulse every day and report any irregular heart beats."
      d.   "Visual disturbances may indicate toxic levels of verapamil."

103. Which one of the following clinical manifestations would the nurse most likely
      find in a patient who is in the compensatory stage of shock?

      a.   Oliguria
      b.   Tachypnea
      c.   Profound hypotension
      d.   Weak peripheral pulses

104. The nurse is administering an initial dose of intravenous penicillin when the
      patient begins to have difficulty breathing. The nurse understands that the patient
      is developing

      a.   hypovolemic shock.
      b.   cardiogenic shock.
      c.   septic shock.
      d.   anaphylactic shock.

105. The primary goal of pharmacological therapy in the treatment of shock is to

      a.   prevent renal ischemia.
      b.   increase cerebral perfusion.
      c.   restore adequate tissue perfusion.
      d.   promote vasoconstriction.

106. Which one of the following clinical manifestations would the nurse most likely
      find in a patient who is in the progressive stage of shock?

      a.   Confusion
      b.   Narrowing of pulse pressure
      c.   Bradycardia
      d.   Cheyne-Stokes respirations

107. What pathophysiological disruption occurs in the vascular system to lead to the development of distributive shock?

    a.   There is a decrease in the amount of circulating blood.
    b.   An alteration in vascular tone causes vasodilation.
    c.   The heart loses its ability to pump effectively.
    d.   Massive vasoconstriction decreases tissue perfusion.

108. A patient who had a transurethral resection of the prostate tells the nurse that he feels an urge to void even though he has a urethral catheter inserted. What should be the nurse's first action?

    a.   Administer pain medication.
    b.   Increase the continuous bladder irrigation flow.
    c.   Encourage the patient to relax.
    d.   Assess the patency of the catheter.

109. The nurse is assessing a dark-skinned patient for cyanosis. Where is cyanosis most likely to be noticed in dark-skinned patients?

    a.   Conjunctivae
    b.   Nail beds
    c.   Ear lobes
    d.   Around the mouth

110. What would be the primary goal of care in a patient with a new tracheostomy as a result of surgery for laryngeal cancer?

    a.   Control pain.
    b.   Reduce anxiety.
    c.   Maintain a patent airway.
    d.   Prevent respiratory infection.

111. Which of the following patients would the nurse most likely encourage to receive the influenza and pneumococcal vaccination?

    a.   Sixty-year-old woman with osteoarthritis
    b.   Ten-year-old boy with allergies
    c.   Forty-five-year-old woman with multiple sclerosis
    d.   Thirty-year-old man who smokes

112.   The nurse should anticipate which of the following treatments in a patient who
has been diagnosed with adult respiratory distress syndrome?

   a.   Oxygen therapy delivered via Venturi mask
   b.   Administration of high dose corticosteroids
   c.   Anticoagulant therapy
   d.   Intubation and mechanical ventilation

113.   Which assessment would be most appropriate for the nurse to make to help
determine if an endotracheal tube is correctly positioned in a patient who is on a
mechanical ventilator? The nurse would assess

   a.   respiratory rate and rhythm.
   b.   ease of suctioning patient.
   c.   lung sounds bilaterally.
   d.   pulse oximeter readings.

114.   The nurse is caring for a patient with ARDS and has established a nursing
diagnosis of ineffective airway clearance related to fatigue. Which of the
following nursing interventions will be most effective in promoting effective
airway clearance for this patient?

   a.   Encouraging the patient to drink 3000 mL/day
   b.   Suctioning the patient if cough is ineffective
   c.   Administering morphine to facilitate rest
   d.   Increasing oxygen flow rate to 4 L/min per nasal cannula

115.   The nurse is caring for a patient who experienced multiple traumas in a motor
vehicle accident. Which of the following signs and symptoms is an early
indication that the patient is developing ARDS?

   a.   Auscultation of lung sounds reveals bilateral wheezing.
   b.   Patient appears lethargic and slow to respond to commands.
   c.   Respirations are irregular, deep, and rapid.
   d.   Oxygen therapy does not relieve the patient's hypoxemia.

116.   A patient's ABG values are pH 7.48; PaO_2, 50 mm Hg; $PaCO_2$, 30 mm Hg;
HCO_3^-, 26 mEq/L. The nurse should be most concerned about which value?

   a. PaO_2
   b. $PaCO_2$
   c. HCO_3^-
   d.   pH

117.   The chest X ray of a patient who was diagnosed with a pneumothorax indicates the patient's lung has re-expanded and the chest tube can be removed. How should the nurse be prepared to immediately care for the wound upon removal of the chest tube?

    a.   Apply petrolatum gauze to wound, cover with dressing, and secure with tape.
    b.   Apply pressure for five minutes and then cover with a sterile 4 × 4.
    c.   Cover wound with steri-strips and instruct patient to keep area dry.
    d.   Cleanse area with normal saline, apply Neosporin ointment and a Band-Aid.

118.   The nurse is assessing the chest tube drainage system of a patient who is recovering from lung surgery due to cancer. The nurse notes fluid fluctuation in the water-seal chamber as the patient breathes. What should the nurse's action be in response to this finding?

    a.   Check the tubing of the drainage system for an air leak.
    b.   Notify surgeon immediately, as it indicates the patient is developing a tension pneumothorax.
    c.   This is a normal finding, and the drainage system is functioning correctly.
    d.   Investigate the tubing for kinks, loops, or obstructions to flow of drainage.

119.   A patient who has been in a motorcycle accident is admitted to the emergency room complaining of difficulty breathing. Upon listening to the patient's lung sounds, which one of the following findings would suggest to the nurse that the patient has developed a pneumothorax?

    a.   Unilateral inspiratory and expiratory wheezing in the right lung fields.
    b.   Absence of breath sounds over the right lung fields.
    c.   Profuse crackles throughout both lungs.
    d.   Pleural friction rub detected over the right lung.

120.   The nurse is caring for a patient who has a chest tube drainage system in place. Which of the following nursing interventions would be appropriate to include in the patient's plan of care?

    a.   Milk the chest tubes every shift to promote drainage.
    b.   Clamp the chest tubes when turning and repositioning the patient.
    c.   Empty collected drainage from the drainage chamber every eight hours.
    d.   Keep drainage system apparatus below patient's waist level when ambulating.

121. The nurse notices that the fluid level has stopped fluctuating in a patient's chest tube water seal chamber. The patient's respirations are 16/min and unlabored. What does this finding most likely indicate to the nurse?

    a.   The patient's lung has re-expanded.
    b.   The drainage tube has become obstructed with a clot.
    c.   The water level in the system is low, and more water should be added.
    d.   The patient's lung has started to re-collapse.

122. The nurse is caring for a ten-year-old boy who has experienced an exacerbation of his asthma. Which of the following instructions should be incorporated into the child's discharge plan as he prepares to return home?

    a.   Limit activities to walking.
    b.   Sleep at night with head of bed elevated.
    c.   Use the peak flow meter to monitor respiratory status.
    d.   Eliminate milk products from diet.

123. A patient is using albuterol (Proventil) for treatment of her asthma. Which of the following signs and symptoms is a side effect associated with the use of albuterol?

    a.   Drowsiness
    b.   Tachycardia
    c.   Hypotension
    d.   Headache

124. Metaproterenol (Alupent) and triamcinolone acetonide (Azmacort) metered dose inhalers have been prescribed for the control of a patient's asthma. What instructions should the nurse incorporate into his teaching plan about the administration of these medications?

    a.   The medications are incompatible and should be taken at separate times.
    b.   The patient should rinse his mouth with water after using the Alupent.
    c.   Azmacort is for short-term use only and should be used sparingly.
    d.   The Alupent inhaler should be used before the Azmacort inhaler.

125. Which of the following assessment findings are indicative of right-sided heart failure in a patient with a long history of COPD?

    a.   Dependent edema
    b.   Orthopnea
    c.   Hemoptysis
    d.   Hypertension

126.   The nurse is caring for a patient who is suspected of having an acute myocardial infarction. An initial priority nursing intervention for this patient is to

    a.   initiate oxygen therapy per nasal cannula.
    b.   obtain a stat EKG.
    c.   place the patient in a supine position.
    d.   administer morphine sulfate.

127.   A patient who is experiencing a myocardial infarction is being treated with streptokinase. The nurse understands that the primary purpose of this drug therapy is to

    a.   stop additional clots from forming.
    b.   decrease the patient's chest pain.
    c.   lyse clots and reduce myocardial damage.
    d.   restore renal tissue perfusion.

128.   With a patient who is experiencing a myocardial infarction, the nurse should be alert to the development of which of the following complications?

    a.   Cardiac tamponade
    b.   Pulmonary hypertension
    c.   Pericardial effusion
    d.   Cardiogenic shock

129.   The nurse can anticipate administering aspirin to a patient with a myocardial infarction to

    a.   treat the patient's low-grade fever.
    b.   provide an anticoagulant effect.
    c.   decrease the patient's chest pain.
    d.   improve peripheral tissue perfusion.

130.   A patient is receiving warfarin (Coumadin) as long-term therapy following a pulmonary embolus. Which of the following instructions would be appropriate to include in the patient's teaching plan regarding Coumadin therapy?

    a.   Use stool softeners to prevent constipation.
    b.   Increase amounts of green leafy vegetables in diet.
    c.   Floss gums after every meal.
    d.   If a dose of Coumadin is missed, double the next dose.

131.   A patient with congestive heart failure is being treated with digoxin (Lanoxin). During an office visit, he tells the nurse that he has been nauseated with occasional episodes of vomiting. His potassium level is 3.0 mEq/L. Based upon these findings, the nurse understands that the patient may be experiencing

    a.   an exacerbation of his congestive heart failure.
    b.   the onset of acute renal failure.
    c.   digitalis toxicity.
    d.   a fluid volume deficit.

132.   A patient with congestive heart failure is taking furosemide (Lasix). Which of the following clinical findings indicate that the furosemide therapy is effective?

    a.   Blood pressure reading of 136/80
    b.   Respirations of 14/min, unlabored
    c.   Urinary output of 800 cc over an eight-hour period
    d.   Weight loss of five pounds in two days

133.   Which of the following signs may be an indication that the patient has developed digitalis toxicity?

    a.   Tachypnea
    b.   Visual disturbances
    c.   Constipation
    d.   Pedal edema

134.   Which of the following electrolyte imbalances can predispose the patient to digitalis toxicity?

    a.   Hypernatremia
    b.   Hypocalcemia
    c.   Hypokalemia
    d.   Hypermagnesemia

135.   Which of the following blood pressure readings, if obtained on at least two separate occasions, would indicate a forty-five-year-old female has hypertension?

    a.   128/76
    b.   136/88
    c.   120/70
    d.   146/80

136. A patient with coronary artery disease is scheduled to have a percutaneous transluminal coronary angioplasty. Postoperatively, the nurse would anticipate implementing which of the following nursing interventions?

    a. Encouraging fluid intake to eliminate dye
    b. Administering oxygen therapy per nasal cannula
    c. Keeping the patient's head elevated 45°
    d. Maintaining the patient on bed rest for eight to twelve hours

137. The nurse is conducting a health history on a patient who is suspected of having uterine cancer. Which of the following is a factor that increases the patient's risk of developing cancer of the uterus?

    a. History of oral contraceptive use
    b. Obesity
    c. Early onset of menarche
    d. Nulliparity

138. Which of the following signs and symptoms is most commonly associated with symptomatic uterine fibroids (leiomyomas)?

    a. Sensation of abdominal bloating
    b. Abdominal pain
    c. Vaginal bleeding
    d. Purulent vaginal discharge

139. A patient who is being treated for a deep vein thrombosis suddenly complains of sharp chest pain. Upon further assessment, the nurse notes respirations of 30 breaths/min, slight cough with hemoptysis, and diaphoresis. Based upon this data, what should be the nurse's **initial** response?

    a. Notify the physician of the patient's condition.
    b. Obtain a pulse oximetry reading.
    c. Administer analgesic for chest pain.
    d. Elevate the patient's head and administer oxygen.

140. A patient has been receiving heparin for treatment of a pulmonary embolus. The physician orders warfarin (Coumadin) to be administered in addition to the heparin. The nurse understands that the reason for administering heparin and Coumadin together is to

    a. allow the Coumadin to achieve therapeutic levels before discontinuing the heparin.
    b. prevent the patient from developing a toxic reaction to the heparin.
    c. increase the effectiveness of the anticoagulant therapy.
    d. prevent more pulmonary emboli from forming.

141.   The nurse is doing a cardiovascular assessment on a sixty-year-old female patient. She tells the nurse that recently she has been experiencing pain in her calf muscles when she walks. The pain disappears when she rests. The nurse understands that these symptoms most likely mean that the patient is

    a.   becoming too sedentary and needs to increase her exercise.
    b.   experiencing intermittent claudication due to ischemia.
    c.   developing varicose veins and needs to wear support hose.
    d.   beginning to demonstrate symptoms related to osteoporosis.

142.   Which of the following assessment findings would be indicative of peripheral vascular disease related to arterial insufficiency?

    a.   Presence of peripheral edema
    b.   Skin ulcer on one of the medial malleolus
    c.   Pallor in extremities when legs are elevated
    d.   Thickened, tough skin

143.   A patient has had a permanent pacemaker inserted. Which of the following statements by the patient indicates he understands the care associated with his pacemaker?

    a.   "I should take my pulse daily and report any rates that fall outside my programmed pulse rate."
    b.   "I cannot submerge my pacemaker in water, so I should not shower or swim."
    c.   "So that the pacemaker can accurately pace my heart rate, my activity level will need to be decreased."
    d.   "It is rare for pacemakers to malfunction, so I don't need to take any special precautions."

144.   The nurse is caring for a patient who has had a myocardial infarction and is on telemetry. On the monitor, the nurse notes a sudden development of a very irregular rhythm with no discernable rate or QRS complex. The patient is unconscious. The nurse recognizes that the patient requires immediate treatment with

    a.   intubation with an endotracheal tube.
    b.   administration of nitroglycerin.
    c.   cardioversion to a normal sinus rhythm.
    d.   defibrillation to reestablish a heart rate.

145.   Which of the following ECG patterns is characteristic of premature ventricular contractions?

   a.   Regular rhythm
   b.   Wide QRS complex
   c.   Early P wave
   d.   Short PR interval

146.   Which of the following medications is most likely to be administered for treatment of premature ventricular contractions?

   a.   Atropine sulfate
   b.   Verapamil (Calan)
   c.   Lidocaine
   d.   Adenosine (Atenolol)

147.   A patient is diagnosed with having sinus bradycardia. Which of the following medications would be used to treat this sinus node dysrhythmia?

   a.   Lidocaine
   b.   Diltiazem (Cardizem)
   c.   Procainamide (Pronestyl)
   d.   Atropine

148.   A patient has been diagnosed with paroxysmal supraventricular tachycardia. The patient complains of dizziness and light-headedness when trying to walk, and feeling fatigued. Based upon this data, which of the following nursing diagnoses would most likely be appropriate for this patient?

   a.   Activity intolerance related to decreased cardiac output
   b.   Impaired gas exchange related to ventilation/perfusion mismatch
   c.   Risk for injury related to dizziness
   d.   Ineffective management of therapeutic regimen related to lack of knowledge

149.   A decreasing pulse pressure is indicative of

   a.   a difference between apical and radial pulse rates.
   b.   a decrease in cardiac output.
   c.   an increase in circulating fluid volume.
   d.   a difference between sitting and standing BP.

150.   The QRS complex on an ECG rhythm strip represents

     a.   atrial depolarization.
     b.   beginning of ventricular repolarization.
     c.   ventricular depolarization.
     d.   travel of impulse from SA node to ventricles.

151.   A patient has had a perineal prostatectomy for prostate cancer. What would be a primary nursing goal for this patient's postoperative care?

     a.   Maintain an adequate nutritional intake.
     b.   Prevent the development of a wound infection.
     c.   Promote the return of peristaltic activity.
     d.   Maintain adequate tissue perfusion to lower extremities.

152.   Which of the following laboratory tests is used to measure the effectiveness of therapy in the treatment of prostate cancer?

     a.   Alkaline phosphate
     b.   Alpha-fetoprotein
     c.   White blood cell count
     d.   Prostate-specific antigen

153.   Which of the following tests is most likely to be ordered to detect the presence of metastatic disease in a patient with prostate cancer?

     a.   Bone scan
     b.   Lung scan
     c.   IVP
     d.   Barium enema

154.   Which of the following factors increases a woman's risk for breast cancer?

     a.   Early onset of menopause
     b.   Multiple childbirths
     c.   Early onset of menstruation
     d.   Moderate alcohol intake

155.   Routine screening recommendations for breast cancer include

     a.   monthly breast self-examination after the age of thirty-five.
     b.   clinical breast examinations every two years after age forty.
     c.   genetic testing in all women with a family history of breast cancer.
     d.   annual mammograms on women after the age of forty.

156. The nurse is developing a teaching plan for a woman who has been diagnosed with benign fibrocystic breast disease. Which of the following would be appropriate for the nurse to include in the teaching plan?

   a. "Increasing your intake of vitamin C will help decrease your discomfort."
   b. "Eliminate coffee, tea, and chocolate from your diet."
   c. "Wear a loose-fitting bra so that the breast tissue will not be irritated."
   d. "Establish a regular pattern of aerobic exercise and walking."

157. A patient has a modified radical mastectomy as treatment for breast cancer. Which of the following discharge instructions would be appropriate for the nurse to give this patient?

   a. "Protect your hands while gardening by wearing gloves."
   b. "You do not need to take any special precautions with your affected arm."
   c. "You will want to limit your arm and shoulder activity for the first week."
   d. "You will not be able to wear a prosthesis until the incision is completely healed."

158. A patient with a diagnosis of acute lymphocytic leukemia is being treated with chemotherapy. The nurse establishes a diagnosis of risk for infection related to bone marrow suppression. Which of the following activities is most important for decreasing the patient's chance of acquiring an infection?

   a. Placing the patient in protective isolation to minimize exposure
   b. Administering prophylactic antibiotics to prevent infection
   c. Emphasizing good hand washing techniques for everyone in contact with the patient
   d. Discontinuing all invasive procedures on patient

159. A patient with acute lymphocytic leukemia has a platelet count of 20,000 mm^3. Which of the following nursing actions would be appropriate based upon this finding?

   a. Check all urine and stools for bleeding.
   b. Encourage the patient to cough and deep breathe.
   c. Take vital signs every two hours.
   d. Limit visitors to immediate family members.

160. The primary clinical problems that a patient with polycythemia vera will develop are related to

   a. increased risk of infection.
   b. decreased cardiac output.
   c. increased tendency toward bleeding.
   d. increased blood volume and viscosity.

161.   A primary nursing goal when caring for a patient with polycythemia vera is to

     a.   promote a diet high in iron.
     b.   encourage adequate fluid intake.
     c.   improve tissue perfusion.
     d.   maintain normal gas exchange.

162.   The nurse should instruct the patient with idiopathic thrombocytopenic purpura to avoid which of the following medications?

     a.   Sedatives
     b.   Iron preparations
     c.   Aspirin
     d.   Antacids containing magnesium

163.   The primary goal of treating disseminated intravascular coagulation is to

     a.   treat the underlying cause of the DIC.
     b.   control the hemorrhaging.
     c.   prevent multi-organ system failure.
     d.   increase tissue oxygenation.

164.   A primary nursing diagnosis for a patient who has been diagnosed with pernicious anemia is

     a.   impaired gas exchange related to hypoxemia.
     b.   alteration in comfort, pain related to altered tissue perfusion.
     c.   self-care deficit related to fatigue.
     d.   activity intolerance related to fatigue.

165.   A teenager who is in sickle-cell crisis is admitted to the hospital with complaints of severe pain. Which of the following is a priority nursing intervention for this patient?

     a.   Determine the precipitating cause of the sickle-cell crisis.
     b.   Evaluate the effectiveness of the pain medication.
     c.   Encourage active range of motion while the patient is on bed rest.
     d.   Evaluate the coping ability of the patient.

166.   The severe pain that can occur in a sickle-cell crisis is caused by the

     a.   accumulation of lactic acid in cells.
     b.   onset of a massive systemic infection.
     c.   tissue ischemia resulting from vessel occlusion.
     d.   onset of an inflammatory process in the joints.

167.   Which of the following can be precipitating factors in the onset of a sickle-cell crisis?

   a.   Smoking and alcohol
   b.   Diet high in protein
   c.   Obesity
   d.   Excessive caffeine

168.   Which of the following clinical manifestations would the nurse expect to find in a patient in the later stages of iron-deficiency anemia?

   a.   Pallor
   b.   Weakness
   c.   Fatigue
   d.   Brittle nails

169.   Prolonged hyperventilation can lead to the development of which of the following acid-base imbalances?

   a.   Respiratory alkalosis
   b.   Respiratory acidosis
   c.   Metabolic alkalosis
   d.   Metabolic acidosis

170.   Prolonged hypoventilation can lead to the development of which of the following acid-base imbalances?

   a.   Respiratory alkalosis
   b.   Respiratory acidosis
   c.   Metabolic alkalosis
   d.   Metabolic acidosis

171.   Primary nursing interventions for preventing hypoventilation include

   a.   positioning the patient in a semi-Fowler's position.
   b.   suctioning the patient to remove excess secretions.
   c.   administering bronchodilating medications.
   d.   encouraging coughing and deep breathing.

172. The nurse is administering an intravenous antibiotic to a patient when the patient
      suddenly begins wheezing and having difficulty breathing. The nurse recognizes
      this as an allergic reaction that

      a.   is a temporary response to the drug that will resolve in a few minutes.
      b.   requires the administration of supplemental oxygen.
      c.   is caused by laryngeal edema and is a medical emergency.
      d.   is best treated by stopping the drug and allowing the patient to rest.

173. The process of shunting can best be described as a condition in which

      a.   blood flows through the capillaries without any gas exchange occurring.
      b.   there is adequate ventilation but inadequate capillary perfusion.
      c.   both ventilation and perfusion are inadequate.
      d.   capillary permeability is altered, allowing fluid to escape into the interstitial
            space.

174. Which of the following is the most common symptom of a respiratory disorder?

      a.   Cyanosis
      b.   Dyspnea
      c.   Cough
      d.   Fatigue

175. Kussmaul's respirations are characterized by

      a.   rapid, shallow respirations.
      b.   slow, deep respirations.
      c.   deep, rapid, regular respirations.
      d.   periods of apnea between respirations.

176. Upon auscultating a patient's lung fields, the nurse hears crackles. The presence
      of crackles in the lungs indicates

      a.   small airway collapse or fluid in the small airways.
      b.   obstruction of large airways with fluid.
      c.   air moving through narrowed airways.
      d.   lack of air moving through the lungs.

177. When a patient develops an unexplained restlessness or confusion, the nurse's
      priority action is to first

      a.   listen to the patient's apical heart rate.
      b.   verify when the patient last had pain medication.
      c.   reorient the patient to the environment.
      d.   check the patient's oxygen saturation levels.

178. The nurse is to obtain a sputum specimen for cytology. When would be the best time for the nurse to obtain the specimen from the patient?

      a.   In the evening
      b.   Early morning
      c.   Before providing oral hygiene
      d.   After an IPPB treatment

179. A patient with allergic rhinitis is using a decongestant nasal spray to relieve nasal congestion. The nurse instructs the patient to limit his use of the nasal spray to no more than four days. What is the reason for these instructions?

      a.   The decongestant spray can cause nasal irritation.
      b.   Use of a nasal spray can lead to the development of a sinus infection.
      c.   Overuse of decongestant sprays can lead to rebound congestion.
      d.   Prolonged use of nasal spray decreases its effectiveness.

180. Which of the following criteria would cause a patient to be considered a candidate for mechanical ventilation?

      a.   A continuous increase in $PaCO_2$ with pH < 7.35
      b.   Respiratory rate of 25 breaths/minute
      c. PaO_2 of 60 mm Hg
      d.   Increasing vital capacity

181. The nurse is caring for a two-year-old who has acute epiglottitis. What precaution should the nurse keep in mind when providing care to the child?

      a.   Epiglottitis is highly contagious and can be easily transferred to other children.
      b.   Use of a tongue depressor or throat culture can precipitate airway obstruction.
      c.   The epiglottis can easily develop into a case of pneumonia.
      d.   A child with epiglottis can easily become dehydrated.

182. Acute laryngotracheobronchitis is usually treated with

      a.   antitussives.
      b.   bronchodilators.
      c.   corticosteroids.
      d.   expectorants.

183.   Which of the following would be a priority nursing diagnosis for the child with croup?

    a.   Ineffective breathing pattern related to fatigue
    b.   Impaired gas exchange related to airway obstruction
    c.   Altered nutrition, less than required related to difficulty breathing
    d.   Fatigue related to persistent, nonproductive cough

184.   A patient who is recovering from a laryngectomy is ready to resume eating. Which of the following foods will be the easiest for the patient to swallow initially?

    a.   Clear liquids
    b.   Soft foods
    c.   Thick liquids
    d.   Pureed food

185.   Which of the following signs and symptoms is an indication that the patient is developing a tension pneumothorax?

    a.   Use of accessory muscles
    b.   Decreased movement on the affected side of the chest
    c.   Percussion of chest wall reveals hyperresonance
    d.   Tracheal deviation towards the unaffected side

186.   Which of the following acid-base imbalances develops in acute respiratory failure?

    a.   Respiratory alkalosis
    b.   Metabolic alkalosis
    c.   Respiratory acidosis
    d.   Metabolic acidosis

187.   One of the criteria used to define acute respiratory failure includes a sudden onset of

    a.   a PaO_2 of 50 mm Hg or less.
    b.   pH of 7.45.
    c. O_2 saturation of 88 percent.
    d.   a $PaCO_2$ of 40 mm Hg or more.

188.   A malignant melanoma lesion most often occurs on the

   a.   hands and feet.
   b.   trunk and lower extremities.
   c.   head and neck.
   d.   lips and eyelids.

189.   Which one of the following lesions is most likely a malignant melanoma?

   a.   Flat brown lesion with regular edges
   b.   Small nodule with pearly borders
   c.   Scaly nodule with ulcerated center
   d.   Bluish-black lesion with irregular edges

190.   The nurse is presenting a community education program about malignant melanoma. Which of the following information should the nurse include in the program?

   a.   Sun exposure should be limited to two to four hours per week.
   b.   Avoid the use of tanning booths.
   c.   Only fair-skinned people are affected by malignant melanoma.
   d.   The elderly are less likely to develop a malignant melanoma.

191.   A patient who has had a subtotal gastrectomy for treatment of stomach cancer has been experiencing episodes of dumping syndrome. Which of the following nursing interventions will minimize the patient's symptoms?

   a.   Increasing fluid intake with meals
   b.   Limiting diet to soft, bland food
   c.   Eating smaller, more frequent meals
   d.   Increasing carbohydrate intake

192.   A complete blood count is obtained from a patient who has been diagnosed with acute myeloid leukemia. The nurse would expect which of the following laboratory values to be reported?

   a.   Decrease in platelet count
   b.   Increase in hemoglobin and hematocrit
   c.   Normal amount of mature leukocytes
   d.   Increase in erythrocytes

193.   Acute myeloid leukemia is most likely to be treated by

     a.   radiation therapy.
     b.   bone marrow transplantation.
     c.   aggressive chemotherapy.
     d.   immunotherapy.

194.   When caring for a child with acute lymphocytic leukemia, the nurse's primary goal of care will be to prevent

     a.   skin breakdown.
     b.   neurological impairment.
     c.   alopecia.
     d.   bleeding and infection.

195.   A child who has been diagnosed with a neuroblastoma is likely to have a/an

     a.   elevated BUN and creatinine.
     b.   elevated urine catecholamines.
     c.   decreased erythrocyte sedimentation rate.
     d.   elevated alkaline phosphatase.

196.   A priority nursing diagnosis for the family of a child who has been diagnosed with a neuroblastoma is

     a.   anticipatory grieving related to perceived loss of a child.
     b.   ineffective management of therapeutic regimen related to lack of knowledge about treatment.
     c.   anger related to diagnosis of terminal illness of child.
     d.   diversionary activity deficit related to restricted hospital environment.

197.   One of the first clinical indications of osteogenic sarcoma may be a

     a.   pathological fracture.
     b.   feeling of fatigue and weakness.
     c.   noticeable limp.
     d.   palpable lump.

198.   The nurse is caring for an infant who has been diagnosed with Wilms' tumor and is scheduled for surgery. What interventions should the nurse implement when caring for the infant preoperatively?

     a.   Establish seizure precautions.
     b.   Avoid palpation of the abdominal mass.
     c.   Monitor urinary output hourly.
     d.   Closely observe the infant for bleeding tendencies.

199.   What postoperative nursing assessments will be most important for the child who has had surgery for a Wilms' tumor?

    a.   Blood pressure and urinary output
    b.   Respiratory rate and lung sounds
    c.   Level of consciousness and pupil reaction
    d.   Pulse rate and abdominal incision

200.   The drug of choice for a patient in anaphylactic shock is

    a.   vasopressors.
    b.   bronchodilators.
    c.   corticosteroids.
    d.   epinephrine.

201.   The nurse is caring for a patient who has been admitted to the hospital with a suspected spinal cord injury from a diving accident. The nurse should closely monitor the patient for the development of

    a.   hypovolemic shock.
    b.   cardiogenic shock.
    c.   neurogenic shock.
    d.   septic shock.

202.   Which of the following patients is most at risk for the development of septic shock?

    a.   Twenty-eight-year-old female with pelvic inflammatory disease.
    b.   Eighty-year-old female with urinary tract infection.
    c.   Fifty-five-year-old male with bacterial pneumonia.
    d.   Sixty-year-old male receiving total parenteral nutrition.

203.   Which of the following clinical findings is indicative of the patient being in the irreversible stage of shock?

    a.   Mottled, cyanotic skin
    b.   Confusion
    c.   Oliguria
    d.   Hypotension

204.   The priority nursing intervention when caring for a patient in shock is to

    a.   implement rapid fluid replacement therapy.
    b.   obtain arterial blood gas values.
    c.   provide emotional support to the patient.
    d.   establish a patent airway.

205.   The most common intravenous fluid administered for shock resuscitation is

    a.   packed red blood cells.
    b.   lactated Ringer's.
    c.   normal saline.
    d.   plasma protein.

206.   Which of the following intravenous fluids would **not** be administered in cardiogenic shock?

    a.   Normal saline
    b.   Albumin
    c.   D5/45 normal saline
    d.   Dextrose with water

207.   The patient who is in hypovolemic shock should be positioned

    a.   supine with legs elevated 45°, trunk horizontal, head level with chest.
    b.   supine with legs flat, trunk horizontal, head level with chest.
    c.   supine in Trendelenburg position with legs elevated and head lower than chest.
    d.   supine with legs elevated 15° and head of bed elevated 30°.

208.   Before administering vasopressor drugs to a patient in shock, the nurse should ensure that

    a.   oxygen saturation levels are within a normal range.
    b.   adequate fluid replacement has been achieved.
    c.   renal perfusion and function is adequate.
    d.   cardiac output is normal.

209.   The nurse is caring for a child who has had a tonsillectomy. Which of the following assessment findings can indicate the child is experiencing active bleeding from the surgical site?

    a.   Pulse rate of eighty
    b.   Frequent swallowing
    c.   Difficulty talking
    d.   Pink-tinged sputum

210. Which of the following comments indicates the parents of a child who has had a tonsillectomy have understood the discharge instructions?

    a. "We will encourage our child to blow his nose with his mouth closed."
    b. "We can feed him anything he wants as soon as the bleeding stops."
    c. "Hot chocolate will make his throat feel much better."
    d. "A warm saline solution can be used to rinse out his mouth."

211. A patient has been diagnosed with sleep apnea. Which of the following instructions should the nurse incorporate into the patient teaching plan?

    a. Eliminate alcohol intake.
    b. Get eight hours of sleep nightly.
    c. Sleep with head of the bed elevated.
    d. Use mild tranquilizers as sleeping aids.

212. Which of the following nursing actions is most appropriate when caring for a child with respiratory syncytial virus?

    a. Administer intravenous antibiotics.
    b. Wear a gown and mask when providing care.
    c. Avoid contact with nasal and conjunctival secretions.
    d. Encourage ambulation to prevent respiratory complications.

213. A patient who has been diagnosed with tuberculosis is receiving streptomycin as part of her therapy. Which of the following side effects is closely associated with the administration of streptomycin?

    a. Anorexia
    b. Hearing loss
    c. Blurred vision
    d. Headaches

214. A patient who is receiving drug therapy for tuberculosis asks the nurse when she will be noninfectious to others. What is the nurse's best response?

    a. "You will always be contagious and need to take special precautions to avoid transmission to others."
    b. "Everyone responds differently to drug therapy. We will need to retest you before we can determine if the drugs have been effective."
    c. "That depends on the drug therapy your doctor prescribes for you."
    d. "After you take your medications for two to three weeks, you will be noninfectious to others."

215.   The nurse is assessing a thirty-year-old patient who is suspected of having active
        tuberculosis. Which of the following signs and symptoms would the nurse
        anticipate finding?

        a.   Night sweats
        b.   Shortness of breath
        c.   Altered mental status
        d.   Wheezing

216.   Which of the following signs and symptoms would the nurse expect to observe in
        a child who has been diagnosed with cystic fibrosis?

        a.   Fever, jaundice
        b.   Foul-smelling, bulky stools
        c.   Peripheral edema, ascites
        d.   Constipation, anorexia

217.   The nurse is teaching the mother of a child with cystic fibrosis about the
        administration of pancreatic enzymes. Which of the following statements
        indicates that the mother understands the instructions?

        a.   "I should dissolve the enzymes in fruit juice to disguise the taste."
        b.   "If my child's blood sugar is high, I should withhold the enzymes."
        c.   "I should give my child the enzymes whenever she experiences diarrhea."
        d.   "The enzymes can be sprinkled directly on food."

218.   What diet is recommended for the child with cystic fibrosis?

        a.   High-protein, high-carbohydrate diet
        b.   Sodium-restricted, low-fiber diet
        c.   High-fat diet with limited dairy products
        d.   Low-protein, high-fiber diet

219.   The parents of a child with cystic fibrosis ask the nurse how their daughter
        developed the disease. The nurse's response will be based on the knowledge that
        cystic fibrosis is caused by

        a.   the mother's exposure to a teratogen during pregnancy.
        b.   factors that are not clearly understood.
        c.   a defective gene that is inherited from both parents.
        d.   a virus that destroys pancreatic tissue.

220.   The parents of an infant with a congenital heart defect express feelings of guilt about their baby's condition. What would be the most appropriate action for the nurse to take in response to these expressed feelings?

       a.   Ask the parents why they think they are guilty of causing their baby's defect.
       b.   Reassure the parents that it is unlikely that they caused the heart defect.
       c.   Explain to the parents that feeling guilty will not benefit their baby.
       d.   Listen attentively and empathetically to the parents' feelings and concerns.

221.   The parents of a young infant have been told their child has a ventricular septal heart defect. They ask the nurse to explain what this diagnosis means. What would be the nurse's best response to this request?

       a.   The ventricles are enlarged.
       b.   There is an abnormal opening between the ventricles.
       c.   The left ventricle is underdeveloped.
       d.   The coronary arteries providing blood to the ventricles are occluded.

222.   The nurse is providing care to an infant with tetralogy of Fallot. The infant begins to cry and becomes acutely cyanotic. What action should the nurse take first in response to this hypercyanotic spell?

       a.   Place the infant in a knee-to-chest position.
       b.   Lay the infant in an oxygen tent.
       c.   Administer a bronchodilator.
       d.   Assess the infant's vital signs.

223.   An infant with patent ductus arteriosus has developed congestive heart failure. Which of the following signs and symptoms indicate the infant is developing pulmonary congestion related to congestive heart failure?

       a.   Fever, purulent sputum
       b.   Coughing, wheezing
       c.   Neck vein distention
       d.   Bradypnea, tachycardia

224.   The nurse is observing the play of a child who has tetralogy of Fallot. Which behavior is most characteristic of a child with tetralogy of Fallot?

       a.   Uncoordinated movements
       b.   Unrelenting cyanosis
       c.   Profuse diaphoresis with activity
       d.   Squatting during periods of activity

225.   The nurse is assessing an infant for signs and symptoms of digitalis toxicity.
       Which of the following findings is most indicative of digitalis toxicity in an
       infant?

       a.   Lowered serum potassium levels
       b.   Decreased muscle tone
       c.   Apical pulse rate below ninety beats per minute
       d.   Irritability, fretfulness

226.   A child is receiving captopril (Capoten) to manage his congestive heart failure
       related to a congenital heart defect. Which of the following medications would be
       contraindicated because the child is receiving captopril?

       a.   Spironolactone (Aldactone)
       b.   Furosemide (Lasix)
       c.   Chlorothiazide (Diuril)
       d.   Torasemide (Demadex)

227.   The nurse is caring for a young child with a congenital heart defect. The child has
       difficulty eating his meals and refuses the high-calorie milkshakes that are
       offered. He has lost five pounds of weight over the last three weeks. He says he
       is "too tired" to eat. Based upon these data, what is the most appropriate nursing
       diagnosis?

       a.   Activity intolerance related to impaired tissue oxygenation
       b.   Altered nutrition, less than body requirements related to fatigue
       c.   Fatigue related to impaired myocardial functioning
       d.   Self-care deficit, feeding related to activity intolerance

228.   The nurse is caring for a young child with a serious ventricular septal defect. A
       goal of care is to decrease the child's cardiac demands. Which of the following
       nursing interventions would be most appropriate?

       a.   Encourage the parent to keep the child on bed rest as much as possible.
       b.   Place the child on a two-gram sodium-restricted diet.
       c.   Implement planned "quiet time" periods throughout the day.
       d.   Ensure that the child gets a minimum of twelve hours of sleep every night.

229.   Which of the following signs and symptoms are classic clinical manifestations of
       a tracheoesophageal fistula?

       a.   Vomiting, failure to thrive, tachypnea
       b.   Rales, hemoptysis, clubbing
       c.   Circumoral pallor, diminished breath sounds, dyspnea
       d.   Coughing, choking, cyanosis

230.   An infant with a tracheoesophageal fistula is at risk for developing which of the
        following complications?

        a.   Aspiration pneumonia
        b.   Pulmonary edema
        c.   Malabsorption syndrome
        d.   Congestive heart failure

231.   An infant with a suspected tracheoesophageal fistula should be placed in which
        position?

        a.   Fowler's position at all times
        b.   Supine with head of bed elevated 30–45°
        c.   Prone position with head positioned to the right side
        d.   Side-lying position with back roll for support

232.   The parents of an infant who was born with a cleft lip are shocked and distraught
        over their child's appearance. They are reluctant to hold and comfort their baby.
        Based upon these data, which nursing diagnosis would be most appropriate at this
        time?

        a.   Anxiety related to lack of knowledge about cleft lip
        b.   Altered family processes related to birth of a child with a deformity
        c.   Risk for altered parenting related to presence of facial deformity
        d.   Ineffective coping skills related to unanticipated defect of a newborn

233.   When feeding an infant with a cleft lip, which of the following feeding difficulties
        should the nurse anticipate? The infant will

        a.   not display a normal rooting reflex.
        b.   be reluctant to feed.
        c.   not be able to breathe while feeding.
        d.   have difficulty creating enough pressure to suck.

234.   The nurse is teaching the parents of a child who has had a cleft lip and cleft palate
        repair about potential follow-up care the child will need. Which of the following
        problems is the child likely to experience?

        a.   Obstructed nasal passages
        b.   Difficulty swallowing
        c.   Speech impairments
        d.   Impaired taste sensations

235.   Which of the following interventions should the nurse implement following cleft lip surgery to prevent trauma to the suture line?

    a.   Keep the suture line covered with an occlusive dressing.
    b.   Apply soft restraints to the infant's elbows.
    c.   Administer small doses of sedatives PRN.
    d.   Instruct the parents to keep the infants fingernails trimmed.

236.   A young child is recovering from surgery for the repair of a cleft palate. Which of the following foods would be most appropriate to serve to the child while the sutures are healing?

    a.   Soft or blended foods
    b.   Clear liquids sipped from a cup
    c.   Fruit juice and milk sipped through a straw
    d.   Regular diet with no restrictions necessary

237.   The nurse is assessing a newborn. Which of the following findings would be indicative of a possible imperforate anus?

    a.   Lack of peristalsis
    b.   No passage of meconium
    c.   Distended abdomen
    d.   Hyperactive anal reflex

238.   Immediately following the surgical repairs of an imperforate anus, which of the following goals would receive priority when planning nursing care?

    a.   To develop a bowel retraining schedule
    b.   To help the parents cope with their child's deformity
    c.   To prevent the development of nutritional deficits
    d.   To prevent infection of the perineal incision

239.   Hirschsprung's disease (congenital aganglionic megacolon) is characterized by which of the following pathophysiological processes?

    a.   Inflamed mucosa in the gastrointestinal tract
    b.   Rapid transit of food from stomach to duodenum
    c.   Decreased motility of the intestine
    d.   Malabsorption of nutrients in the small intestine

240.   The nurse is caring for an infant with Hirschsprung's disease. The infant becomes lethargic and develops a fever and explosive, watery diarrhea. Which nursing action would be most appropriate for the nurse to take first?

    a.   Administer liquid acetaminophen to reduce the fever.
    b.   Increase fluid intake by increasing IV flow.
    c.   Provide skin care to the perineal area to prevent excoriation.
    d.   Notify the physician of the infant's signs and symptoms.

241.   The nurse is preparing an infant who has Hirschsprung's disease for surgery to create a temporary colostomy. Which of the following nursing actions will be a part of the preoperative care?

    a.   Administer cleansing saline enemas.
    b.   Teach the parents how to change the colostomy pouch.
    c.   Cleanse the infants abdomen with an antiseptic solution.
    d.   Implement a full liquid diet forty-eight hours before surgery.

242.   Which of the following assessment findings may be indicative of biliary atresia in a newborn?

    a.   Abdominal distention
    b.   Straw-colored urine
    c.   Jaundiced sclera
    d.   Constipation

243.   The nurse is providing care instructions to the parents of a toddler who had biliary atresia. Which of the following comments indicates the parents have understood the instructions?

    a.   "We should limit the amount of protein in our child's diet."
    b.   "It is important to keep our child's fingernails trimmed."
    c.   "It will be important to force fluids so that our child does not get dehydrated."
    d.   "With proper care we can avoid the need for a liver transplant."

244.   The nurse is performing an assessment on a six-week-old infant and notices asymmetrical gluteal and thigh folds. The nurse understands that this finding is indicative of

    a.   cerebral palsy.
    b.   muscular dystrophy.
    c.   congenital scoliosis.
    d.   developmental hip dysplasia.

245. Which of the following assessment findings would indicate the adolescent may have scoliosis?

    a. Limp present when walking
    b. Asymmetrical hip height
    c. Lower lumbar pain
    d. External rotation of the hip

246. The nurse is conducting a well-baby assessment on a four-month-old infant. Which of the following findings would be a source of concern about the infant's level of development? The infant

    a. lacks head control.
    b. cannot sit without support.
    c. is not crawling.
    d. cries when held by the nurse.

247. The nurse is providing prenatal instructions to a group of women. Which of the following instructions would be appropriate for decreasing the occurrence of myelomeningocele and other neural tube defects?

    a. "Increase your daily intake of iron by taking supplements."
    b. "Eliminate all caffeine from your diet."
    c. "Increase your intake of foods rich in folic acid."
    d. "Do not expose yourself to secondhand smoke."

248. The nurse is caring for a newborn with spina bifida. The nurse should focus assessments of the infant's

    a. cardiovascular status.
    b. nutritional intake.
    c. vision and hearing.
    d. neurological status.

249. The laboratory values of a child who has muscular dystrophy will include a/an

    a. elevated serum creatine phosphokinase.
    b. decreased serum aspartate aminotransferase.
    c. elevated serum calcium.
    d. decreased white blood cell amount.

250. An infant has been diagnosed with phenylketonuria. Which of the following dietary restrictions is appropriate for this infant?

    a. Decrease sodium intake
    b. Restrict high-protein foods
    c. Eliminate sugars from diet
    d. Decrease fat intake

251. The nurse is helping her mother to feed her infant who has Down syndrome. The infant is having difficulty sucking, repeatedly pushing the nipple away from the mouth with is tongue. The mother tells the nurse "I just can't get him to eat. He acts hungry but keeps pushing the nipple away." Based upon these data, which nursing diagnosis would be most appropriate?

    a. Ineffective breathing pattern related to difficulty feeding
    b. Altered growth and development related to cognitive impairment
    c. Ineffective coping related to having an infant with Down syndrome
    d. Potential for altered nutrition, less than body requirements related to protruding tongue and difficulty sucking

252. When caring for an infant with hydrocephalus the nurse should closely observe the infant for signs of

    a. electrolyte imbalances.
    b. respiratory distress.
    c. seizure activity.
    d. mental retardation.

ANSWERS TO PRACTICE EXAMINATION

1. __	43. __	85. __	127.__	169.__	211.__
2. __	44. __	86. __	128.__	170.__	212.__
3. __	45. __	87. __	129.__	171.__	213.__
4. __	46. __	88. __	130.__	172.__	214.__
5. __	47. __	89. __	131.__	173.__	215.__
6. __	48. __	90. __	132.__	174.__	216.__
7. __	49. __	91. __	133.__	175.__	217.__
8. __	50. __	92. __	134.__	176.__	218.__
9. __	51. __	93. __	135.__	177.__	219.__
10. __	52. __	94. __	136.__	178.__	220.__
11. __	53. __	95. __	137.__	179.__	221.__
12. __	54. __	96. __	138.__	180.__	222.__
13. __	55. __	97. __	139.__	181.__	223.__
14. __	56. __	98. __	140.__	182.__	224.__
15. __	57. __	99. __	141.__	183.__	225.__
16. __	58. __	100.__	142.__	184.__	226.__
17. __	59. __	101.__	143.__	185.__	227.__
18. __	60. __	102.__	144.__	186.__	228.__
19. __	61. __	103.__	145.__	187.__	229.__
20. __	62. __	104.__	146.__	188.__	230.__
21. __	63. __	105.__	147.__	189.__	231.__
22. __	64. __	106.__	148.__	190.__	232.__
23. __	65. __	107.__	149.__	191.__	233.__
24. __	66. __	108.__	150.__	192.__	234.__
25. __	67. __	109.__	151.__	193.__	235.__
26. __	68. __	110.__	152.__	194.__	236.__
27. __	69. __	111.__	153.__	195.__	237.__
28. __	70. __	112.__	154.__	196.__	238.__
29. __	71. __	113.__	155.__	197.__	239.__
30. __	72. __	114.__	156.__	198.__	240.__
31. __	73. __	115.__	157.__	199.__	241.__
32. __	74. __	116.__	158.__	200.__	242.__
33. __	75. __	117.__	159.__	201.__	243.__
34. __	76. __	118.__	160.__	202.__	244.__
35. __	77. __	119.__	161.__	203.__	245.__
36. __	78. __	120.__	162.__	204.__	246.__
37. __	79. __	121.__	163.__	205.__	247.__
38. __	80. __	122.__	164.__	206.__	248.__
39. __	81. __	123.__	165.__	207.__	249.__
40. __	82. __	124.__	166.__	208.__	250.__
41. __	83. __	125.__	167.__	209.__	251.__
42. __	84. __	126.__	168.__	210.__	252.__

ANSWERS TO PRACTICE EXAMINATION

1. __	43. __	85. __	127.__	169.__	211.__
2. __	44. __	86. __	128.__	170.__	212.__
3. __	45. __	87. __	129.__	171.__	213.__
4. __	46. __	88. __	130.__	172.__	214.__
5. __	47. __	89. __	131.__	173.__	215.__
6. __	48. __	90. __	132.__	174.__	216.__
7. __	49. __	91. __	133.__	175.__	217.__
8. __	50. __	92. __	134.__	176.__	218.__
9. __	51. __	93. __	135.__	177.__	219.__
10. __	52. __	94. __	136.__	178.__	220.__
11. __	53. __	95. __	137.__	179.__	221.__
12. __	54. __	96. __	138.__	180.__	222.__
13. __	55. __	97. __	139.__	181.__	223.__
14. __	56. __	98. __	140.__	182.__	224.__
15. __	57. __	99. __	141.__	183.__	225.__
16. __	58. __	100.__	142.__	184.__	226.__
17. __	59. __	101.__	143.__	185.__	227.__
18. __	60. __	102.__	144.__	186.__	228.__
19. __	61. __	103.__	145.__	187.__	229.__
20. __	62. __	104.__	146.__	188.__	230.__
21. __	63. __	105.__	147.__	189.__	231.__
22. __	64. __	106.__	148.__	190.__	232.__
23. __	65. __	107.__	149.__	191.__	233.__
24. __	66. __	108.__	150.__	192.__	234.__
25. __	67. __	109.__	151.__	193.__	235.__
26. __	68. __	110.__	152.__	194.__	236.__
27. __	69. __	111.__	153.__	195.__	237.__
28. __	70. __	112.__	154.__	196.__	238.__
29. __	71. __	113.__	155.__	197.__	239.__
30. __	72. __	114.__	156.__	198.__	240.__
31. __	73. __	115.__	157.__	199.__	241.__
32. __	74. __	116.__	158.__	200.__	242.__
33. __	75. __	117.__	159.__	201.__	243.__
34. __	76. __	118.__	160.__	202.__	244.__
35. __	77. __	119.__	161.__	203.__	245.__
36. __	78. __	120.__	162.__	204.__	246.__
37. __	79. __	121.__	163.__	205.__	247.__
38. __	80. __	122.__	164.__	206.__	248.__
39. __	81. __	123.__	165.__	207.__	249.__
40. __	82. __	124.__	166.__	208.__	250.__
41. __	83. __	125.__	167.__	209.__	251.__
42. __	84. __	126.__	168.__	210.__	252.__

PRACTICE EXAMINATION ANSWER KEY

1.	b	43.	b	85.	d	127.	c	169.	a	211.	a
2.	d	44.	d	86.	a	128.	d	170.	b	212.	c
3.	c	45.	a	87.	b	129.	b	171.	d	213.	b
4.	d	46.	b	88.	c	130.	a	172.	c	214.	d
5.	a	47.	c	89.	a	131.	c	173.	a	215.	a
6.	d	48.	b	90.	d	132.	d	174.	b	216.	b
7.	a	49.	d	91.	b	133.	b	175.	c	217.	d
8.	b	50.	d	92.	c	134.	c	176.	a	218.	a
9.	c	51.	c	93.	d	135.	d	177.	d	219.	c
10.	a	52.	d	94.	a	136.	a	178.	b	220.	d
11.	c	53.	b	95.	b	137.	b	179.	c	221.	b
12.	b	54.	a	96.	d	138.	c	180.	a	222.	a
13.	d	55.	c	97.	d	139.	d	181.	b	223.	b
14.	a	56.	c	98.	a	140.	a	182.	c	224.	d
15.	b	57.	b	99.	c	141.	b	183.	b	225.	c
16.	d	58.	a	100.	b	142.	c	184.	c	226.	a
17.	b	59.	d	101.	a	143.	a	185.	d	227.	b
18.	c	60.	c	102.	c	144.	d	186.	c	228.	c
19.	a	61.	b	103.	b	145.	b	187.	a	229.	d
20.	a	62.	c	104.	d	146.	c	188.	b	230.	a
21.	a	63.	a	105.	c	147.	d	189.	d	231.	b
22.	d	64.	c	106.	a	148.	a	190.	b	232.	c
23.	c	65.	c	107.	b	149.	b	191.	c	233.	d
24.	d	66.	a	108.	d	150.	c	192.	a	234.	c
25.	b	67.	d	109.	a	151.	b	193.	c	235.	b
26.	b	68.	b	110.	c	152.	d	194.	d	236.	a
27.	b	69.	c	111.	c	153.	a	195.	b	237.	b
28.	c	70.	a	112.	d	154.	c	196.	a	238.	d
29.	d	71.	c	113.	c	155.	d	197.	c	239.	c
30.	b	72.	b	114.	b	156.	b	198.	b	240.	d
31.	b	73.	d	115.	d	157.	a	199.	a	241.	a
32.	d	74.	a	116.	a	158.	c	200.	d	242.	c
33.	c	75.	c	117.	a	159.	a	201.	c	243.	b
34.	a	76.	b	118.	c	160.	d	202.	b	244.	d
35.	b	77.	b	119.	b	161.	b	203.	a	245.	b
36.	d	78.	d	120.	d	162.	c	204.	d	246.	a
37.	c	79.	c	121.	a	163.	a	205.	c	247.	c
38.	a	80.	a	122.	c	164.	d	206.	b	248.	d
39.	d	81.	b	123.	b	165.	b	207.	a	249.	a
40.	b	82.	a	124.	d	166.	c	208.	b	250.	b
41.	c	83.	b	125.	a	167.	a	209.	b	251.	d
42.	b	84.	c	126.	a	168.	d	210.	d	252.	c